ELEMENTARY
SCHOOL
HEALTH
EDUCATION

HARPER'S SERIES IN

SCHOOL AND PUBLIC HEALTH EDUCATION,
PHYSICAL EDUCATION, AND RECREATION
Delbert Oberteuffer, EDITOR

ELEMENTARY SCHOOL HEALTH EDUCATION

CURRICULUM - METHODS - INTEGRATION

JAMES H. HUMPHREY
Professor of Health Education and Physical Education
University of Maryland

WARREN R. JOHNSON
Professor of Health Education and Physical Education
University of Maryland

VIRGINIA D. MOORE
Supervisor of Elementary Schools
Board of Education of Anne Arundel County, Maryland

HARPER & BROTHERS, *Publishers*
NEW YORK

CONTENTS

FOREWORD   by William H. Creswell, Jr.   vii

PREFACE   ix

1 ORIENTATION TO ELEMENTARY SCHOOL HEALTH
  EDUCATION   1

2 ORGANIZATION AND ADMINISTRATION OF THE
  ELEMENTARY SCHOOL HEALTH PROGRAM   14

3 CHILD HEALTH AND PHYSICAL FITNESS   26

4 WAYS OF OFFERING HEALTH IN THE ELEMENTARY
  SCHOOL CURRICULUM   43

5 TEACHING AND LEARNING IN HEALTH EDUCATION   58

6 ORAL COMMUNICATION AND LANGUAGE IN RELATION
  TO HEALTH   71

7 PLANNING FOR HEALTH TEACHING   94

8 CRITERIA FOR THE SELECTION OF HEALTH TEACHING
  CONTENT   149

9 HEALTH TEACHING CONTENT FOR THE VARIOUS
  GRADE LEVELS   164

10 TEACHING AIDS AND MATERIALS   200

11 INTEGRATION OF HEALTH AND ARITHMETIC   231

12 INTEGRATION OF HEALTH AND LANGUAGE ARTS   257

13 INTEGRATION OF HEALTH AND SOCIAL STUDIES   307

14 INTEGRATION OF HEALTH AND SCIENCE   323

15 INTEGRATION OF HEALTH AND PHYSICAL EDUCATION   342

16 INTEGRATION OF HEALTH AND CREATIVE EXPRESSION   360

APPENDIX: SOURCES OF HEALTH TEACHING AIDS AND
          MATERIALS   381

INDEX   387

FOREWORD

Health education has long been recognized as an important responsibility of the schools. Too frequently, however, the gap between what is attempted and what is accomplished has been a source of serious concern to school officials. Teaching health effectively so as to make a significant difference in the lives of boys and girls requires certain essential conditions. There must be a fully qualified teacher, adequate teaching materials, and a well planned curriculum. While *Elementary School Health Education* provides some orientation to the total school health program, the authors focus on developing a curriculum that makes good teaching possible.

For the teacher in the self-contained classroom faced with the increasingly difficult task of mastering an expanding body of teaching content, this book should prove a useful tool. Recognizing that the task of carrying forward health teaching will rest primarily with the classroom teacher, the authors have made an impressive effort to come to grips with the "hows" of curriculum arrangement.

The authors have presented a most searching and systematic study of integrated health teaching. They have analyzed in great detail the content structure of health education, arranging health concepts sequentially from the simple to the more complex. Each area of the elementary school curriculum is developed as it relates to health. There is a sense of how pupil learning is reinforced and enriched with the development of these relationships between health and the other curriculum areas. As health is related to learning arithmetic and as arithmetic is related to learning health concepts, the dividends of truly integrated teaching are more fully appreciated.

To the specialist this book reveals a fresh approach to content arrangement; to the classroom teacher it goes beyond theory to provide as well a comprehensive source of practical suggestions.

William H. Creswell, Jr.
Consultant in Health Education,
American Association for Health,
Physical Education, and Recreation

PREFACE

For many years there has been a need to combine into a single volume all of the elements needed to prepare elementary school teachers for the teaching of health. That is, there has been a need for a volume which would depict the nature and structure of modern health education, define the meaning of child health and fitness, propose a health curriculum suitable for the several school grades, present the principles of teaching methodology, and spell out specific ways in which health might be taught in conjunction with other curriculum areas, i.e., by integration. This book has been prepared for the express purpose of meeting this need.

The titles of most of the chapters of this volume are self-explanatory. However, the matter of *integration* would seem to require special comment here. Integration is now highly recommended as perhaps the most feasible way to include health teaching in the elementary school curriculum. For example, at the recent World Confederation of Organizations of the Teaching Professions it was reported that: "Educational authorities in the United States generally agree that health education at the elementary level should be integrated with all of the other educational experiences and activities."

Yet, in spite of the many recommendations for using this approach in health teaching at the elementary school level, there is almost no literature which discusses integration techniques thoroughly. In this book, rather extensive treatment has been given to ways of integrating health and arithmetic, language arts, social studies, science, physical education, and creative expression. It is hoped that the present material will shed additional light on how integration of health in the elementary school curriculum might be successfully accomplished; and it is hoped that it will encourage further experimentation with this procedure.

The reader will note that each chapter begins with a number of questions. The intended functions of these questions are: (1) to set forth a study guide for the reader at the outset of each chapter, (2) to give a ready reference to the problems to be considered in a particular chapter, and (3) to provide a device by which the reader can evaluate his present knowledge of the subjects discussed in each chapter.

The authors have been guided by the successful experiences of many outstanding elementary school classroom teachers, administrators, and supervisors with whom it has been their pleasure to associate through the years. In fact, these individuals provided much of the stimulus which resulted in the decision to prepare this volume. To them the authors wish to express their most sincere gratitude for the contributions, both direct and indirect, that they have made to the book.

A debt of gratitude is also due to the publishers of other texts who have given permission to use previously published materials.

J. H. H.
W. R. J.
V. D. M.

ORIENTATION TO ELEMENTARY SCHOOL HEALTH EDUCATION

1

1 *What are some of the essential functions of school health service?*

2 *What does the healthful school living aspect of the school health program involve?*

3 *In what ways has health teaching in the elementary schools changed through the years?*

4 *What are some of the outstanding highlights in the development of health education in the elementary school?*

5 *How are the objectives of elementary education and health education compatible?*

The sound treatment of any segment of education requires a basic understanding of the framework within which that particular segment functions in the total educational program. Therefore, it is important to establish the place of health education in the entire area of elementary education. We will attempt to do so in this chapter by discussing (1) the scope of elementary education; (2) the scope of the school health program; (3) the development of school health programs in elementary schools; and (4) the compatibility of the objectives of elementary education and health education.

SCOPE OF ELEMENTARY EDUCATION

It would perhaps be quite difficult to identify all aspects of elementary education by discussing it on a nationwide basis. However, the scope of elementary education can be classified in two general

1

ways: the scope of *curriculum areas* or *subjects,* and the scope in terms of *grade* and *age levels.*

Scope of Curriculum Offerings

Curriculum development in modern elementary education is based largely on the needs of children in a given locality. Due to this fact, there is little national standardization in curriculum offerings and elementary schools in different areas provide different learning experiences for children.

However, although the range of specific curriculum areas may vary from one school to another, there are certain constant areas of study that will be found in virtually all the elementary schools of the United States. These are the so-called "tool subjects" or "fundamentals" that involve the communication skills of reading and writing, and the concept of number involving the study of arithmetic. In addition, most schools include some sort of instruction in the area of social studies. This area of the curriculum may include the study of history, geography, science, civics, and health and safety.

Some school districts, depending upon such factors as available funds and the number of pupils enrolled, extend their curriculum offerings to include such areas as the various forms of industrial and graphic arts, creative activities, music, art, physical education, and foreign languages.

It should be borne in mind that the modern elementary school curriculum should not be interpreted only in terms of subject-matter areas. On the contrary, the curriculum as it is conceived today consists of all the school experiences which in one way or another influence the pupil. The modern approach to an understanding of the place of subjects in the curriculum is that learning which results from the experiences in the various subjects, rather than the subjects themselves, should be considered the real curriculum content. Consequently, merely considering the number of subjects in a given elementary school would not necessarily indicate the scope or extent of the learning experience afforded the pupils.

Scope of Age and Grade Levels

As in the case of the scope of curriculum offerings, there is variation among elementary schools with regard to lower and upper age and grade levels. However, this variation is not likely to be as pronounced, because age and grade ranges are generally standardized in terms of the type of organizational plan under which a given school system functions.

The lower age and grade limits have been fairly well defined. It has been traditional in most public tax supported elementary schools to start children in the first grade at approximately 6 years of age. However, the practice of starting children at the *kindergarten* level at around 5 is becoming popular in many parts of the country. Since this country's first kindergarten was founded in 1855 the idea of starting children in school before the traditional first grade has received widespread emphasis. In 1947 a survey of 203 school systems in cities of over 30,000 population showed kindergartens operating in 139 systems. In 1950 about 750,000 4- and 5-year olds were enrolled in public kindergartens.[1] In a more recent survey the National Education Association reported that by 1958 there were kindergartens in 79 percent of those elementary schools where the supervising principal was the chief administrator.[2]

Fluctuation in the upper grade limit of the elementary school depends largely upon whether the school system recognizes the junior high school (Grades 7, 8, and 9) as a separate educational level in its organizational pattern. In those schools that operate on what is known as the 8–4 plan, the junior high school as such does not exist. In this plan the elementary school consists of Grades 1–8 and the high school consists of Grades 9–12.

Two of the more prevalent plans of organization are the 6–6 plan and the 6–3–3 plan. In both of these plans, the elementary school consists of Grades 1–6. In the 6–6 plan the junior and senior high school is generally combined into one unit, while the 6–3–3 plan involves a separate unit for the junior high school (Grades 7, 8, and 9) and the senior high school (Grades 10, 11, and 12). According to the NEA survey a large majority of elementary schools end with Grade 6—79 percent go through Grade 6 while 20 percent continue through Grade 8.[3]

[1] Emma Reinhardt, *American Education, An Introduction*, rev. ed., New York, Harper, 1960.
[2] Research Division of the National Education Association, *NEA Research Bulletin*, December, 1958, p. 108.
[3] *Ibid.*

In considering the range of grade levels in the elementary school it might be well at this point to describe some of the terms used in connection with the various divisions of grade levels. In the eight-year elementary school the first three grades are generally referred to as the *primary* level; Grades 4, 5, and 6 may be called the *middle* grades; and Grades 7 and 8 are known as the *upper* grades. In the six-year elementary school the most common practice seems to be to designate the first three grades as the *primary* level and the last three as the *intermediate* or *upper elementary* level. Sometimes the six-year elementary school is divided into three levels as follows: Grades 1 and 2, primary; Grades 3 and 4, intermediate; and Grades 5 and 6, upper elementary.

In keeping with what appears to be the prevailing practice, we will consider the lower and upper grade limits of the elementary school as kindergarten through Grade 6. Grades 1–3 will be referred to as the *primary* level, and Grades 4–6 will be referred to either as the *intermediate* or *upper elementary* level.

The range of *age* levels considered will be from approximately age 5 to approximately age 12. This is based on the assumption that a great majority of children who start at kindergarten level enter at about 5. At the completion of kindergarten the child is approaching or has reached the age of 6 years. Similarly, the first-grade child is approximately 6 years of age at the start of the first grade and is approaching or has reached the age of 7 at the end of the school year. The following scale is based on these age and grade level assumptions:

GRADE IN SCHOOL	APPROXIMATE AGE LEVEL
Kindergarten	5–6
First grade	6–7
Second grade	7–8
Third grade	8–9
Fourth grade	9–10
Fifth grade	10–11
Sixth grade	11–12

It is important to recognize age levels at the various grades, because children at each age level tend to have certain distinct physical, social, emotional, and intellectual traits.

SCOPE OF THE SCHOOL HEALTH PROGRAM

The field of school health is characterized by the somewhat unusual distinction of having a proposed list of standardized terms. This is mentioned here because the scope of the various areas of school health might be better understood if these areas are specifically defined.

Attempts at standardization of terms in school health were brought about through the efforts of a committee on terminology of the Health Education Section of the American Physical Education Association. The recommendations of this committee were published in 1934.[4] In view of the fact that many of the health education areas took on new and different meanings in the intervening years, a new Committee was organized in 1949 for the purpose of redefining terms and bringing clarity to certain features in school health. This group became known as the Joint Committee on Terminology in School Health Education and represented the American Association for Health, Physical Education and Recreation and the American School Health Association. This Joint Committee's recommendations were published in 1951.[5]

The terminology and definitions of the various areas of school health used throughout this volume will be based as far as possible on the recommendations of the Joint Committee. However, it should be borne in mind that attempts to standardize terminology in such a rapidly changing and expanding area precludes a static list of terms. Consequently, terminology and descriptions or definitions of the various areas of school health will deviate from the Joint Committee's recommendations as it seems necessary in terms of modern theories and practices.

It is a generally accepted idea that the entire *school health program* involves those school procedures that contribute to the understanding, maintenance, and improvement of the health of pupils and school personnel. In carrying out these functions, the total

4 Committee Report of the Health Education Section of the American Physical Education Association, "Definition of Terms in Health Education," *Journal of Health and Physical Education,* December, 1934.

5 Report of the Joint Committee on Terminology in School Health Education, *Journal of the American Association for Health, Physical Education and Recreation,* September, 1951.

school health program is composed of three areas: *school health service, healthful school living,* and *health teaching.* These three areas are interrelated and to some extent interdependent upon each other, but, in order to delineate the scope of the entire school health program, each will be discussed separately.

School Health Service

This phase of the school health program attempts to conserve, protect, and improve the health of the school population. This objective is achieved in part through such procedures as (1) appraising the health status of pupils and school personnel; (2) counseling with pupils, parents, and others involved regarding the appraisal findings; (3) helping to plan for the health care and education of exceptional children; (4) helping to prevent and control disease; and (5) providing for emergency care for sick and injured pupils.

The maximum function of school health service would consist of providing all that is needed in the way of health supervision to contribute to the optimal health of all children. Naturally, such service depends upon the availability of such specialized resources as physicians, dentists, nurses, psychologists, and others who can make worthwhile contributions to the health of children. The type of service which is actually provided in a given school system also depends upon such factors as available funds, size of school enrollment, and availability of properly trained personnel. Because of these factors the range of school health services varies markedly from one school system to another.

The extreme importance of the health service aspect of the school health program is obvious when one considers the range of anomalous health conditions of the school population. For instance, some estimates indicate that out of every 100 children of school age, one has heart disease, 20 have visual disorders, 10 have some degree of hearing impairment, 15 have nutritional disturbances, 10 have some sort of growth problems, 85 have dental disease, and 20 have emotional disturbances. Add to these estimates the fact that many children are only partially immunized and countless others live under conditions of poor hygienic practices which involve lack of sleep, fresh air, and sunshine.

Adequate school health service can do much to help eliminate these conditions. This is particularly true at the elementary school level because the younger a child is at the time a deviation from normal health is discovered the greater the opportunity for proper care and possible recovery.

Healthful School Living

This aspect of the school health program involves procedures which provide for the most satisfactory living conditions within the school plant. Healthful school living is concerned with such factors as (1) organizing the school day on a basis commensurate with the health and safety of all pupils; and (2) providing for physical aspects of the school plant such as proper ventilation, heating, lighting and the like, which are essential in preserving an optimum health status.

As in the case of school health service there is likely to be a wide range of standards of healthful school living from one school system to another. The standard of healthful school living that a given school system provides will be governed largely by available funds and specialized personnel, particularly in the area of school maintenance.

Health Teaching

This phase of the school health program is the primary concern of the text. Subsequent chapters will deal extensively with health curriculum content at the various grade levels of the elementary school as well as the best accepted teaching procedures.

It is the aim of health teaching[6] to provide desirable and worthwhile learning experiences which will favorably influence knowledge, attitudes, and practices pertaining to individual and group health. In recent years there has been a growing recognition of the fact that if people are going to be healthy, they should be educated in matters pertaining to health. For instance, since a child must eat certain foods that are good for him, it is important that he be taught why, so that when away from the control of his parents he will be able to take into account the nutritional needs of his body, and not necessarily choose foods only on the basis of what tastes best to him.

6 The term "health teaching" may also be referred to in the literature as *health education* or *health instruction*.

Moreover, if he has never been taught what constitutes a good diet, it is not likely that he will know how to select one even if he should become aware of its importance for vigorous health, weight control, and bodily efficiency.

Recognition of the importance of health teaching during the early years of life has gradually resulted in a national tendency to place greater emphasis upon health in the curriculum at all grade levels. More and more schools are making a definite effort to cover a series of topics which are considered vital to the present and future health of the child. Many states have laws which require that certain health topics be presented. These required topics were at first quite limited, commonly amounting only to the effects of alcohol, tobacco, and narcotics upon the body. However, at the present time there is a definite trend to go far beyond teaching only those health topics required by law.

DEVELOPMENT OF SCHOOL HEALTH PROGRAMS IN ELEMENTARY SCHOOLS

Over the years the structure, function, and curriculum offerings of elementary schools have taken many forms. Although the development of elementary education has at times met with a great deal of adverse criticism, it can be said that, for the most part, attempts have been made to gear this segment of education to meet the needs of the times.

The importance of health of school children was, of course, recognized long before it was considered an essential aspect of the school program or a specific function of the school as such. However, shortly after the establishment of the first elementary school with a graded program at Quincy, Massachusetts, in 1847, the place of health as it related to children in schools became an increasingly important matter.

Before this time some European schools did make attempts to improve health conditions in schools. The first efforts were primarily concerned with the sanitary conditions of schools. For example, in 1830 there was a regulation in Paris concerning the inspection of the sanitary aspects of schools.

The groundwork for the shift in emphasis from school sanitation to the personal health of the school population can perhaps be attributed in part to the following declaration by Horace Mann in 1843: "The study of human physiology—by which I mean both the laws of life and hygiene or the rules and observances by which health can be preserved and promoted should be undertaken in schools. No person is qualified to have the care of children for a single day who is ignorant of the leading principles of physiology."[7]

Some two decades later other states began recognizing the importance of providing for more healthful conditions in schools. In this particular connection the following state law passed in California in 1866 is of interest: "Instruction shall be given in all grades of schools, and in all classes, during the entire school course, in manners and morals, and the laws of health; and due attention shall be given to such physical exercises for the pupils as may be conducive to health and vigor of body, as well as mind; and to the ventilation and temperature of school rooms." (Rev. school law. Approved March 24, 1866, sec. 55.)[8]

Around 1880 there was a wave of legislation for instruction in the effects of alcohol and narcotics. This might be considered as forerunner of our modern offerings in health education because it carried instruction in physiology and hygiene into many of the schools in the country. At about the same time the need for improvement in healthful living conditions in schools became more noticeable and in 1880 the Los Angeles Board of Education passed a rule stating that teachers should give attention to the ventilation and temperature of their classrooms. Many other school systems also adopted rules which provided that windows should be opened a number of times during the day.

Shortly before the turn of the century interest in the health of children was largely a matter of concern for only the immediate family and there was little public interest in child health. However, around this time public interest was generated by certain communicable disease epidemics in the schools. Because of the large number of cases of diphtheria and scarlet fever in the schools of Boston in 1894, the city Board of Health appointed a number of

[7] From the *Sixth Annual Report of the Massachusetts Board of Education 1843*, cited in, Federal Security Agency, U.S. Office of Education, *Supervision of Health and Physical Education as a Function of State Departments of Education*, Bulletin 1940, No. 6, Monograph No. 14, Washington, D.C., p. 1.

[8] *Ibid.*

physicians whose task it was to detect contagious diseases. The need for complete physical examinations of children became readily apparent when the physicians noticed that while inspecting for communicable disease, various other kinds of defects were discovered.

By 1912 seven states had provided mandatory laws for medical examination of children. During the First World War, the large numbers of individuals rejected for military service because of poor health gave further impetus to the promotion of better health for the school population.

Interest in school health was again stimulated as a result of the still relatively large number of draft rejections during the Second World War. This is not to say that the poor health of young men examined for military service could be blamed directly on the nation's schools. However, the health of the nation's population as revealed by the number of physically and mentally unfit individuals during this time of national emergency indicated that the schools might well be considered an important area in American society where a start could be made to improve such conditions in the future. This has been a primary reason for the widespread expansion in the various areas of the school health program in recent years.

One of the most recent actions which has had an impact upon the growth and development of health programs was the President's Conference on Fitness of American Youth which convened in 1956. This was the first peacetime fitness conference ever held under White House auspices. One of the important developments resulting from the conference has been the stress placed upon the total fitness of children in our rapidly changing society. School administrators, teachers, and others connected with school work are becoming more and more "fitness minded." This attitude tends to develop a better understanding of the need for improved school health programs.

It might be said that current interest in elementary school health education is at its greatest peak in history. Many schools are expanding school health services as well as attempting to improve conditions of healthful school living. In addition, more serious attempts are being made to provide satisfactory and interesting health learning experiences for elementary school children. However, this does not mean that anyone in the area of elementary education can become lethargic as far as this aspect of the school program is concerned. Continued effort toward improvements is essential in order to insure the highest possible level of health for all children.

OBJECTIVES OF ELEMENTARY EDUCATION AND HEALTH EDUCATION

Although the area of school health might well be considered an innovation of the twentieth century, health as an educational objective is certainly not new. For example, in 1550, Francois Rabelais suggested that, "The aim of education is not so much to fill thee with learning as to train both thy mind and thy body. . . . Without health, life is no life."[9]

In its statement of objectives, the Commission on the Reorganization of Secondary Education, in 1918, gave recognition to health as a fundamental purpose of the school. Although these objectives are listed as the Cardinal Principles of Secondary Education, they have also served as a basis for objectives of elementary education. The Cardinal Principles are: (1) health, (2) command of fundamental processes, (3) worthy home membership, (4) vocational efficiency, (5) good citizenship, (6) worthy use of leisure, and (7) ethical character.[10]

About two decades later, in 1938, a statement of purposes by the Educational Policies Commission of the National Education Association indicated that four aspects of educational purpose might focus around the areas of: (1) the individual, (2) the individual's relationships to others in the home and the community, (3) the creation and use of material wealth, and (4) sociocivic activities. More concretely stated these four areas were concerned with self-realization, human relationships, economic efficiency, civic responsibility.[11]

This set of objectives emphasized the importance of health as a major function of the school in that such things as "sight and hear-

9 Francois Rabelais, *The Works of Francois Rabelais*, trans. Sir Thomas Urquhart and Motteux, London, Bohn, 1849.
10 U.S. Office of Education, *Cardinal Principles of Secondary Education*, Washington, D.C., 1918, Bulletin No. 35.
11 National Education Association, *The Purpose of Education in American Democracy*, Washington, D.C., 1938.

ing," "health knowledge," "health habits," and "public health" are included among the objectives of self-realization.

One of the more recent statements of purpose of elementary education is that of the Ninth Conference on Elementary Education held at the U.S. Office of Education in 1956. Delegates to this conference included representatives from 62 national organizations whose programs reflected an interest in children of elementary school age. The members of the conference agreed that it was the job of the elementary school to: "cooperate with the home and community to lay foundations for healthful living—physical and mental health, safety protection—in the light of the great pressures and tensions which affect children."[12]

Modern educators are now generally agreed that the goal of elementary education is to stimulate and guide the growth of an individual so that he will function well in life activities involving vocation, citizenship, and enriched leisure, and that he will possess as high a level of physical, social, emotional, and mental health as his individual capacity will permit. More succinctly stated, the purpose of the modern elementary school should be in the direction of the *total growth and development* of the child during the formative educational years. Health education is necessarily concerned with the whole individual. The World Health Organization has defined health as "a state of complete *physical, mental,* and *social* well being and not merely the absence of disease or infirmity." Consequently, health education must be considered an essential and integral part of elementary education if the general objectives of the elementary school are to be realized.

REFERENCES

Anderson, C. L., *School Health Practice*, 2nd ed., St. Louis, Mosby, 1960, chap. 1.

Efraemson, M. W., "Summary of Health Goals of Elementary Education," *The Journal of School Health*, November, 1956.

Haag, Jessie Helen, *School Health Program*, New York, Holt, 1958, chap. 1.

[12] U.S. Department of Health, Education, and Welfare, Office of Education, *Report of the Ninth Conference on Elementary Education, May 7, 8, 9, 1956,* Washington, D.C.

Harnett, A. L., and J. H. Shaw, *Effective School Health Education*, New York, Appleton-Century-Crofts, 1959, chap. 2.

Merrill, M. H., "Immediate Concerns in Child Health Supervision," *California's Health*, September 15, 1957.

Nichols, H. L., "Problems in Developing an Adequate Health-Instruction Program," *The Journal of School Health*, September, 1958.

Oberteuffer, D., "Philosophy and Principles of the School Health Program," *The Journal of School Health*, April, 1953.

Oberteuffer, D., *School Health Education*, 3rd ed., New York, Harper, 1960, chaps. 1, 2.

Sliepcevich, Elena M., "Echoes from the Past," *The Journal of School Health*, May, 1960.

Veselak, K. E., "Historical Steps in the Development of the Modern School Health Program," *The Journal of School Health*, September, 1959.

ORGANIZATION AND ADMINISTRATION OF THE ELEMENTARY SCHOOL HEALTH PROGRAM

2

1 *What are some general plans of organization of the school health program?*
2 *What are some teacher responsibilities in the organization and administration of the school health program?*
3 *What are some aspects of organization and administration of health service, healthful school living, and health teaching?*
4 *How can the school health program be coordinated?*
5 *What are some of the functions of the school health council or committee?*

Because state of health is of such particular urgency in childhood and because it bears so directly upon learning efficiency, health is a prime consideration in the elementary schools. At other school levels, and especially among older groups generally, it is assumed that responsibility for health resides primarily with the individual. It is also usually assumed that beyond the elementary school level an intelligent awareness of personal and group health needs will lead to healthy behavior. Studies of the health knowledge and practices of older groups suggest that this assumption is not justified; yet, at any rate, the fact remains that school officials and personnel have recognized the inability of the young child to provide for his own health needs and health education. Thus, traditionally, even in schools dedicated almost exclusively to the "3 R's," a health program of sorts has been taken for granted. Just as the responsibility for the health of the infant is that of the parents, responsibility for the health of the child during the school day has been accepted by the elementary school.

It is probable that the ability of the elementary school child to understand his own health needs and to direct his own health practices has been underestimated. Because of this underestimation, relatively little emphasis has been placed upon providing a substantial, systematic, and well-rounded program of health teaching. The great emphasis in the elementary school health program has been upon providing a healthful and safe environment and the services needed to attend to illness, first aid, health-screening programs, and referrals. These considerations involve both the public education and public health programs.

ORGANIZATION AT THE STATE LEVEL

In a somewhat unusual way, the public education and public health programs converge upon the elementary school child. Although in past years there was considerable controversy as to who was responsible for school health—the board of education or the board of health—at present a cooperative approach involving both boards seems to be the most feasible one. State laws set the pattern to be followed in the schools, although individual communities may go as far as they wish beyond these standards. State laws may specify that all children are to be tested for sight and hearing, that all teachers must be examined yearly for evidences of communicable diseases, and that "hygiene and sanitation" must be included among the subjects taught in schools. Clearly, carrying out these directions requires consultation between the public health and school officials, and ample leeway is allowed for local administration.

Usually, school health facilities and personnel are augmented and supplemented by public health programs. For example, at the state level it is common for school and public health officials to engage in cooperative planning to establish policies, to consider school health needs, and to attempt the solution of specific school health problems. In some cases, these liaisons are further augmented by state school health councils composed of both public health and school personnel and concerned with health problems and needs of children.

ORGANIZATION AT THE COMMUNITY LEVEL

A great deal of variation is found in the organization of school health programs at the local level. In some instances, the city or county board of education plays the dominant role, while in others responsibility is mainly in the hands of the board of health. Two counties in one eastern state may serve to illustrate markedly different, but quite effective, approaches to conducting a school health program. Both typify the excellent cooperation of school and public health personnel in the interests of a functional and efficient school health program. Moreover, both programs are considered highly satisfactory by those involved in them, and both are considered outstanding by outside observers. It is noteworthy that the focus of attention in both cases is upon healthful school living and health services.

In one of these counties, a well-trained and experienced supervisor of health education, employed by the board of education, has organized and supervised an extensive program of health screening and arranged for the operation of clinics (including hearing, vision, dental, and mental health) for the diagnosis of children referred. She has also organized an active county health council composed of lay citizens, teachers, school administrators, and medical and other health personnel who are concerned with school health and who are able to assume leadership in studying and coordinating suitable approaches to health problems. This intimate relationship between boards of health and education in this particular county may be further illustrated by the fact that although the so-called "nurses-aides" who are responsible for first aid in the secondary schools of the county are under the supervisor administratively, the public health nurses, who routinely visit the elementary schools, work closely with the aides, the teachers, the school administrators, and the supervisor. Screening, immunization, and other programs represent some of the additional cooperative activities engaged in.

In contrast, the other county has no health education supervisor employed by its board of education. Most of the responsibilities of the supervisor in the previous example are in the hands of the county health officer (a physician) and his staff. The county officer's intense interest in the health of children leads to a considerable emphasis on the school aspect of the total community health program. His health educator maintains very close contact with the schools and is of service to them in many ways. On the other hand, although leadership in conducting the health service aspect of the school program is mainly in the hands of public health officials, school personnel at all levels demonstrate an active and continuing interest in the program. It should be added, as a reflection of interest in the teaching aspect of school health, that the school officials of both of these counties frequently invite professors from a nearby university to conduct courses for their teachers on the school health program and the teaching of health.

ORGANIZATION AT THE INDIVIDUAL SCHOOL LEVEL

It has been pointed out that the total school health program is composed of three major aspects—health services, healthful school living, and health teaching. These form the basis for both organization and administration of individual programs, and consideration of them may serve as a guide to the evaluation of existing programs.

In addition to protection provided by official supervision of school building construction, individual schools receive a great deal of guidance from coordinating and supervising groups in regard to health services and environmental considerations. However, it should be stressed that none of the aspects of the school health program can be taken care of "once and for all" and then forgotten. For example, it is frequently found, especially in some older schools, that lighting in various parts of classrooms is far below the recommended minimum standard and is affecting pupil performance in reading and other close work; stairways, locker areas, and play areas may become unsafe; cleanliness standards may be relaxed by inadequately supervised custodial staffs and the absence of campaigns involving pupil participation; emotional tensions and/or perhaps factory-like regimentation may become inordinate; and so on. These general developments illustrate the need for continual alertness to and evaluation of the environmental aspects of the school health program, which are basic to healthful school living.

School Health Services

The health services aspect of the school health program is the chief medium whereby public and school forces join in the interests of child health maintenance and disease detection and treatment. Thus, the health service maintains a continuing scrutiny of school children for evidences of behavior indicative of health disturbances; it has to do with seeing that such evidences are diagnosed by properly qualified persons; and it also has to do with utilizing available sources for the treatment of disturbances that are discovered.

Numerous illustrations of the functions of the school health service could be cited. For example, it sometimes happens that, as a result of cooperative planning by the board of education and the board of health, arrangements are made for the dental screening of the children in a particular grade. The parents of all children showing evidence of tooth decay or other defects are advised of the problem and encouraged to provide dental treatment. In similar ways, vision and hearing screening programs may be conducted. If parents are unable to provide suitable treatment by private therapists, efforts are made to take care of the child through other possible public means. Benevolent organizations frequently offer help in such cases and on request provide such things as glasses and hearing aids for children in need.

At the elementary school level, perhaps the most common plan for availing school children of public health resources is to have public health nurses assigned to one or more schools. Routine visits (monthly, weekly, semiweekly, or biweekly, depending upon personnel available in relation to the number of schools) by the nurse to the school put her in a position to provide information to teachers —information on current health problems, valuable health materials, visual aids, immunization and screening programs, and so on—and to acquire information about the health of individual children and general health conditions of the school. Under qualified leadership, cooperative programs of this kind are in relatively efficient operation all over the country, with little or no evidence of a conflict as to jurisdiction between boards of education and boards of health.

Responsibility for the School Health Services Program. Consideration of the foregoing information suggests that, generally speaking, school *and* public health personnel are responsible for the school health services program. We think first of the medical orientation of this aspect of the school program. Nurses are key figures, for they move freely between school and health board facilities in order to bring all available resources to bear in the interest of child health. Moreover, medical and other therapeutic clinics, such as those for speech, dentistry, hearing, mental health, and remedial fitness, may be established to serve child needs. Of course, great sensitivity to the health needs of school children and awareness of the school situation on the part of health officials is essential for the satisfactory operation of this program.

However, the role of school personnel is also paramount in the health services program. Understanding and encouragement on the part of school administrators is indispensable for its full development. Numerous services may be available from public health departments, but unfortunately they are utilized only to a minimum extent in many schools. This situation is frequently traced to lack of enthusiastic leadership on the part of school administrators. On the other hand, where these programs are flourishing there is almost invariably strong administrative support behind them. Apparently, the intimate relationship between health and learning efficiency is still not fully appreciated, and child health, therefore, is considered by some to be the concern of a program other than general education.

As may easily be surmised from the foregoing, the teacher is of utmost importance in a satisfactorily conducted school health program. Not only is it essential that the teacher cooperate in the various screening and immunization programs, but, of perhaps even greater importance, it is the teacher who must make the necessary referrals to the nurse or other personnel. Thus, when teachers fail to play their role fully in the program, they may readily frustrate the efforts of others to provide information and services and to handle referrals.

The teacher may make a further vital contribution to the school health services program by utilizing its activities to teach children the functions and importance of medical and other community health services in their lives. Such teaching can be of the utmost importance for the child's future. Moreover, skillful teaching can be a vital factor in avoiding or reducing the intense fears commonly associated with dental and medical examinations and treatment. Fears of this kind are not to be underestimated, for numerous individuals in need of and able to pay for dental treatment refuse to make or keep appointments because of fear of the clinical situation. Many people undergo marked rise in heart rate and blood pressure whenever they enter a clinic or hospital, and thus medical diagnosis may be confused. And as everyone knows, many children and adults are inordinately afraid of hypodermic needles. Skillful teaching can be an important factor in encouraging a more positive attitude toward medical and dental diagnoses and treatment.

Healthful School Living

Vast experience in school construction has led to the accumulation of plans and recommendations which should insure basically healthful and safe school plants. Also, construction codes, including electrical and fire regulations, sanitary requirements, and the like, tend to make new buildings quite satisfactory for educational purposes. Unfortunately, planners sometimes fail to benefit from past experience, with the result that locker areas, dressing rooms, hallways, dining facilities, and gymnasium and play areas sometimes contain hazardous or potentially unsanitary conditions. Unfortunately, too, older buildings are sometimes allowed to become unsafe, and inadequate attention may be given to such vital factors as proper lighting in hallways and study and work areas. In fact, experience has shown that when teachers in even relatively modern buildings make lightmeter studies of their classrooms, they sometimes discover that the lighting is far substandard and, therefore, not conducive to visual health. Similarly, seats may be of poor design, thus making for poor lighting of working surfaces, while at the same time discouraging good posture. Ventilation problems, too, are far from nonexistent, and, with increasing tendencies around the country to extend school work into the summer months, suitable cooling systems become vital considerations.

The healthful school living aspect of the program should also take into account the general element of interpersonal relationships among the various individuals and groups associated with the school, in particular, children, teachers, parents, and administrative and supervisory personnel. For example, excessively used public address or intercommunication systems, or listening devices that give an impression of spying on the classroom; "snooper-vision" types of supervision; chronically complaining or favor-seeking teachers; poor disciplinary practices by individual teachers; inept grouping of mentally inferior or emotionally disturbed children; overly solicitous or misguided parents—all these are factors which can interfere with the emotional-social health climate of the school. In addition, healthful school living takes into account the mode of operation of the school as this mode affects the people in the school. For example, an atmosphere of haste and of high-pressure operation, in the factory sense, is as little conducive to emotional health as slovenliness is to efficiency.

Responsibility for Healthful School Living. The obvious answer to the question, "Who is responsible for ensuring healthful school living?" is "Everyone in the school." The position of leadership in individual schools is, of course, that of the school principal. Upon his awareness of the meaning of healthful school living and how to implement it depends, to a considerable extent, the success of this aspect of the program.

Although there is no question that the principal's leadership is of prime importance to the satisfactory conducting of the environmental aspect of the school health program, the importance of other personnel should certainly not be underestimated. Thus, teachers play a major role in seeing that they and their children participate in the program. Moreover, the teacher is in an ideal position to keep the school administration sensitive to new problems and developments which *require* action that is beyond his own scope or that of any individual class.

The children of the school, too, should be considered active participants in the maintenance of healthful school living. And, of course, the teacher can use the program as a means of teaching basic principles of cleanliness and sanitation that are essential to group living.

The role of certain other personnel in the maintenance of healthful school living is so obvious as to require only brief mention to round out the total picture. Nurses, doctors, custodial and cafeteria staffs, and public health inspectors are all vitally concerned with healthful living in the schools. Occasionally, health and safety problems may arise which require the attention of parent-teacher organizations, as well as professional groups.

Health Teaching

The present volume is especially concerned with the health teaching aspect of the school health program. Without disputing the importance, even the indispensability, of healthful school living and health services, it must be emphasized that health teaching which is designed to increase the individual's ability to live healthily and deal intelligently with his own health problems is basic to the whole concept of healthful living.

Health teaching is handled in various ways in different school systems, depending upon the administrative plans and policies that are in operation. In some situations a renewed attention to the need for specialists in various subject-matter areas has given rise to a considerable amount of departmentalization in some elementary schools. Moreover, it is to be expected that there will be some variation from school to school within the same system. In some cases, health teaching is dealt with in the form of specific projects or units on health topics. In some cases, too, resource persons such as nurses, health agency personnel and safety specialists, are invited to teach particular subjects. However, in the great majority of cases health is taught in connection with other subject-matter areas, such as life science and social studies. It is for this reason that integration and techniques of integration are emphasized in subsequent chapters of the present book.

Perhaps the major problem and point of chief justifiable criticism that may be leveled at teaching health through integration is that, through ignorance of the concept, this approach may tend to relegate health to secondary, incidental, or even insignificant importance. The teacher may bring in the health aspect of a topic if it happens to occur to him or her to do so. For example, one year a teacher may include excellent material on mental health in a social studies unit because of stimulation from newspapers and television programs on the subject which happens to coincide with certain material scheduled for teaching. Another year, without the stimulation of current publicity, mental health may be forgotten in that unit of instruction. For another example, a physical education teacher may do important teaching on the subject of elementary human reproduction because at about that same time he or she may *happen* to be taking a university course on the subject, or because questioning from pupils *happens* to set the stage for such teaching.

The crucial point in this discussion is that health knowledge and guidance is far too important to human welfare to be left to such chance encounters with provocations for teaching. To integrate health with the various other curriculum areas of the elementary school is *not* to relegate it to chance but to place it carefully in a natural setting.

On the other hand, in a few elementary schools, health teaching is considered a subject-matter area in its own right and is treated as a major theme into which other subjects are integrated. Quite commonly the individual teacher has little or no choice as to which general type of approach he will use, but in any event excellent teaching can be done.

Responsibility for Health Teaching. Quite clearly the major responsibility for health teaching in the elementary school rests with the classroom teacher. However, in many situations the teacher has numerous resources to draw upon in the way of free and inexpensive materials and various health and safety personnel connected with either the school or the local public health organization. The teacher is responsible for utilizing these in such a way that they fit into the sequence of learning experiences.

In elementary schools where physical education teachers are available, they may be utilized for extremely important health teaching which may be integrated into various aspects of their programs. For example, they may communicate basic health concepts, especially as these relate to matters of nutrition, effects of physical activity, importance of proper rest and sleep, effects of smoking, and so on.

Coordination of the School Health Program

In most schools a need is felt for some coordinating body to maintain a continuing scrutiny of the entire school health program. No matter how earnestly the principal of the school may try to encourage the program; how anxious the individual teacher is to teach important health concepts, or to observe the children carefully so as to make suitable referrals and work closely with nurses and other personnel; or how eager the nurse is to bring the services of community health programs into the schools—the entire program is in constant danger of failing in its function if it lacks some sort of means of coordination.

Some examples should serve to clarify this point. School pupils often complain that they do not like "health." This reaction is paradoxical because "health" is one of those subjects that has to do with the child himself—his growth, vigor and efficiency—and should be of great interest to him. However, a negative attitude is often traceable directly to the fact that more than one teacher has taught the pupils exactly the same material, perhaps several times. By implication it may safely be assumed that in such instances of unintentional and pointless repetition, certain other equally important health topics are being neglected completely. Clearly there is a need for school-wide planning of the health teaching curriculum and materials, just as there presumably is in other subject-matter areas.

As a further example, teachers A and B see a need for improving the selection of foods by children in the cafeteria. However, no school-wide effort is pointed in this direction, with the result that neither other teachers nor pupils nor cafeteria personnel become involved in the effort and, indeed, may inadvertently interfere with or block it. Similarly, efforts of individual teachers to institute hallway or playground safety measures, cleanliness measures or child fitness programs may fail or be only partially successful because of a lack of school-wide coordination and the cooperation of key persons.

Various approaches may be made to the forming and conducting of a health coordination program. One common procedure is for the principal to appoint a council or committee composed of key personnel and chaired by the individual whose interest is greatest and who is best qualified by training and experience to assume this responsibility. In addition to teachers and administrative personnel, the health committee should include the nurse who services the school, an especially interested member of the Parent-Teacher Association, a school physician if available, and perhaps one of the more mature children in the school who can represent the pupils' point of view. Custodial staff members, cafeteria personnel, and resource persons are invited as needed, depending upon the particular problems under consideration.

A school health committee of this kind might well be divided into subcommittees, one devoting its special attention to each of the three major aspects of the total school health program—health services, healthful school living, and health teaching. In this way care can be taken that all aspects of the program receive continuing scrutiny, and planning and action can, when appropriate, take into account the entire school and the community. For example, an immunization or screening program can, with planning, be a vehicle for health learning experiences involving the entire school and extending out into the community.

Needless to say, there is a great deal of variation from school to school in the emphasis that is placed upon the activities of health committees. In some schools, the committee merely concerns itself with problems that arise, serves as a liaison between the school and the health department, and does a certain amount of curriculum planning so as to distribute health topics through the grades and avoid excessive overlap or repetition. In other schools, where the greatest importance is attached to health, the health committee is exceedingly active and seeks aggressively to improve all aspects of the total program. Where such programs are found, administrative leadership is usually very much in evidence.

REFERENCES

Anderson, C. L., *School Health Practice,* 2nd ed., St. Louis, Mosby, 1960.

Haag, Jessie Helen, *School Health Program,* New York, Holt, 1958, Part 8.

Harnett, Arthur L., and John H. Shaw, *Effective School Health Education,* New York, Appleton-Century-Crofts, 1958, chap. 4.

Irwin, Leslie W., James H. Humphrey, and Warren R. Johnson, *Methods and Materials in School Health Education,* St. Louis, Mosby, 1956, chap. 2.

Oberteuffer, Delbert, *School Health Education,* 3rd ed., New York, Harper, 1960, chap. 16.

Turner, C. E., C. M. Sellery, and S. Louise Smith, *School Health and Health Education,* 3rd ed., St. Louis, Mosby, 1957.

CHILD HEALTH AND
PHYSICAL FITNESS

3

1 *What is meant by "total personality" health?*
2 *What are the various elements of total personality health?*
3 *What is meant by "physical fitness" as it pertains to the elementary school child?*
4 *What are some general aspects of physical fitness?*
5 *What are the responsibilities of the elementary school classroom teacher with regard to health and fitness of children?*

Sound health and fitness are basic requirements for success in school—if by "success" we mean performance at or near the child's capacity in the total educative process. Not only do we mean the obvious, that "ill children make poor pupils," we also mean that the child who is not ill but whose level of health and/or fitness is "below par" is to some degree a *handicapped* child. He is handicapped with respect to one or more of the objectives of education.

CASE STUDY

An 8-year-old boy was referred to our Clinic[1] because of poor large-muscle coordination. Unlike most of the children referred to the clinic he had no physical defect of a medical kind—he was not emotionally disturbed,

[1] Children's Physical Developmental Clinic, College of Physical Education, Recreation and Health, University of Maryland. Cases cited in this chapter are all from this Clinic's files. These studies are not unique, since a number of other universities conduct somewhat similar programs and have had generally similar results. However, these cases were selected as a matter of convenience and are merely illustrative of a considerable number that could be drawn upon.

got top marks in school, and showed precocious skill in working with his hands. On the other hand, he never played with other children and was very timid and submissive when in contact with them. He was fat and moved awkwardly and was generally found sitting, making something, or watching television.

Individualized attention and skillful introduction of this child to basic physical skills and gymnasium activities quickly led him to "make friends with his body," that is, to realize that his body too could be trusted to serve him in what he wanted to do. In a very short time he gained the confidence to participate fully in the activities of other children and on an equal basis with them. In keeping with his intelligence, his classroom work remained at a high level.

COMMENT. This case was somewhat unusual in that most physically inadequate and socially maladjusted children do not "turn to their studies" and other eye-hand coordination work, but perform poorly in these areas as well. This boy was like a seed in the sun, needing only a little water to make it spring into life. When his basic need for physical activity and skill were satisfied and certain minor dietary adjustments were made, the child's response was quick and lasting. He was no longer *handicapped* with respect to the social, emotional, and fitness objectives of the educative process.

MEANING OF "TOTAL PERSONALITY" HEALTH

No modern definition of health fails to take into account a combination of mental, emotional, and social, as well as physical, aspects of human behavior. Writers on the subject of health commonly describe health as being a delicate and complex balance of these aspects—very much as Walter Cannon described homeostasis as being a complex, ever fluctuating balance of bodily functions which remain about the same in spite of stresses and strains in the environment.

On the other hand, a great deal of clinical and experimental evidence indicates that a human being must be considered as a whole —an organism interacting with other organisms—and not a collection of parts. This, of course, is the psychosomatic approach to health. According to this point of view, when a worried parent's stomach "knots up," when a beginning teacher trembles and perspires, or when a nervous child stutters or becomes nauseated, a mental state is *not* causing a physical symptom. On the contrary, a pressure imposed upon the organism causes a series of reactions which include thought, verbalization, digestive processes, and muscular functions. This distinction as to cause and effect may appear trivial, but it is basic to psychosomatic thinking. Mind does not cause the body to become upset; the total organism is upset by a situation and reflects its upset in several different ways, including disturbances in thought, feeling, and bodily processes. The whole individual responds in interaction with the social and physical environment. And, as the individual is affected by his environment, he, in turn, has an effect upon it.

However, because of a long tradition during which either physical development *or* mental development, rather than physical *and* mental development, have been glorified, we are accustomed to dividing the two in our thinking. The result is that we sometimes pull human beings apart with this kind of thinking too. Consider, for example, the case described earlier in this chapter. That boy's parents were affectionate and provided an excellent intellectual environment for him. But their lack of provision for his physical needs, which resulted in the undermining of his self-confidence and emotional and social development, literally forced the situation which finally required remedial attention.

A great deal of evidence from our own Clinic could be used to illustrate this point further. Traditional attitudes which separate mind and body tend to lead to unbalanced development of the child with respect to mind and body and/or social adjustment. To understand total personality health, the human organism can be seen in terms of a triangle. The three sides—physical, emotional, and intellectual aspects of the total personality—form a single figure, with the physical as base. An arrow, extending from the center of the triangle upward through one of the sides, is designated "social" to represent interpersonal relationships. The arrow is pointed at both ends to suggest a two-way operation: The individual is affected by those around him, and he affects them (largely by way of verbalizations). The whole figure, the triangle, is dependent upon a balance of all its parts, and if one part of the triangle is changed, the entire triangle is affected. It is interesting to draw diagrams in which one after another of the sides is shortened—as in one kind or another of developmental failure or retardation—and see how this affects the triangle. It is also interesting to make personal applications such as the following: "What happens to my intellectual performance when I am worried or have a stomach ache?" "What changes occur in my body when I 'feel' frightened, embarrassed, or angered?" "How would I do in a test if I had just received bad news from home?" And so on. Obviously, similar applications can be made to children.

In this day when great emphasis is placed upon social adjustment —but when perhaps our major problems involve faulty interpersonal relationships—it is reasonable to make special note of the interaction between the individual and his environment. The quality of the individual's interpersonal relationships affects all the other aspects of his personality. How well do you drive when someone is shouting at you? How well can you study when you think someone is "talking about you?" What happens to the appetite, interests, appearance, and activities of the young person in love? Of the child whose home is in a state of upheaval? All of these are social circumstances which affect the total physical, intellectual, and emotional organism.

But this matter of social considerations, of interpersonal relationships, is still more fundamental to health than the foregoing illustrations suggest. For example, it has been found that infants and very young children who are deprived of a reasonable amount of mothering—that initial and basic social experience—actually stop growing in one or more aspects of their personality, even though all of their other needs are met. Thus, some fail to grow mentally and become idiots. Some actually stop growing both physically and mentally and remain infants as long as they live. Still others are affected mainly at the emotional level. That is, if they are deprived of love and given, instead, nonloving care, they may fail to grow emotionally and not be capable of human feeling as we generally think of it. This may be the cause of the so-called psychopathic personality, that most unfeeling, antisocial, "wolf in the fold" of criminal types. In brief, the quality of interpersonal relationships in the early years tends to set the pattern of subsequent attitudes and behavior toward other people, authority, and the "rules of the game" of life generally. Early and later social relationships also have a profound influence upon physical and emotional health and intellectual performance, as the following case illustrates. (All of the cases cited in this chapter are true and not so very unusual. If they appear extreme, bear in mind that they are selected to make a point and that the *principles* involved apply in less extreme cases.)

CASE STUDY

A 13-year-old girl, Ann, had become the outlet for her stepfather's frustrations and maladjustments from about age 9. Even worse than his shocking treatment of her physically was his continual discrediting of all aspects of her behavior, ranging from her intelligence to her table manners. She became the black sheep of the family, entirely inept in all that she did because, as a child will, she accepted her stepfather's evaluation of her as true. Her low level of self-esteem literally forced her to the worst possible performance in all social relations and in school, where she did failing work and was a constant source of irritation to her teachers. After several trials she was permanently excluded from class. Her low opinion of herself was expressed further in nail-biting, bed-wetting, and pulling out her hair. She had frequent accidents and took a certain amount of pleasure in the pain involved.

Since the professional people who attempted to deal with her numerous symptoms were not fully aware of the pathological father-daughter relationship, treatment that was attempted was focused upon the girl's emotions on the supposition that some immaturity or other inadequacy must be responsible. Finally, however, the mother was helped to realize that no treatment could succeed which failed to get at the fundamental problem of interpersonal relationships. She separated from her husband and lived alone with her daughter. Within a few months the symptoms of stress and self-abuse (i.e., wetting herself in her sleep, disfiguring her finger nails, pulling out her hair, and making disparaging remarks about her own appearance and intelligence) had disappeared; social adjustment with other children became normal, and home study revealed Ann to be a bright child entirely capable of keeping up with her class, even after having fallen far behind.

"Verbalization" deserves special comment as an aspect of social interaction. The infant's first social contact is by way of his skin, as he is fed, fondled and caressed. This communication via the skin expresses the warm relationship between mother and child and is a kind of "language of the body" which both understand deeply and which will linger throughout life as a fundamental way of "expressing" love and affection.[2] But as the child develops intellec-

---

[2] The controversy over breast versus bottle feeding is probably not so much a nutritional as a social matter. The breast-fed baby must experience the intimate contact with the mother—with all that this implies for loving care, safety, and security; but the bottle-fed baby *may* be robbed of this initial social experience if left alone habitually with the bottle.

tually, verbalization replaces touch as the prime medium of social interaction. Gradually, verbalization in spoken and written form becomes a major influence in the child's environment. Far too little consideration is given to the implications of the quality of verbalization for the total health of the individual. For example, in many homes mealtime is a time of gossip, a period of criticizing and ridiculing friends, neighbors, fellow workers, and so on. Or perhaps worse, it is a time of intrafamily verbal conflict. Not only is such talk and the model that it constitutes in the child's mind of questionable value from a social health point of view, but also the aroused emotions are likely to affect digestion adversely and to establish certain deep-seated attitudes regarding eating and meals. (Have you ever seen angry people literally attack their food as though it were an enemy?)

Moreover, the parent's authoritative suggestions regarding food and eating are likely to have far greater influence upon the child's subsequent health attitudes and behavior than their accuracy or importance warrants. For example, one hears the common harping: "You eat that or you'll get sick," "If you eat such and such foods together, you'll get sick," "If you want to be healthy and strong you have to clean up your plate," and so on. Overeating in adulthood is sometimes a direct hangover from childhood when an enormous capacity and plate-cleaning were held up as signal virtues. Similar kinds of applications could be made with respect to all aspects of health. For example, adult verbalization regarding the child's body build ("He's too skinny," "He isn't husky enough," "He's a frail child") can have the effect of making a perfectly normal though naturally lean and not red-faced child profoundly suspicious as to the adequacy of his body—which is to say, of himself.

No discussion of verbalization in relation to health would be adequate without consideration being given to the fantastic barrage of television, radio, magazine, and newspaper advertising on health topics. The advertiser, whose function is to sell a product and not to elevate the public health, uses every trick of language and other symbols to instill the desired point of view in the mind of the listener or reader. Sometimes the product is of value and sometimes it is harmless, but frequently the advertisement represents a seductive effort to get people of all ages to acquire a dangerous habit. It may be fair to say that *all* health advertising is suspect because, as we have said, the advertiser's objective is sales and not public health. Unfortunately, however, recent studies indicate that health advertising in the mass media of communication are exceedingly effective in shaping children's thinking as to the merits of products in a health sense.

This then is the basis of total personality health—a complex balance of psychophysical and social considerations which qualify the individual for the fullest, most socially valuable, productive, and adventuresome living. Childhood is the time when healthful attitudes and patterns of living are set or not set, and it is therefore of urgent importance that parents and educators concern themselves with meeting the total health needs of children.

MEANING OF PHYSICAL FITNESS

We will now devote our attention to physical aspects of personality health.

In earlier eras of human existence, education was primarily a matter of developing physical skills and prowess, because success in life depended heavily upon a man's might and endurance. Emotional education was also of great importance because certain attitudes were needed which would make men able to face what they had to do and able to withstand their own fears and doubts.

Today a man's success depends upon his skill with relatively small muscle responses, such as those of the hands, eyes, and vocal chords, and upon abstract thinking. Consequently, education concerns itself mainly with developing those skills and with the manipulating of symbols such as words and numbers. Education of the physical aspect of the personality is generally considered of minor importance in general education. Under present circumstances of making a living, this seems reasonable—until we stop to consider the violence that it does in terms of the biological heritage of man and the nature of children. It is encouraging to note that in very recent years, there has been a growing awareness of the importance of fitness in children.

Traditional thinking, as we have noted earlier, has tended to bring about a separation of mind and body, with the result that physical fitness is commonly considered an isolated quality of the individual and having no special relationship with other aspects of the personality. Thinking back to the triangular representation of the human personality, however, we are reminded that the physical aspect is an integral part of the total organism.

CASE STUDY

Robert, age 12, was referred to our Clinic by the psychiatry department of a children's hospital because of his physical inadequacy, which seemed in part responsible for his meager response to treatment. He had a slight neurological disorder, but his major symptoms were of an emotional and social nature. When in public, his arms were folded habitually around his body as though for protection, and upon entering a situation where there were other people, he would shrink down visibly and appear to be attempting to disappear into the wall. Although this boy was very intelligent, the quality of his school work fell far short of the limits of his capability.

Great care and, of course, individual attention were needed in order to get Robert to attempt the various activities utilized in the Clinic. However, his clinician succeeded in befriending the boy, and because there was little possibility of failure and because he did not have to compare his performance with that of other children, he soon began to respond. As his motor skill and fitness improved and his feeling of confidence in what he could do was strengthened, his posture and manner of walking became more assured. As strength, eye-hand coordination, and ball-handling skills improved, he began to be observed playing ball with neighborhood children, riding his bicycle with them, and being, in general, no longer a person apart. For the first time in several years, he became able to sleep well (preoccupation with his inability to sleep had been a major fear playing on his mind), and his appetite became greatly improved. His heightened confidence was reflected in his schoolwork, in which he showed greater ability to concentrate and to address himself to new tasks of all kinds.

COMMENT. Robert's case was interpreted as being one in which a child was brought more nearly into harmony with his biological heritage and the nature of other children. The efforts of the Clinic were heartily reinforced by the parents who, upon gaining insight into the basic concepts of the Clinic, did everything possible to encourage a fitness attitude in the home. Highly educated though they were, these parents had no awareness of the physical activity and fitness needs of their son, nor of the possible relationship of these needs to his emotional and social problems. Like a great many other people, they had not realized how basic to the whole personality the physical aspect is.

It is not claimed that the fitness and skills program "cured" the psychological problems which underlay Robert's maladjustment. However, it does seem fair to say that the program heightened his self-esteem as he gained respect for his ability to do exciting things requiring courage, skill, and perseverance. An improved ability to associate with his peers on an equal footing also helped to put Robert in a much better position to live with, handle, and perhaps in time overcome his other problems.

The foregoing illustration suggests some of the various factors that are involved in physical fitness. These, too, may be conceived in terms of a triangular relationship because of their interdependence and the implied need for balance of the factors. The triangle of physical fitness suggests that there are three major components of fitness, all of which have to be taken into account for the improvement and maintenance of fitness at all age levels. The three components are movement (physical activity, exercise), nutrition, and rest and relaxation.

Movement (Physical Activity, Exercise)

One of the most fundamental characteristics of life is movement; whatever else they may involve, all of man's achievements are based upon his ability to move. Obviously, the very young child is not an intelligent being in the sense of performing abstract thinking, and he only gradually acquires the ability to deal with symbols and intellectualize his experiences in the course of his development. On the other hand, the child is a creature of movement and feeling. Any efforts to train or educate the child must take this relative dominance of the intellectual versus movement and feeling into account. The following diagram is an approximation which is intended to show how, in the course of developing, the child only gradually becomes able to deal with life on an intellectual basis and how, in the meantime, he responds to life primarily in terms of movement and feeling.

The two lines in the diagram can only be suggestive of a tendency and cannot be precise in terms of the rate of convergence, but the principle under consideration is indisputable. Intellectualizing and verbalizing ability is still at the zero point long after life has been totally a matter of moving and feeling for a very considerable period. The diagram suggests why it is that classroom teachers are

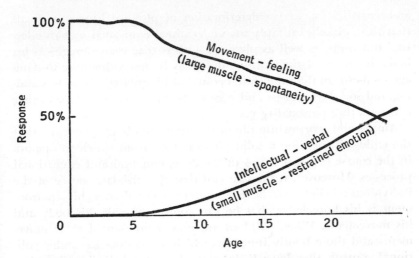

The Development of the Intellectual-Verbal Response to Environment.
High muscle movement and feeling and low intellectualization-verbalization
are the characteristic responses in childhood. With increasing maturity the
intellectual-verbal responses gradually become more important.

continually having to attempt to motivate their children to want to
learn to deal with the symbols and abstractions of the established
curriculum, and it also suggests why the teacher of physical and outdoor education and the camp counselor have few problems of
motivation. They have the advantage of dealing with the child
"where he lives." It is exactly for this reason that many teachers
of young children, both normal and those designated "atypical,"
utilize a play approach to learning, using games, dances, and gym-
nastic activities as means of conveying concepts of number, social
studies, life sciences and so on.[3]

As the years pass, the discrepancy between the intellectual and the
physical (movement-feeling) narrows, and in a great many people
there is a complete reversal of the dominance of the two—although,
of course, some maintain a proper balance. The common result of
such a reversal is a life centered around small-muscle movements

3 For an elementary school physical education book that emphasizes this
approach, see James H. Humphrey, *Elementary School Physical Education: With
Emphasis upon Its Integration in Other Curriculum Areas*, New York, Harper,
1958.

and verbalization and a deterioration of physical fitness—with all that this is likely to imply for undermined emotional and intellectual functions, as well as physical. This is true even though, as his body deteriorates, the mature adult may be less vulnerable to damaged self-esteem than the child because of his greater self-understanding and social awareness and because he may have developed other compensating personality resources.

Ample and worthwhile physical activity tends to guarantee that the child will develop a solid physical base from which to operate in the course of his progress in the developmental and educational processes. Moreover, it may be said that the ultimate source of the individual's belief that he can exercise control over his environment is his knowledge that he can control himself, his body and his movements. When children are unable to control their movements and those bodily functions which are ordinarily under volitional control, they have little or no basis for believing that they can exercise control over anything external to them. It is for this reason that numerous children who are deficient in all or even some of the usual activities expected of children suddenly spring into the range of "normal" when their physical base is improved.

Case 1

Bruce was an intelligent boy of 10 whose only serious fitness problem was that he had practically no skill with his hands. He could scarcely draw and could not write in a legible way at all, nor could he sustain the effort for any but short periods. His schoolwork was suffering so badly because of his handicap that it was decided to attempt to teach him typing as an alternative solution.

The Physical Developmental Clinic began a program to elevate Bruce's general fitness so as to be sure of a solid base of operation, happy adjustment to the environment, and enough self-confidence to be assured of success in what was asked of him. Then, during rest periods between activities he was asked to draw and write about what he had been doing—how he bounced on the trampoline and what this felt like, for example. Bruce's writing skill quickly improved and he soon rose to the level of performance in school that was appropriate to his ability.

COMMENT. There are reasons to believe that such problems as inability to read and write may sometimes have psychological bases, and the contention here is not necessarily in conflict with that possibility. However, the point is that given sufficient motivation in the form of physical-emotional experiences, it is evidently quite possible to reach a point at which desire to *do* outweighs and overwhelms blockages causing inability to do, regardless of the cause of blockage.

CASE 2

Donald, age 8, was an entirely normal child except that he was very timid, entirely unwilling to become involved in the play of other children, readily dominated by other children including his sisters, and lacking in confidence in virtually all activities of his life. Although not inadequate, his body type was sufficiently light to encourage this tendency—and certainly was not large enough to provide an easy compensation.

The eight-week activity and exercise program (one session per week) provided by his clinician in the Fitness Clinic established the fact in Donald's mind that he was competent physically and that he could learn to do what he wished to do. He became more confident of himself in all aspects of his life, willing to stand up for himself, and, too, he became an enthusiastic participant in play and games.

Ideally, all parents should know a great deal about the basic needs of their children and how to guide them into activities most likely to encourage good physical development and the acquisition of physical and recreational skills. Since this is frequently not the case, however, a rather tremendous responsibility is passed on to the classroom teacher. Out of recognition of this responsibility, most states require a certain amount of physical education study in the preparation of their elementary school teachers. It is highly desirable, too, that properly qualified physical educators and other people of this general type be available for teaching, for remedial fitness, and for assisting classroom teachers in the development of good fitness and skills programs.

Nutrition

As the triangle of physical fitness shows, nutrition is an inseparable part of the fitness picture, for it may literally be said that we *are* what we eat. This is a sobering thought which leads to concern as to just what we and our children *do* eat.

There are a number of important hazards to good nutrition at the present time. However, instead of condemning certain kinds of foods or glorifying others, for advertising and commercial rather than for health reasons, it is perhaps more appropriate to emphasize fundamental nutritional needs.

In the modern American diet, there is virtually no need for concern about getting enough in the way of fats, sugars, and carbohydrates. Unfortunately, the foods that are likely to be inadequate in the diet are the vitamins and minerals and, particularly in the case of growing children, proteins. As a general recommendation, it is suggested that fruits and vegetables of a wide variety be given special consideration and be used much more widely as "snack foods" and "nibble foods" than candy and pastries.

Numerous books may be consulted for recommendations as to just what diets are recommended for children. However, one precaution is suggested. There is a tendency for some writers on nutrition to make what appear to be rather dogmatic statements as to just what types and quantities of various foods should be eaten by everyone, how much milk and orange juice and eggs and so on. Still, it is well to keep in mind two facts. The first is that it is entirely possible for children to be very healthy without any one of the much-praised foods. For example, oranges are an excellent food but many a healthy, young Swiss of a few years ago never saw them except, perhaps, on Christmas. Milk, too, is an excellent food but not indispensable. Meat is a valuable food but various religious groups, vegetarians, and peoples who cannot afford the luxury of meat have demonstrated that substitutes are entirely satisfactory.

The second fact is that eating is an individual matter. The problem is not so much one of following an arbitrary diet but of learning to know on what foods and proportions of foods one functions best—just as every person needs to discover just what his own sleep needs are. In the early years, of course, this judgment is in the hands of parents and must be based upon (1) close and intelligent observation of the child, (2) awareness of the basic nutritional needs of children and what combinations of proteins, vitamins, minerals, carbohydrates, and fats will meet those needs, and (3) appreciation of the balanced relationship of physical activity, nutrition, and rest and relaxation, as indicated in the triangle of physical fitness. To put it very simply, if a child is normal (in the medical sense), if his rest and sleep are adequate, and if his physical activity level is reasonably high (which may seem *very* high to a sedentary adult), his appetite for most foods that are put before him will be good.

CASE STUDY

David, age 9, was slight of build, generally weak and poorly coordinated. As is customary, his clinician evaluated his dietary practices, as well as his movement capabilities, and discovered that his intake of protein foods was very low. For example, he would eat no meat and cared little for milk. Since the basic theme of the clinic is to foster in both the child and parents a "fitness attitude," the clinician emphasized to the child the importance of proper eating if the desired physical development were to take place. By the third week of the clinic the child was happily eating meat and other recommended foods. This nutritional consideration was undoubtedly a major factor in the improvements that were soon noted in his physical development.

Overeating and overweight are also of importance in the development of some children. Of course fat performs vital functions in the body, but beyond a point it must be regarded as *non-payload*—like useless bricks thrown into a cargo plane. Moreover, beginning even in youth, excessive amounts of fat may be associated with the onset of certain serious degenerative diseases.

Children become fat for various reasons. Sometimes these reasons are psychological—as in cases where heavy eating is related to a serious disturbance in parent-child relationships or when excessive eating is a compensation for inadequacy of other satisfactions—and in a few cases fatness is apparently due to certain endocrine gland disturbances. However, it is likely that most cases of fatness among children today are not due to such complicated problems but to such factors as (1) naturally adopting the pattern of heavy eating and little physical activity of the adults in the family; (2) the temptation of passive recreation, such as television and comic books, plus the easy availability of high-energy foods; and/or (3) the lack of availability of attractive play and activity areas and facilities—as in the nation's vast apartment house areas where adequate provision to meet the activity needs of children is rarely made. All of these things are indicative of a widespread lack of "fitness attitude" in our society.

Basically, weight control is a simple question of energy intake and energy expenditure. When intake exceeds expenditure (as in heavy fat-sugar-carbohydrate intake, plus much sitting and little moving), fatness is likely to result. With children, as with adults, when energy intake is reduced (fruits replacing most candy and pastries) and energy outlay increased (more play, walking, swimming, hiking, gymnastics), weight tends to adjust itself to the maximum functional level of the individual.

Numerous cases could be cited to show that, when weight of children is properly adjusted to their body type and strength, their physical performance improves; they handle their bodies more easily and confidently and therefore more safely; and their improved ability to do what their peers do, with lessened tendency to attract ridicule, results in happier social adjustment.

Rest and Relaxation

The third side of our triangle of physical fitness is concerned with rest and relaxation. Just how much of these are needed by any given child depends upon a number of factors, including age, body type and activity level.

As a general rule, it may be said that if the child is quite active, physically speaking; if his nutritional state is satisfactory; if he is not being excessively stimulated by the excitement of certain forms of entertainment; and if he is not being placed under emotional pressure by family problems or various forms of competition, his rest and relaxation needs will tend to take care of themselves. The physically active child who is not under emotional pressure is ready to sleep when evening comes.

Many physical educators and other teachers make a considerable point of teaching children how to relax, how to pause from time to time to get into a comfortable position and slowly bring their muscles into a state of relaxation. Often, music and the teacher's voice quietly directing the children to relax set after set of muscles can be an important and valuable experience in how to gain a brief and worthwhile respite during the course of the day.

EVIDENCES OF DISTURBANCE IN HEALTH AND/OR FITNESS

It is not really necessary for the teacher to be able to identify a single disease as such. It is not his or her business to distinguish measles from chicken pox or other diseases.[4] On the other hand, the teacher does have an obligation to be able to distinguish good health and fitness from poor, and this obligation is dependent to a great extent upon being very sensitive to these states and observing the children closely from day to day.

The alarm signals of most diseases are readily noted, and include fever with flushed appearance, digestive upset, paleness, loss of alertness in the eyes (perhaps redness), fatigue, and lack of desire to move about. Chronic ailments may be much more difficult to spot because change in the child's appearance or behavior may be very gradual and thus not so readily noted. For example, the child may slowly lose weight, become more pale, or become less active and more readily fatigued. Disturbances of these kinds require special alertness on the part of the teacher and the assistance of such devices as periodic weighing and measuring and perhaps anecdotal records. Growth grids such as the Iowa and Wetzel Grids, which have the advantage of taking into account the individualized nature of growth, can be extremely useful in telling whether the child's growth is within the range of normalcy and does not depart markedly from its unique pattern.

At any time the teacher observes evidence of acute or chronic illness, the school's procedure for getting proper medical attention should immediately be followed. In perhaps the great majority of elementary schools, a public health nurse makes periodical visits and is thus the logical person to whom questionable cases should be referred. The nurse is informed as to the availability of clinics and other facilities which are maintained for the diagnosis of difficulties ranging from hearing testing to speech, dental fitness, and mental health evaluations.

Symptoms of poor mental health should also give rise to prompt referral so that they may receive early attention, and, if possible, their causes—which might involve a disturbance in the home—be dealt with. The teacher does not have to be able to identify neurotic or psychotic symptoms, but should realize that withdrawn behavior, extreme aggressiveness, hostility, timidity, inordinate daydreaming, and "vegetable salad" or garbled kinds of speaking are all evidences

---

[4] Most local and state health departments will provide charts showing specific symptoms of disease and related information to teachers who request them.

that something is wrong and that the child is in need of specialized evaluation and help.

Evidences of poor physical fitness and/or coordination are fairly obvious but are overlooked surprisingly often because most teachers are not trained to notice them. Such symptoms as awkward bodily movements, toes pointing out and weight falling to the inside of the feet, lack of grace or assurance in walking or ease in climbing or descending stairs, incompetence in throwing and catching balls, and lack of ability to be active for reasonably extended periods are important in themselves and may also be related to how the child feels about himself and to his ability to be an active member of his group. Unfortunately, there are few fitness therapists to whom children may be referred, and the teacher is left to her own resources in providing whatever instruction and practice is attempted. Where physical education teachers and/or supervisors are available, they should be of great value in determining the nature of the child's fitness problems and the most suitable plans for solving them. Of course, in extreme cases of this kind a highly individualized approach is essential, and recognition of the possible medical basis of the problem must be given utmost attention.

REFERENCES

Broer, M. R., *Efficiency of Human Movement*, Philadelphia, Saunders, 1960.

Caplan, G., ed., *Emotional Problems of Early Childhood*, New York, Basic Books, 1955.

Dunbar, H. F., *Mind and Body: Psychosomatic Medicine*, New York, Random House, 1955.

Layman, Emma, *Mental Health Through Physical Education and Recreation,* Minneapolis, Burgess, 1955.

Mayer, J., "Exercise and Weight Control," in Warren R. Johnson, ed., *Science and Medicine of Exercise and Sports*, New York, Harper, 1960, chap. 16.

Metheny, Eleanor, *Body Dynamics*, New York, McGraw-Hill, 1951.

Rarick, G. Lawrence, "Exercise and Growth," in Warren R. Johnson, ed., *Science and Medicine of Exercise and Sports*, New York, Harper, 1960, chap. 23.

Weiss, E., and O. S. English, *Psychosomatic Medicine*, 2nd ed., Philadelphia, Saunders, 1958.

WAYS OF OFFERING HEALTH IN THE ELEMENTARY SCHOOL CURRICULUM

4

1 *What are some general ways of arranging health teaching content in the elementary school curriculum?*

2 *What are some ways in which health learning experiences may be provided for elementary school children?*

3 *What is the general purpose of unitary teaching in the elementary school as far as health education is concerned?*

4 *What does the concept of educational integration involve in the curriculum area of health education?*

5 *How does curriculum organization influence health teaching in the elementary school?*

There are various facets and ramifications of the elementary school curriculum which in one way or another tend to influence the way in which health learning experiences should be provided. Personnel in the field of school health education are continually seeking the most desirable ways and means of selecting, organizing, and presenting those learning experiences which will favorably influence the health knowledge, attitudes, and practices of children. Obviously, there is no standard set of procedures which satisfactorily meets the needs of all elementary schools, because of the varying conditions existing from one school system to another. Consequently, there are certain basic considerations which should be taken into account, involving an understanding of (1) the general ways of arranging health teaching content; (2) the specific ways of providing health learning experiences; and (3) how health teaching functions in the various types of elementary school curriculum organization.

An attempt will be made in this chapter to help the reader resolve some of the problems connected with establishing health in the curriculum in the most desirable manner. Discussions will include consideration of certain advantages and disadvantages encountered when making application of the various procedures.

GENERAL WAYS OF ARRANGING HEALTH TEACHING CONTENT

One of the more difficult problems involved in curriculum construction in the area of health education is that concerned with the general grade placement of learning experiences. This involves the arranging of health teaching content in one of two ways.

One method is known generally as the *continuous plan* and the other as the *cycle plan*. Theoretically, there is one essential difference between the two plans. The former provides for learning experiences in specific health topical areas at *each* of the grade levels. On the other hand, the latter allows the study of given topical areas at a particular grade within a range of grade levels. Taking the topical area of nutrition as an example, when the continuous plan is employed, a sequential order of learning experiences concerning nutrition would be provided at every level from Grades 1 through 6. In the cycle plan the topic of nutrition would be taken up once during the primary level and once during the intermediate level.

The Continuous Plan

This means of arranging health teaching content is the one most prevalent in the modern elementary school. Proponents of this plan feel that continuity of learning experiences is assured from one grade level to another. Moreover, it appears likely that the child's present and future health needs can be satisfied best when learning experiences are presented at each stage of his development. It is suggested also that retention of health knowledge is more likely to occur when learnings follow a sequential order from year to year, thus providing for suitable articulation between maturity levels in terms of the child's readiness to learn.

There has been some criticism of the continuous plan on the basis that there is likely to be too much repetition of health content from one grade level to another. However, it is questionable whether or not this can be considered a valid argument against the plan itself. On the other hand, when this condition exists, a part of the fault might be due to a lack of progressive sequence as far as learning experiences in the school's curriculum guide or course of study are concerned. Unquestionably, some repetition of health teaching content may be unavoidable from grade to grade. When it does occur it need not necessarily be a cause for great concern, because a certain amount of repetition of material is not only justifiable, but may be highly desirable in some cases.

The Cycle Plan

As mentioned, the cycle plan provides for presentation of given health topics at a particular grade level within a range of levels. This plan was probably established originally because of its adaptability for use in small elementary schools, evidenced in part by the following excerpt from an early course of study which the State of Indiana published some three decades ago.

One of the features of the organization of this course of study is the cycle arrangement whereby the general plan of having each of the major topics taught once during the first three grades, a second time on a higher level during the second three grades, and a third time on a more scientific and technical level in the seventh and eighth grade is followed. For the teacher in the one-room elementary school, we recommend that all pupils in the first three grades could be handled as one group for health instruction; pupils in the fourth, fifth and sixth grades in a second group; pupils in the seventh and eighth grades in a third group. In this way each group could cover the material as outlined in a way that would save time in the school schedule.[1]

In general, the factors which would tend to favor the continuous plan would be the same ones that might be suggestive of some shortcomings in the cycle plan. For example, some persons feel that gaps in health content left from one grade level to another in the cycle plan would tend to militate against the importance of presenting materials at each age level of the child's development. In defense of

[1] State of Indiana Department of Public Instruction, *Tentative Course of Study in Physical and Health Education,* Grades One to Eight, 1933, p. 132. (This tentative course of study has been revised and supplemented on various occasions since this publication.)

the plan it might be said that needless repetition of health content is likely to be avoided when aspects of health topics are presented only four times during the twelve years of elementary and secondary school. Many school systems have reported varying degrees of success with both plans.

WAYS OF PROVIDING HEALTH LEARNING EXPERIENCES

There are a number of ways in which learning experiences in health may be organized for elementary school children. All of these procedures have met with varying degrees of success when applied under certain conditions. This suggests that almost any procedure will be effective when applied under the right conditions at the right time by the right personnel.

The following ways of providing such experiences will be reviewed here: (1) health as a separate subject; (2) opportunistic teaching of health; (3) integrating health with other curriculum areas. It should be understood that these procedures do not necessarily include all of the possible ways of organizing and providing health learning experiences. However, they do involve some of the better known procedures as far as health teaching in the modern elementary school is concerned. Although discussed as separate entities, it should be borne in mind that a great deal of overlapping may exist; moreover, in some situations it might be desirable to use a combination of two or more of the procedures rather than to resort to a single one in absolute form.

Health as a Separate Subject

This procedure has sometimes been referred to by school health educators as "direct teaching" of health. Establishing health as a separate subject in the curriculum at the *secondary* school level is a generally recommended practice because it then tends to enjoy the same status as the other subjects in the curriculum. Moreover, it lends itself well to the departmentalized way in which most secondary schools are organized.

Offering health as a separate subject at the elementary school level has been considered impractical in some cases, largely because of the way in which most elementary schools are organized. For example, the prevalent plan of organization in the primary school is the "one teacher per grade or class plan"[2] in which one teacher is responsible for virtually all subjects. In those cases where there is departmentalization—usually in the intermediate grades—and promotion from one level to another is done on the basis of individual subjects, presenting health as a separate subject tends to be more adaptable. This should not be interpreted to mean that the elementary school must be departmentalized in order to offer health on a separate-subject basis. It may be done in the so-called "self-contained classroom" situation with some degree of success if the entire curriculum organization is the subject version. (The various versions of curriculum organization will be discussed in an ensuing section of this chapter.)

Perhaps one of the main advantages of having health as a separate subject is that a specified time will be allotted for it and thus more likely that teachers will be apt to treat it with the same importance as other curriculum areas.

Criticism of the idea of health as a separate subject in the elementary school centers around the thought that the use of separate subjects might tend to place undue emphasis on the subject to the neglect of a child-centered program.

Opportunistic Teaching of Health

Utilizing health learning opportunities as they arise is a practice employed in some elementary schools. This procedure, sometimes referred to as involving "teachable moments," perhaps has little to offer if it is used to the exclusion of other types. When this condition prevails it appears likely that health learnings will occur more or less on an "incidental" basis. However, when combined with one or more other means of presenting health experiences it can become a satisfactory practice.

There appear to be various disadvantages to the plan when it is the sole way of presenting health education. Chief among these is the fact that a satisfactory opportunity for developing a given health concept may never present itself. Moreover, it has been found that those health areas where incidental health opportunities occur may

2 This plan may be generally referred to in the literature as the "self-contained classroom."

be limited. For example, in analyzing incidental health teaching in the fourth grade Ness[3] found that most incidental opportunities occur in the category of personal hygiene, anatomy and physiology, foods, and environmental hygiene.

Advocates of the plan counter by suggesting that it is up to the teacher to provide the type of classroom climate where such opportunities will be likely to prevail. The difficulty here lies in the fact that even the most skillful teacher may need to spend an inordinate amount of time setting the stage in anticipation of a given teachable moment.

Another objection to the practice of relying entirely upon opportunistic health teaching is that the opportunity may arise under catastrophic conditions. For example, it is questionable if there is much merit in a procedure which defers teaching of certain school safety practices until someone is seriously injured.

Perhaps one of the major advantages of this procedure is that there is little question that interest of the children will be at a high level. This is especially true when an opportunity for teaching about a certain aspect of health originates in the immediate environment. In this case motivation is likely to be of an intrinsic nature, and interest in the lesson should be relatively easy to maintain.

Integration of Health and Other Curriculum Areas

In order to provide for a better understanding of how health might be integrated with other areas of study in the elementary school curriculum, it appears necessary to discuss briefly the general nature of integration in education.

The term *integration* has taken on different meanings through the years, and as a consequence it may mean many different things to many different people. In simplest terms integration means the process of making whole. To integrate is to bring together the parts of the whole in order to derive some sort of functional unity.

An analysis of the literature suggests that educators appear to use the concept of integration in terms of the *psychological, sociological,* and *educational* areas. The psychological aspect of integration concerns the total personality of the individual. This concept accepts

[3] Carmen Oved Ness, *An Analysis of Incidental Health Instruction in the Fourth Grade of Selected Indiana Elementary Schools,* Doctoral Dissertation, Bloomington, Indiana University, 1957.

the individual as a *total* being consisting of the highly interrelated and interdependent physical, social, emotion, and intellectual facets of personality.

Social integration is concerned with three different aspects. These include (1) the relationship between personalities, such as pupil with pupil and pupil with teacher; (2) the need for a desirable relationship between the individual and various agencies of society; and (3) consideration of the relationship between these various agencies of society.

The third concept, educational integration, is the one that we are primarily concerned with here. This procedure involves teaching methods and techniques which relate and unify various subject-matter areas and skills through units of learning and specific fields for the purpose of providing problem-solving as a way of learning. Educational integration tends to recognize that all areas of the curriculum in the elementary school in one way or another complement one another in the solution of problems for the learner.

Although modern educators have provided possibilities for the implementation of educational integration this concept is by no means new. For example, Quintilian in the first century postulated that children differed in individual capacity and that teachers should take this into account. A possible forerunner to the modern concept of integration was Quintilian's interrogation, "Are we first to deliver ourselves up to the sole services of the teacher of literature, and then similarly to the teacher of geometry, neglecting under the latter what was taught us by the former?"[4]

Theoretically, educational integration can be accomplished in two different ways. First, it may be concerned with teaching procedures which bring together various subject-matter areas through units of work, contributing to the development of the concepts or understandings[5] of the unit. Secondly, integration may be accomplished

---

4 *The Institutio Oratoria of Quintilian*, Book 1, English translation by H. E. Butler, New York, Putnam, 1921, p. 195.

5 A concept has been defined as "an idea of representation of the common element or attribute by which groups or classes may be distinguished" (Carter V. Good, *Dictionary of Education*, 2nd ed., New York, McGraw-Hill, 1959, p. 118). Lee and Lee suggest that there is little to distinguish between the two terms "concepts" and "understandings" and that they may be used interchangeably (J. Murray Lee and Dorris May Lee, *The Child and His Curriculum*, 2nd ed., New York, Appleton-Century-Crofts, 1950, p. 506).

by relating and unifying two or more subject-matter fields in such a way that the content of each area helps to provide for a better realization of the understandings to be developed in the other.[6]

In many cases the process of integration has been recommended as one of the best means of providing health learning experiences for elementary school children. One of the more recent pronouncements in this regard is the following statement from the United States summary report of the World Confederation of Organizations of the Teaching Profession: "Educational authorities in the United States generally agree that health education at the elementary level should be integrated with all of the other educational experiences and activities."[7]

The extent to which the integration of health learning experiences with other curriculum areas is practiced in elementary schools is not entirely clear. Moreover, not too much is known about how successful this procedure has been in practical situations. A recent study[8] should help to shed some light on the extent to which this process is used, as well as the degree of success associated with it.

The study involved the extent to which selected superior classroom teachers accomplish the integration of certain health education activities in the various areas of the elementary program in the light of present day philosophy and practice.

One hundred and thirty-two selected superior classroom teachers of Grades 4, 5, and 6 participated in the study involving the extent to which health education activities were used in all phases of the elementary program. The activities for this study were compiled from courses of study, health textbooks, and current educational literature. There were 118 activities arranged in 7 categories, including the subject areas of social studies, science, language arts, art, arithmetic, physical education, and miscellaneous activities. All the activities received some emphasis as evidenced by the percentage of affirmative replies for each of the seven categories.

[6] Both of these procedures will be elaborated in detail in subsequent chapters.
[7] William H. Creswell, Jr., *WCOTP Inquiry on Child Health and the School*, Unpublished report, American Association for Health, Physical Education and Recreation, Washington, D.C., 1960.
[8] Lois S. Barber and Virginia D. Moore, *The Extent to Which Health Activities Are Integrated with Other Areas of the Elementary School Curriculum*, Unpublished materials in health education, College Park, University of Maryland, 1960.

In the interpretation of the activities in the responses received, the social studies category showed that 55 percent of the participants integrated health activities with social studies. However, 71 percent of the teachers had either excellent or good success with this category.

In the science, language arts, art, and arithmetic categories a lower percentage of the participants integrated health activities with the respective categories. It is interesting to note, however, that in all four of these curriculum areas the respondents had approximately the same degree of excellent to good success (at least 70 percent or more) as those who reported success with the social studies activities.

A more detailed analysis of these four categories revealed that (1) 48 percent of the respondents had a 70 percent degree of excellent to good success in integrating health and science activities; (2) 42 percent had a 70 percent excellent to good success integrating health and language arts activities; (3) 24 percent had a 70 percent excellent to good success integrating health and art activities; and (4) 41 percent had a 72 percent excellent to good success integrating health and arithmetic activities.

For the health education activities used in the physical education category, 67 percent of the respondents had an 81 percent excellent to good success. This high degree of successful integration perhaps may be partially due to the fact that physical education activities provide for learning through active participation rather than passive responses.

Almost 50 percent of the teachers reporting integrated health activities with other types, such as pantomiming, dramatic play, dramatizing stories, role-playing, show and tell, and telling stories. These teachers had a 78 percent degree of excellent to good success in using these learning activities in all areas of the curriculum.

Because of the nature and scope of this study it appears obvious that whatever conclusions may be reached, it is essential that they be somewhat generalized. For example, this study would seem to indicate that teachers are barely "scratching the surface" of the possibilities for integrating health education activities into the elementary school program. The degree of success which teachers reported offers some evidence that health education activities afford an excellent medium for cooperative effort in utilizing the elementary curriculum in a more functional way. Other results of the study seem to indicate that the integration of health education activities in the different parts of the curriculum may serve as a means of contributing simultaneously to the broader purposes of education. The study also revealed a need to explore further the possibility of integrating more health activities with other areas of the curriculum.

There is much to be said for the use of educational integration as a means of interrelating the various curriculum areas in providing the most desirable problem-solving experiences. However, like any educational endeavor this procedure is not without its pitfalls. One of its main limitations perhaps lies in the difficulty of arranging a natural relationship between subject areas when two or more are integrated to help develop a particular health concept. In the ideal situation a health concept would be an inherent aspect of, say, a science experiment. Perhaps a very skillful teacher could show a relationship in areas that are somewhat unrelated. However, this procedure would tend to cause the teacher to "force" one curriculum area in developing a concept in another, and certainly this procedure is not recommended. However, forceful mention should be made here that the skillful teacher can easily circumvent this problem by using various ways and means of unifying curriculum areas with health. Numerous practical procedures designed to help the teacher carry this out effectively will be recommended in later chapters.

HEALTH TEACHING IN VARIOUS TYPES OF CURRICULUM ORGANIZATION

Over the years various theories have been advanced with regard to curriculum organization in the elementary school. Obviously, there are certain advantages and disadvantages in any kind of approach to curriculum organization when a particular organization is applied in absolute form. It is perhaps for this reason that modern educators tend to select procedures from various forms of standard curriculum organization and then make those adaptations which best meet local needs. For example, all types of curriculum organization should be designed to orient learning experiences in such a way that they make an optimum contribution to the total growth and development of elementary school children. If satisfactory results are to accrue, the curriculum must be developed in such a way as to make learning experiences desirable, beneficial, and worthwhile to all children.

There are various approaches to curriculum organization through which this objective might be accomplished in specific situations. Some of the better known approaches to curriculum development in the elementary school are the *subject version*, the *broad fields version*, and the *areas-of-living version*.[9] All versions should be considered, and the best ideas from each might well be taken and adapted to local conditions. The main objective at this point will be to attempt to familiarize the reader with some of the advantages and limitations of the various versions, especially when a single one is employed in absolute form to the entire exclusion of certain of the desirable elements of the others. Also, a major point of concern will be the way in which the provision of health learning experiences might fit into each version. This is absolutely essential because, in order to function at its greatest potential level, health teaching must be compatible with the over-all existing curriculum organization.

The Subject Version

The separate-subject approach has been considered the traditional type of curriculum organization. Essentially, the separate-subject approach tends to allot a specified amount of time in each school day to the various subjects making up the curriculum. A typical list of elementary school subjects might include reading, writing, arithmetic, spelling, art, music, physical education, and health.

One reputedly important feature about a separate subject is its uniqueness in relation to others. Critics of this form of curriculum organization sometimes consider such uniqueness a distinct disadvantage. They tend to argue that because of this the subject has been so emphasized as to become "subject-centered," with more emphasis placed on subjects than on children. However, it should be remembered that this might not necessarily be a fault of the ap-

9 This version may also be referred to by other names, such as, "problems-of-living" or "activities-of-daily-living."

proach itself. This may be brought out more clearly when we consider that teachers who use the subject approach have two rather extreme alternatives to follow. They can teach for the sake of the subject in terms of merely imparting information, or they can be concerned with the needs and interests of children, and provide for desirable learning experiences for them in the various subject areas. When the latter procedure is practiced it becomes the responsibility of the teacher to help children understand the important relationships between subjects, to the extent that various subjects may be drawn upon in the solution of problems. The degree to which teachers may accomplish this purpose will be directly related to the prevailing philosophy of the local school administration, in terms of the interpretation placed on the various subject-matter areas.

Health can fit in very nicely with the separate-subject approach. If health is a part of the subject-matter offerings under this plan, then it will be assured a specified amount of time on a daily or weekly basis. It then becomes a *subject* in the curriculum, to be taught in much the same manner as history, reading, or any other.

It should be brought to the attention of the reader that the separate-subject approach does not necessarily mean that all subjects in the elementary school will be taught by different teachers, as is the case in many secondary schools. On the other hand, the self-contained-classroom idea can be retained, with the same teacher handling all subjects. In this case it is advisable and worthwhile for the teacher to attempt to *integrate* health with the other subjects, so that children may understand it in terms of its relationship to the other areas.

The health unit approach may be used to advantage in the separate-subject type of curriculum organization. Teaching units may be constructed by the teacher in terms of specific health topics, and unitary teaching may be accomplished by utilizing the other subjects as needed to help solve the problems of the unit.

The Broad Fields Version

As many new subjects began to find their way into the elementary curriculum through the years, it seemed a feasible plan to combine some subjects into broad areas. Curriculum development approached in this manner does not necessarily mean that subject-matter areas are entirely deleted, but rather that the emphasis is on broader areas of study instead of individual subjects. An example of one of the broad fields at the upper elementary level has been the combining of such individual subjects as history, geography, and civics into the broad field of social studies.

One of the main problems in organizing the elementary curriculum on the broad fields basis is that its content must necessarily be developed in terms of broad concepts that are inherent in the various individual subjects that combine to make up a broad area. Further complication of this problem concerns the fact that it may be difficult to develop the broad concepts and understandings over a range of grade levels. Even though this procedure may be difficult to accomplish, it is offset to a certain extent because of the latitude and flexibility inherent in the broad-fields plan. Proponents of this approach to curriculum development feel that it helps children to see relationships between learnings in a general area, whereas the separate-subject approach might tend to neglect this important relationship.

In the broad fields version, health is most likely to be incorporated in the area of social studies. When this occurs health topics are usually presented as units in social studies. For example, a unit on food or clothing may be a part of a larger unit of work in the general area of social studies. Another broad area may combine the study of science and health and be referred to as either "science-health" or "health-science." Perhaps the close relationship between these two areas would tend to give health some status in a broad area of this type.

The Areas-of-Living Version

This version of curriculum organization is primarily concerned with those life problems which confront children in our modern complex society. It is more or less dependent upon the different stages of development of children, as well as individual differences in traits and characteristics. Herein lies a major difference in the areas-of-living approach from the separate-subject and broad fields versions because the latter two are more dependent for their organization upon subject matter or subject content. Persons who favor the areas-of-living version believe that the experiences of the child should be directly associated with his environment, and that he will develop the skills he needs as he progresses through his various phases of development.

A major criticism of the areas-of-living approach is that basic skills and the so-called "fundamentals of education" may be neglected. Advocates of this plan feel that it may not be an entirely valid criticism, because the ability to perform certain skills will be necessary if problems are to be solved. It is suggested that the basic skills in this approach may be taught and learned as they are needed for a given problem-solving situation. In this way children will perhaps be more apt to see the need for learning certain of the basic skills, whereas if they are taught skills independently of their use in solving problems of living, skill-learning may be somewhat intangible and consequently less meaningful to them.

In teaching health in the areas-of-living approach, activities of a class will center upon the solution of a given health problem that is closely related to the immediate environment. For example, a class of third-grade children may work for a given period of time on a unit designed to "make our playground a safer place." The teacher and children plan together in terms of the approach that they are going to take in solving the problems of such a unit. Unitary teaching is employed for the most part in the areas-of-living approach.

Although the various approaches to curriculum development have been discussed in terms of their application in absolute form, it is re-emphasized that it would be most difficult to make a rigid and clear-cut separation of them. This is to say that in the better-than-average elementary school the curriculum is organized for the most part to meet the particular needs of the children in the local situation. Good aspects of each form of curriculum organization are combined to form the best approach for a given situation. When this procedure is employed it permits more flexibility than if one approach is followed in absolute form. This is extremely important in the case of health education, some degree of latitude being needed in curriculum organization so that health teaching may be incorporated in the curriculum in a way that is most beneficial to children.

REFERENCES

Cornacchia, Harold J., "How We Developed Our Elementary Health Education Curriculum," *Journal of Health-Physical Education-Recreation,* April, 1958.

Irwin, L. W., "Basic Needs in Health Education," *Journal of Education,* April, 1959.

Klausmeier, Herbert J., *Teaching in the Elementary School,* New York, Harper, 1956, chap. 4.

Oberteuffer, Delbert, *School Health Education,* 3rd ed., New York, Harper, 1960, chap. 7.

Rucker, W. Ray, *Curriculum Development in the Elementary School,* New York, Harper, 1960.

Starr, Helen M., "Putting Health Instruction to Work for You," *National Elementary Principal,* February, 1960.

TEACHING AND LEARNING
IN HEALTH EDUCATION

5

1 *How are health knowledge, health attitudes, and health practices involved in teaching and learning?*

2 *How can we differentiate between "learning activities" and "learning experiences"?*

3 *What are some criteria for evaluation of health learning activities?*

4 *What are some of the factors which might influence learning as the elementary school child passes through various stages of growth and development?*

5 *What are some of the competencies and experiences which appear to be essential for successful health teaching in the elementary school?*

BASIC CONSIDERATIONS

It is most important that teachers have as full an understanding as possible of the role of teaching and learning in elementary school health education. Because of this it appears necessary to preface some of the subsequent discussions in this chapter with various fundamental considerations for good teaching.

The concepts of learning that an individual teacher or a group of teachers in a given school subscribe to are directly related to the kind and variety of health learning activities and experiences that will be provided for children. For this reason it is important for beginning teachers to explore some of the factors that make for most desirable and worthwhile learning. Among the factors which should help to orient the reader with regard to some basic understandings in the teaching of health in the elementary school are (1) an understanding of the meaning of certain terms, (2) an understanding of the derivation of teaching methods, and (3) an understanding of *knowledge, attitudes,* and *practice* in health teaching and learning.

Meaning of Terms

Due to the fact that certain terms, because of their multiple use, do not actually have a universal definition, no attempt will be made here to *define* terms. On the other hand it will be the purpose to *describe* certain terms, rather than to attempt to define them. The reader should view the descriptions of terms that follow with this general idea in mind.

Learning. Without exception, most definitions of learning are characterized by the idea that learning involves some sort of change in the individual. This means that when an individual has learned, his behavior is modified in one or more ways. It should be obvious that all learning is not necessarily desirable learning. For example, a child may develop a health misconception because of the way he has learned something. It is the job of the teacher to see that this situation does not prevail.

Teaching. Several years ago one of the authors was addressing a group of teachers on the matter of teaching and learning. Introducing the discussion in somewhat abstract terms the speaker asked, "Can anyone tell me what teaching is?" After a short period of embarrassing deliberation, one member of the group interrogated the following answer with some degree of uncertainty. "Is it imparting information?" This kind of thinking is characteristic of that which reflects the traditional meaning of the term "teaching." In more recent years we have come to think of teaching not as merely imparting information, but in terms of the guidance and supervision of behavior that results in desirable and worthwhile learning. Lee and Lee express it in this way: "You can't 'teach' a child anything; you only can provide an opportunity for him to learn."[1] In other words, it is the job of the teacher to guide the child's learning rather than impart to him a series of unrelated and sometimes meaningless facts.

Method. In general, "method" is concerned with doing some-

[1] J. Murray Lee and Dorris May Lee, *The Child and His Development,* New York, Appleton-Century-Crofts, 1958, p. 341.

thing in such a way that desirable objectives will be achieved. It has been suggested that learning results in modification of behavior, and that teaching is the guidance of behavior that results in learning. If the best results are to accrue for elementary school children as far as their present and future health is concerned, it is essential that provisions be made for the most desirable health learning experiences. The procedures that teachers use in the guidance and direction of these learning experiences are known as *teaching methods*.

Derivation of Teaching Methods

Beginning teachers often ask, "Where do we get our ideas for teaching methods?" For the most part this question should be considered in general terms. In other words, although there are a variety of acceptable teaching procedures utilized in the modern elementary school, all of these methods are likely to be derived from two somewhat broad sources.

The first of these involves an accumulation of knowledge of educational psychology and what is known about the learning process in providing for health learning experiences. The other is the practice of successful teachers.

In most instances undergraduate preparation of prospective elementary school classroom teachers includes at least some study of educational psychology as it applies to the learning process and certain accepted principles of learning. With this basic information it is expected that beginning teachers have sufficient knowledge to make application of it to the practical situation.

It has been the observation of the authors over a period of years that many beginning teachers tend to rely upon the practices of successful teachers as a source of teaching methods. The validity of this procedure is based on the assumption that such successful practices are likely to have as their bases the application of fundamental psychological principles of learning. Certainly, no teacher should rely entirely upon this source for teaching methods. It should be the responsibility of every teacher to become familiar with the basic psychological principles of learning and to attempt to apply these in the best possible way in the process of providing the most desirable and worthwhile health learning experiences for children.

Knowledge, Attitudes, and Practices

For children to benefit most from the health learning experiences that are provided for them, it is essential that these experiences eventuate into desirable *health practices*. Thus the ultimate goal should be in the direction of a kind of conduct that will insure optimum present and future health for the individual. However, before the most desirable health practices can be achieved, there is a need for a certain amount of health knowledge, along with a proper attitude in making application of it to health practice.

While it is obvious that "to know" is not necessarily "to do," nevertheless, that which is done wisely will depend in a large measure upon the kind and amount of knowledge an individual has acquired. In the accumulation of health knowledge the child should be taught *why* it is beneficial for him to follow a certain practice. When this is done it is more likely that the child will develop a desirable attitude toward certain health practices. If he has a sufficient amount of desirable health knowledge and has developed a proper attitude, then he will be more apt to put the knowledge into practice. Moreover, he should be in a better position to exercise good judgment in matters pertaining to his health if he has obtained the right kind and amount of health knowledge.

The following illustration may help to clarify the points made in this discussion. Let us say that we are attempting to develop a concept involving the proper way of safely crossing the street with a group of first-grade children. A learning activity which results in a desirable learning experience is provided, whereby the children acquire knowledge of the safest way to cross the street. During the process of acquiring this knowledge some sort of attitude will develop as a result of what the child is currently learning and what his past experiences have been. Obviously, obtaining the knowledge of the best acceptable way of crossing the street in a safe manner is not in itself complete assurance that the child will behave in this manner. However, it is much more likely that he will put into practice this way of crossing the street if he has been given the knowledge. Of course this is contingent upon knowledge accumulating through the most worthwhile and desirable learning experiences.

THE NATURE OF LEARNING IN
HEALTH EDUCATION

It should be understood at the outset that teaching and learning in health education is not essentially different from teaching and learning in other curriculum areas. However, the nature of the curriculum content of health education is such that it should provide for more interesting problem-solving opportunities than some of other subject areas. The basic reason for this is that most health topics contain aspects that are in one way or another closely related to the everyday life experiences of children.

The theory accepted here is that learning takes place in terms of a reorganization of the systems of perception into a functional, integrated whole due to the result of certain stimuli. This implies that problem-solving is *the* way of learning and that learning takes place through it. In that so much of the health curriculum content involves material applicable to solving health problems that should be of interest and importance to children, excellent opportunities exist in this area.

There are certain features involved in purposeful learning. Klausmeier *et al.* suggest five such features, as follows:

1. The individual is motivated; and the goal, which constitutes an incentive to action in a given direction, becomes associated with the motive.
2. He consciously directs his attention toward the goal and expends energy directed thereto.
3. He engages in intelligent trial-and-error activity to find a new method of reaching the goal or to refine already developed methods.
4. He applies previous experiences to the task, differentiating various elements of the present situation in order to perceive the appropriate method more clearly and integrating already developed responses into a new or higher-level response.
5. In the process of differentiation and integration he drops inappropriate methods, confirms the correct response, and incorporates the new method into a learned behavior pattern where it is available for use in other situations.[2]

The following discussion highlights some procedures a teacher might use in applying the above five-step pattern of purposeful learning in the development of a particular health concept with

[2] Herbert J. Klausmeier *et al., Teaching in the Elementary School,* New York, Harper, 1956, pp. 74–75.

a class of fifth-grade children. It involves the *selection of clothing suitable for extremes of weather.*

In some cases with elementary school children it might be important for the teacher to set the stage for learning by the use of an interesting introductory activity. Let us say in this particular instance the teacher decides to use the following experiment for this purpose. Two pieces of ice of equal size are placed in an area in the classroom where the sun will shine through the windows on them (if possible it would be better to put them outside in the direct sunlight). A bit of heavy dark-colored cloth and a light-colored patch are placed over the separate pieces of ice. The children are asked to observe which piece melts first. It can be assumed that some of the children will want to know "why" the piece of ice with the dark-colored cloth over it was the first to melt.

Their aroused curiosity will stimulate various questions, and thus attention is directed toward the goal. The teacher at this point may engage in a short discussion about body temperature with the pupils. Pictures of persons dressed for swimming at the beach and for ice skating may be shown.

To help the pupils engage in intelligent trial-and-error activity, various learning experiences are provided, under the skillful guidance of the teacher. The teacher may help the children relate some of their past experiences to the present learning situation. For example, she might ask if they have ever noticed, when coming in from playing on a cold day, how they felt after leaving their warm clothes on for a time. Or she might ask if they have ever experienced shivering when they came out of swimming into the cold air.

The learning experiences that the children have as a result of engaging in such a typical activity should help them to understand why proper kinds of clothing should be selected for various kinds of weather. Theoretically, a learned behavior pattern is developed and available for use when the child is confronted with a related problem or choice.

Learning Activities and Experiences

Oftentimes the terms learning "activities" and learning "experiences" are used interchangeably. However, it appears advisable to make a clear-cut distinction between the two. Learning activities may be considered as the things that children *do* in order to learn.

The personal feelings that they derive as a result of engaging in these activities comprise the learning experiences. When thought of in these terms it should be considered that *anything* a person does is a potential learning activity. The following partial list of activities includes some of the things that children do in the school situation which are designed to help them learn.

1. Collecting	13. Observing
2. Constructing	14. Organizing
3. Creating	15. Planning
4. Demonstrating	16. Playing
5. Dramatizing	17. Reading
6. Drawing	18. Sharing
7. Experimenting	19. Singing
8. Exploring	20. Speaking
9. Imagining	21. Studying
10. Inquiring	22. Thinking
11. Investigating	23. Writing
12. Listening	

The list might serve as worthwhile material for teachers in planning health learning activities and experiences. It should be remembered that it is by no means complete and that it might be expanded to include other desirable learning activities.

Since practically anything a person does is a potential learning activity, there is an extremely vast range of possible learning activities from which the teacher may draw. Within this range are found concrete activities, or those which involves direct purposeful experience. On the other hand there are numerous kinds of abstract activities which deal essentially with verbal symbols. In between the concrete and the very abstract activities, lie numerous possibilities for health learning which involve such aspects as contrived experiences, demonstrations, field trips, motion and still pictures, and a variety of other kinds of visual symbols. (Numerous examples of these and other types of health learning activities appear in subsequent chapters of the book.)

Whenever possible, it appears advisable that health learning activities for the elementary school level should be concrete. For example, there is a good opportunity for children to learn to brush their teeth in the best accepted way through actually doing it. Of course in some cases it is not practical or desirable for children to participate firsthand in the direct reality of learning. For instance, in studying about the human heart it is obvious that the experience should be "contrived." This can be accomplished by having pupils study a model.

In various cases and under certain conditions it is most advisable for pupils to work with the teacher in planning the learning activities for the study of different aspects of health. However, in the final analysis the responsibility for providing the most desirable and worthwhile activities will rest with the teacher. This is as it should be because the classroom teacher should be in a favorable position to understand the health needs and interests of a particular class. It appears advisable for teachers to devise certain criteria for the selection and evaluation of health learning activities. The following four general criteria are submitted as suggestive:

1. Are the health learning activities selected on the basis of how well they might meet the needs and interests of pupils?
2. Are the health learning activities within the ability level of the pupils?
3. Are the health learning activities sufficiently varied so as to provide for individual differences of all pupils?
4. Are the health learning activities compatible with the objectives of a given health unit or lesson?

QUALIFICATIONS OF TEACHERS

It might be said that there are certain *general* abilities required for teaching in any of the subject-matter areas, and that teaching about health in the elementary school does not differ extensively from teaching in the other curriculum areas. On the other hand it should also be recognized that, by the very nature of the content of some curriculum areas, *specific* abilities may be needed for teachers to be most successful in certain of these areas. This is no doubt true in the area of health education. While understanding should certainly be a general requirement for all teachers, the need for it is perhaps more pronounced in the area of health education because health teaching content is inherently involved in understanding the child and how he learns.

Understanding the Child

As the child progresses through various stages in his growth and development, certain distinguishing characteristics can be identified which furnish implications for effective teaching and learning in health education.

The range of age levels from 5 through 7 years usually includes pupils from kindergarten through Grade 2. During this period the child begins his formal education. In our culture he leaves the home and family constellation for a part of the day to take his place in a classroom of pupils approximately the same chronological age. Not only is he taking an important step toward becoming increasingly more independent and self-reliant, but as he learns he moves from being a highly self-centered, egotistical individual to becoming a more socialized group member.

This stage is characterized by a certain lack of motor coordination, because the small muscles of the hands and fingers are not as well developed as the large muscles of the arms and legs. Thus, as he starts his formal education the child needs to use large crayons or pencils as one means of expressing himself. His urge to action is expressed through movement and noise. Pupils at these age levels thrive on vigorous activity. They develop as they climb, run, jump, hop, skip, or keep time to music. An important physical aspect at this level is that the eyeball is increasing in size and the eye muscles are developing. This factor is an important determinant in the child's readiness to see and read small print, and thus involves a sequence from large print on charts to primer type in preprimers and primers.

Even though he has a relatively short attention span, he is extremely curious about his environment. At this stage the teacher capitalizes upon his urge to learn by providing opportunities for him to gain information from firsthand experiences through the use of the senses. He sees, hears, smells, feels, and even tastes to learn. For instance, the child learns that citrus fruits are different from the apple family, or he learns about the different parts of plants that we eat (root, stem, leaf) through actually handling and examining fruits and vegetables.

The age range of 8 and 9 years is the period which usually marks the time spent in the third and fourth grades. The child now has a wider range of interest and longer attention span. While strongly individualistic, he is working from a position in a group. Organized team games afford opportunities for developing and practicing skills in good leadership and followership, as well as body control, strength, and endurance. Small muscles are developing, manipulative skills are increasing, and muscular coordination is improving. The eyes have developed so that the children can, and do, read more widely. They are capable of getting information from books and are beginning to learn through vicarious experience. However, experiments carry an impact for learning at this age by capitalizing upon the child's curiosity as he tests or proves a hypothesis. This is the stage in his development when skills of communication (listening, speaking, reading, and writing) and the number system are needed to deal with situations both in and out of school.

At the age range of 10 through 12 most children complete the fifth and sixth grades. This is a period of transition for most, as they go from childhood into the preadolescent period of their growth and development. They may show concern over bodily changes, and are sometimes self-conscious about appearance. At this range of age levels children tend to differ widely in physical maturation and in emotional stability. Greater deviations in growth and development can be noted within the sex groups than between them. Rate of physical growth can be rapid, sometimes showing itself in poor posture and restlessness. Some of the more highly organized team games such as softball, modified soccer, and the like, help to furnish the keen and wholesome competition desired by these pupils. It is essential that the teacher recognize that at this level prestige among peers is more important than adult approval. A definite interest in clothes and a desire to improve personal appearance provide a particular readiness for effective health teaching. During this period the child is ready for a higher level of intellectual skills involving reasoning, discerning fact from opinion, noting cause-and-effect relationships, drawing conclusions, and using various references to locate and compare the validity of information. He is beginning to show proficiency in expressing himself through oral and written communication.

Thus, during the years between kindergarten and the completion of Grade 6, the child grows and develops (1) socially, from a self-centered individual to a participating member of a group; (2) emotionally, from a state manifesting temper tantrums to a higher degree of self-control; (3) physically, from childhood to the brink of adolescence; and (4) intellectually, from learning from firsthand experiences to learning from technical and specialized resources.

If the child is to be educated as a growing organism, aspects of growth and development need the utmost consideration of the teacher in planning and guiding health learning activities which will be most profitable for the child at his particular stage of development.

Competencies and Experiences Needed by Teachers

One of the modern approaches in meeting the needs of teachers for proficiency in a given curriculum area involves the acquisition of certain *competencies* and *experiences* in that area. The following statement by Snyder and Scott lends some insight to the meaning and relationship of the terms "competency" and "experience."

A competency is defined as a skill, insight, understanding, qualification, fitness, or ability which is used to meet a life situation. An experience is defined as the conscious interaction of the individual with the environment. Competencies provide the individual with intelligent ways of doing things or a means of behavior which resolves the tension between the organism and the environment. A person who is competent can successfully meet his personal and professional problems. Since learning takes place through experience, the development of competencies *must* come through that medium. If the individual is provided with sound learning experiences, she should develop the desired competencies.[3]

Various attempts have been made by group as well as individuals to identify competencies and experiences essential to proficient on-the-job performance of the elementary school classroom teacher in the area of health teaching. One such recommendation emphasizes the need for specific competencies and experiences for prospective elementary classroom teachers, and that which is incorporated in the Report of the National Conference on College Health Education, "Health Education for Prospective Teachers." Excerpts from this report pertinent to the abilities, techniques, and experiences needed by elementary teachers in the area of health teaching follow.

The teacher should:

Learn how to formulate the objectives for a program of health education;
Examine the *scope* of health education in elementary schools;
Learn how to utilize the experiences of children to provide health teaching content;
Learn how to utilize family and community health problems as an area of emphasis in health education;

[3] Raymond A. Snyder and Harry A. Scott, *Professional Preparation in Health, Physical Education and Recreation*, New York, McGraw-Hill, 1954, p. 115.

Learn how to interpret statistical information which points to the major health problems of the school age child;

Learn how to plan and organize experiences for direct instruction to include certain basic needs of pupils such as nutrition, physical activity, rest, relaxation and recreation, emotional health, safety, first aid and emergency care, cleanliness, grooming, dental health, education in family living, vision and hearing, and health examinations;

Learn how to enrich the understanding of pupils through integrated health instruction in those areas where there is a natural relationship such as science, social studies, art education;

Develop awareness and sensitivity to the opportunities for incidental teaching inherent in special situations;

Learn how to motivate health teaching so that desirable changes in health behavior take place;

Learn how to evaluate the results of health teaching;

Recognize the importance of maintaining a high level of personal health himself as an example to the children.

Some learning experiences which the prospective elementary teacher should have are:

The planning of interesting and effective lessons;

Adapting group techniques such as problem solving, role playing, pupil-teacher planning, to help stimulate interest in desirable health behavior;

Selecting and using appropriate audio-visual aids to supplement and enrich the program;

Using and evaluating printed materials such as texts, references, free and inexpensive materials;

Using the results of health appraisals for determining health teaching content;

Observing and participating in health teaching experiences;

Supervised teaching of health;

Having opportunities for the observation of children in school situations which have health and safety teaching implications such as school lunch period, recess and play periods, bus transportation, and community groups (Sunday School, Boy Scouts);

Consulting resource personnel about matters pertaining to health problems of children;

Utilizing organized community health resources in health education.[4]

---

[4] American Association for Health, Physical Education and Recreation, "Health Education for Prospective Teachers," *Report of the National Conference on College Health Education*, Washington, D.C., 1956.

It can be readily seen from the discussion in this chapter that the job of the elementary school classroom teacher as it pertains to teaching and learning in the area of health education is a complex one. Many important competencies, abilities, and experiences are needed by the teacher in order to provide health learning activities and experiences in the most desirable way. Much of the material in some of the subsequent chapters is designed to help the prospective teacher or teacher-in-service acquire these essential abilities, which are so important to successful health teaching in the elementary school.

REFERENCES

Atkins, J. Myron, *An Analysis of the Development of Elementary School Children in Certain Selected Aspects of Problem Solving Ability,* Doctoral Dissertation, New York, New York University, 1956.

Humphrey, James H., Warren R. Johnson, and Virginia D. Moore, "Recent Research in Methods of Teaching and Its Implications for Elementary School Health Education," *Journal of Health, Physical Education, Recreation,* October, 1960.

Irwin, Leslie W., James H. Humphrey, and Warren R. Johnson, *Methods and Materials in School Health Education,* St. Louis, Mosby, 1956, chap. 7.

Lee, J. Murray, and Dorris May Lee, *The Child and His Development,* New York, Appleton-Century-Crofts, 1958, Part III.

Means, Richard K., "Learning Principles Applied to Elementary School Health," *Health Education Journal,* January, 1961.

Mogar, Mariannina, "Children's Causal Reasoning about Natural Phenomena," *Child Development,* March, 1960.

Muldoon, Mary Warren, *Learning to Teach,* New York, Harper, 1958.

Phillips, Beeman N., Ralph L. Duke, and M. Vere DeVault, *Psychology at Work in the Elementary School Classroom,* New York, Harper, 1960, Part II.

U.S. Department of Health, Education, and Welfare, Office of Education, *Educating Children in Grades Four, Five and Six,* Washington, D.C., 1958.

ORAL COMMUNICATION AND LANGUAGE IN RELATION TO HEALTH[1]

6

1   *Why is effective speaking of major importance in health education?*

2   *What are some of the characteristics of audiences that should be taken into account when talking about health?*

3   *What are some important aspects of group discussion as it pertains to health education?*

4   *What are some of the major considerations which should be given to the area of semantics as it pertains to health education?*

5   *What are some of the important factors related to health advertising which should be taken into account by the elementary school teacher?*

The purpose of this chapter is to indicate some of the characteristics of oral communication and some principles which make for effective speaking. In addition, this chapter is intended to call attention to and illustrate the enormously important role that language plays in human health and health education, as well as in human relations generally.

It is recognized that teachers are not orators and that younger elementary school children are not prepared to organize "formal talks." However, many elementary teachers and other school personnel do find themselves in the position of wishing to express their point of view on health and other matters effectively before groups

[1] The authors are grateful to Dr. Richard Hendricks, Professor of Speech and Hearing Science at the University of Maryland, for his critical reading of this chapter.

and in discussions; and, indeed, certain of the recommendations made here have important implications for good classroom teaching. Furthermore, when pupils are ready to make statements before their classmates, they are doubtless prepared to learn *how* to do so effectively and responsibly.

It should be noted that the objectives of speakers determine what is, for them, "effective" speaking. Some speakers, such as political propagandists and advertisers, are concerned primarily with swaying an audience emotionally and persuading it to accept the argument or position of the speaker. Thus, if by haranguing, you convince me that I am a member of the master race, and this conviction has been your purpose, then you have spoken effectively. And if by harping at me repeatedly in a commercial that "Fresh" is the best applesauce in the land, and I go out and buy some Fresh, then you have spoken effectively. On the other hand, some speakers are concerned primarily with instructing an audience and/or requiring it to think seriously about something. In such cases, too, the effectiveness of the speaking will depend upon the extent to which the speaker's objectives are achieved.

Of course it is not necessary to make either the emotional or intellectual extremes one's objective when speaking, for presentation can and should be both intelligent *and* persuasive. "Effective" speaking, in the present discussion, is not meant to imply either an emotion-heavy appeal for health or a coldly logical presentation of facts. Rather, it is intended to mean a communication between speaker and audience concerning a matter of mutual interest and in which that interest is highlighted and given direction. Since an "audience," like a speaker, is a feeling *and* thinking organism, neither its feelings nor its capacity to understand and gain new insights should be ignored.

EFFECTIVE SPEAKING

Perhaps somewhat paradoxically we will begin by considering the particular audience rather than the speaker—for this is what the speaker must first take into account.

"Lecturing" is suspect as a means of oral communication, not because it is necessarily intrinsically unsatisfactory as a form of

oral communication, but because many professors and other lec-
turers do not bother to take their *particular* audience adequately
into account. Their oral communication tends to be "speaker and
speech" centered. Thus they are talking to themselves more than
to their audience. In effect, they place a deluge of verbiage in front
of their audience, implying, "This is my message, this is what has
come out of me, take it or leave it and make what you can out
of it."

The speaker who is seriously interested in communicating with
his audience studies the particular audience. He informs himself, if
possible, as to its current status of knowledge of and interest in the
subject under consideration; he takes into account the audience's
motives for being present. He considers the time of day and other
factors—that is, Is the audience tired? Is it hungry? Hot? Otherwise
uncomfortable?

Following are some characteristics of audiences which should be
considered by any serious speaker.

1. Unless it is in a school situation, the audience is generally not a
   "captive audience," that is, it has some interest in the subject, perhaps
   as individuals, parents, or community-minded persons.
2. The audience is likely to be poorly to moderately well informed on the
   subject under discussion; but there is likely to be a considerable amount
   of misinformation in evidence.
3. There is likely to be an initial period of interest and alertness on the
   part of the audience, regardless of who the speaker is, because he is
   assumed to have something worthwhile to say.
4. In general, audience interest tends to be complete when a speaker begins, but declines at a rapid rate unless countermeasures are taken
   by the speaker. That is, the audience is likely to be tired and to become
   apathetic unless visual aids or other devices are utilized.
5. The average audience is not in the habit of concentrating on a talk
   (as a student is who is likely to be tested on details of a lecture), is
   likely to have a short attention span, and is not likely to discriminate
   between important and relatively unimportant points unless the important points are emphasized, repeated, and reviewed. In this connection it is interesting to ask people to recall the best speech they have
   heard in recent years. They can usually identify their favorite and
   tell how it made them feel, but they can rarely remember so much as
   a point or two that the speaker made.

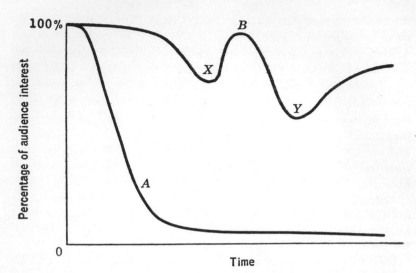

Audience Interest Span. Line *A* shows the likely sharp drop in audience interest unless countermeasures are taken. Line *B* shows the effects of countermeasures used in an effective presentation. The rise at *x* may be due to film, anecdote, or other device; the rise at *y* indicates revival of interest brought about by a good conclusion.

6. The average audience is not familiar with professional jargon and technical terms. The field of health is full of terminology that is unknown or only vaguely known by people untrained in the field.
7. The audience is likely to be sensitive to certain "loaded" words and terms such as: *insanity, syphilis, socialized medicine,* as well as numerous sex-related words.
8. Modern audiences are very sophisticated in terms of showmanship. By virtue of conditioning, the audience is accustomed to the rapid fire and very professional presentations of television, radio, and the movies. All speakers tend to be judged by these professional standards.

Preparation and Presentation of "Talks"

Oral presentation should be prepared with due regard for the fact that unlike written material, spoken material cannot be re-examined by the audience later on at its leisure. Except in the classroom situation where preliminary teaching, follow-up, and outside reading may be given, "talks" are "one-shot" affairs which have a single opportunity to have an effect. That is, if it is to convey information, or modify attitudes or behavior, the talk must do so by means of its single opportunity. To point up the contrast between written and oral communication, one writer has compared hearing a speech to watching a parade through a narrow slit in a fence, each element of the parade having a single momentary opportunity to present itself to a viewer peering through the slit.[2] Generally speaking this situation calls for relatively short and simple sentences (the uncertain listener cannot relisten as an uncertain reader can reread), and for nontechnical vocabulary (the listener cannot stop in mid-sentence to reach for a dictionary), unless the speaker wishes deliberately to introduce and define particular terminology.

Although numerous books on public speaking may be consulted for far more detailed information, the following basic pointers have been useful to many speakers.

1. Begin by making a careful outline with special reference to three major headings: introduction, content, and conclusion. There is a saying among practiced speechmakers: "First tell them what you're going to say, say it, then tell them what you said."

2. Have an interest-arousing introduction that, perhaps, raises a question or presents a challenge. Humor may be useful in this regard, but it is dangerous. That is, a joke or humorous story may be effective in launching the presentation, but it may also make what follows seem anti-climactic. It might better be used later in the talk as a means of re-arousing interest which is almost bound to be lagging.

3. The presentation should include not more than three or four main points if the speaker is interested in retention of information. To put across information the speaker should not make point after point, but rather he should concentrate on "selling" the essentials, arousing interest in them, elaborating on their importance, and illustrating their significance to the individuals in the audience. Thus, the talk previews, develops, elaborates, demonstrates (for example, with audio-visual aids), and reviews the essential points.

4. Every talk should give a conclusion which is clear-cut, and which summarizes and emphasizes the main points of the talk. This may be done by simple reiteration of the key points, the presentation of the original challenge.

5. Although reading a speech is an almost sure way to "kill it," a short reminder-outline may be referred to without detracting from the presentation.

[2] L. Schubert, *A Guide for Oral Communication*, New York, Prentice-Hall, 1948, p. 31.

GROUP DISCUSSIONS

By "democracy" some people seem to mean everyone doing or saying whatever happens to cross his mind at the moment. This raises questions of discipline and control, and an illustration will indicate our reasons for placing emphasis upon the idea that group discussions, if they are to be democratic, must be in control.

Earlier in this book the chapter concerned with child health and physical fitness utilized case studies from our Children's Physical Developmental Clinic. It was noted that some children referred to the Clinic were awkward and unable to make bodily movements that were appropriate to the needs or wishes of the child involved. Indeed, in rather extreme cases (certain palsies—and always in early infancy, for that matter) movement is more or less random.

Now the question is, does this *undisciplined movement,* this *lack of control,* make for freedom of the individual? Quite the contrary. These individuals are the slaves of their lack of control. Their inability to *inhibit* all possible movements but the *one movement desired* renders them helpless. So their movements are random and they get nowhere. The function of the clinicians is to help the children achieve disciplined movement and thus to achieve *control* and—paradoxically perhaps—*freedom* of movement. So it is with oral communication, in this case with special reference to group discussion.

If a group discussion is "to get somewhere" it must be under control; and let us stress that democracy, like freedom of movement, implies discipline and control.

Children understand games. They soon realize that a game is "no fun"—it gets nowhere—if it is lacking in clearly defined rules which every player agrees, tacitly, to observe. A poor sport is unpopular with the other players of the game, not for "moral" reasons, but because he stops, interrupts, or impedes the flow of the game. So it is with group discussions.

Group discussions, like baseball games, must operate under rules which are agreed upon in advance by the group; and certain individuals must be accepted as moderators or officials who assume responsibility for keeping the discussion or game moving within the agreed-upon framework. In other words, the officials should interfere if a baseball game threatens to become a boxing match, or if someone starts to walk off with the ball.

To repeat, children understand games. Group discussion is a kind of sociointellectual exercise (involving numerous bodily movements, of course) just as basketball is a kind of sociomovement exercise (involving too, higher mental functioning). Both imply individual discipline to keep play moving and within bounds, and both require moderators (or officials) overseeing, though not participating in, the play in a manner that is objective and aloof from the heat of differing views (or competition). In brief, disciplined, controlled group discussion can be a training ground for living in a society in which both individual and group interests are profoundly respected—just as games can serve a comparable function.

In group discussion, the group in effect agrees to concern itself with a particular subject—and no other. It agrees to accept the further controlling influence of a chairman and a time limitation (with adults, this time limit does not usually exceed one hour). It then proceeds to "talk the matter over."

The purposes of group discussion have been summarized as (1) to make people think; (2) to increase agreement as to what action to take and increase cooperation; (3) to reveal present conditions as the group sees them; and (4) to give people a chance to get things off their chests.[3] With these purposes in mind it is evident that group discussions of health subjects can occur under numerous circumstances. However, for present purposes, the more formal types of group discussions such as those intended for classroom or meeting are considered here.

Thoughtful teachers can develop numerous applications of the above purposes in health teaching. For example, classroom group discussions might take into account such questions as:

What additional health department services are needed in our community?
What are our playground safety hazards?
What can we do about our physical fitness? Our home recreation facilities? Our between-meal eating practices?
How should children dress for play day? Closing exercises for elementary school? Preteen dance?
Under what conditions do we enjoy eating, working, and studying?

3 *Ibid.,* p. 173.

It has often been protested that most group discussions are nothing more than a pooling of ignorance—and there is no question that this is often true. However, in some situations a teacher may wish to know the status of knowledge (or ignorance) of a class concerning a health topic before a new unit is begun, and an informal class discussion of that topic may be useful. (Indeed, a recording may be made of such a discussion to be contrasted with a second recording to be made at the termination of the unit.) However, discussions are likely to be far more fruitful if preparation is made for them in advance. That is, to avoid being "a pooling of ignorance," a group discussion should be preceded by careful study of the subject under consideration by those who are to discuss it.

The Discussion Leader

Perhaps the main functions of the discussion leader are to keep the discussion on its subject and to keep individuals from dominating it. The leader, then, must view himself as being more an official than a player, and he must be ready with tact—but with firmness— to settle disputes, "shut off" individuals if necessary, reword questions or statements so that they will be understood, and to keep the discussion within its time limits. He should insist upon recognizing discussants before they speak and prevent unrecognized speakers from making statements. In a word, he keeps the game in control. Moreover, by asking questions he "passes the ball around," drawing all into the discussion. He may terminate the discussion by summarizing what has been said, the conclusions reached and, perhaps, the agreed-upon plan of action.

Clearly, leading a discussion is a complex and difficult skill, and pupils should not be expected to be able to do it well without guidance. The teacher may prepare them for this responsibility by setting up situations which are likely to occur in the course of discussions (that is, disputes, individuals attempting to do all the talking, and so on) and discussing with the class how such problems might be handled effectively.

Panel Discussions and Symposiums

Panel discussions are another means of oral communication which may be very effective for bringing new health information into the classroom or other meeting place, stimulating thought concerning health needs and problems, and suggesting uses for newly acquired knowledge.

Panel discussions are most valuable if they are preceded by study and thought on the subject under consideration by the individual panelists. A class may be divided into panel groups (usually five to eight persons per panel), each assigned to the study of a health or fitness topic; for example, food elements essential to daily diets; things to consider when shopping for school clothes; control of communicable disease in our community. Prior to the presentation of their discussion, each panel should select a chairman and plan the course that the discussion will take. The specific points and questions to be dealt with should be decided upon in advance. It is the responsibility of the chairman to introduce the subject and tell what the plan of the discussion is. He should also see that all the panelists participate, that the discussion is not sidetracked, and that all of the time allotted is not spent on only part of the subjects agreed upon. Time may be set aside at the end for a forum, that is, questioning and commenting by the audience. Audience members wishing to raise questions should be recognized by the chairman, and then address their question to the appropriate panelist. Panel discussions in the fifth and sixth grades usually prove to be a motivating technique that can stimulate effective oral communication in relation to the subject matter of health.

The symposium is quite similar to the panel discussion, except that each member in turn makes a short speech (perhaps five minutes) on his subject.

After each symposium member (usually three to five) has made his statement, a panel discussion among the members may follow, and audience participation may be invited. Still another variation is for the chairman to ask each symposium member a challenging question related to a statement the latter made before the audience is invited to participate.

Question-and-Answer Sessions

One of the commonest forms of oral communication utilized in the classroom is the question-and-answer session. It is frequently used as a means of testing pupils so as to discover whether they have carried out their assignments and to determine their understanding of specified material. However, many teachers find such sessions to be extremely valuable ways not only of examining pupil thinking but of stimulating it.

The so-called Socratic method of thinking through problems by means of raising questions can be used to require more and more clear and reasonable replies from pupils, and it can encourage greater skill in problem-solving. Intelligent inquiry can also help pupils to acquire greater skill in logical reasoning; seeing relationships; predicting outcomes; evaluating content, situation, and characters; making comparisons; and interpreting figurative language.

Activities for elementary school children which involve questioning include preparing thought-provoking questions on health topics, preparing quiz programs as summary activities for a topic or unit, and interviewing specialists on some phase of health.

Among the commonest mistakes made by teachers questioning pupils are that (1) the questions are more or less random rather than being well thought out and "going some where" sequentially, (2) the questions are asked in such a way that they suggest their own answers or can be satisfied by a guessed yes-or-no answer, and (3) the questions are asked in such a way that the pupil is made to feel under pressure to parrot information from books or previous lessons, and inadequate attention is paid to exploring and clarifying the meaning of the information for the particular pupil.

HEALTH AND LANGUAGE

A major message of the field of general semantics[4] and certain philosophers (for example, Dewey) is that language itself affects human behavior profoundly. Sometimes, as for example, when a parent or teacher says something that sparks a new insight in a young person, language is of great value. At other times the language used by influential persons has a deadly effect. For example, anyone who remembers hearing the harangues of Hitler must be impressed by the awful effect that words, when spoken under certain conditions, can have on the attitudes and behavior of people. On the other hand, the *language* of love stirs us; the *words* of a trusted

4 See the chapter reference list for sources concerned with language and semantics.

therapist can reassure a patient, helping him to gain or regain self-confidence, or to face up to the inevitable.

Health is a central factor in human affairs because few things can be of greater interest to an individual than how he feels, how effective he is in fulfilling his potential, how long—or whether—he will live, and so on. Because of this universal interest, health has been studied from many different points of view, that is, from the perspectives of the physician, the bacteriologist, the mental hygienist, the physiologist, and the like. However, one of the major factors which affects our health is something that is rarely taken into account at all—namely, how we talk and are talked to about ourselves and our health. Again, the spoken word. Let us consider some examples.

1. A coach *explains* the relationship of nutrition, exercise, and rest and convinces his athletes that changes should be made in their way of life.
2. Some kind of attitude toward foods, health, and illness is formed by repetition of such remarks as, "Eat it or you'll be sick," or "Clean up your plate if you want to be big and healthy."
3. A child protects himself after being *told* by his camp counselor that certain plants, insects, and reptiles are poisonous.
4. Thousands of people rush out and buy a new "health product" bread or drink because of what some television sponsor has *claimed* for it.
5. Realistic *radio programs* have been known to give rise to such symptoms in listeners as feelings of strangulation supposedly resulting from poisonous gas attack, feelings of heat from nonexistent explosions, and loss of consciousness following hysteria.[5]
6. Being *told* that one has a "condition" such as "heart trouble" has brought about radical changes in feelings, appearance, and activities of people—even though subsequent examinations have indicated that the condition did not actually exist.
7. A family *argument* at mealtime disturbs the digestion and later, perhaps, the sleep of some of those present.
8. A child forms some kind of impression upon being *told* that he or something he has said or done is nasty, bad, dirty, or stupid.

However, the point of this discussion is not merely that people's emotions, attitudes, and behavior may be affected by what is said to them; we wish further to direct attention to the fact that specific

[5] J. P. Chaplin, *Rumor, Fear and the Madness of Crowds*, New York, Ballantine Books, 1959.

words are themselves "loaded" in the sense that they are capable of giving rise to various more or less dramatic reactions in people. The following illustrations show how although we thoughtlessly assume that we are reacting to a threat, or at least to *something* in our environment, we are, in fact, reacting to words themselves. Let us emphasize in these examples that the word is what we react to. The "loaded" words are italicized for emphasis.

1. Visitors to a ranch in Arizona become nauseated upon being told that the meat they enjoyed so much at lunch was, indeed, *rattlesnake*. (Observe that the meat itself was fine—until the word *rattlesnake* was introduced.)
2. A child gets some kind of feeling about himself upon being told that he is *skinny*—or husky—as the case may be. Of course the "skinny" child may be exceptionally healthy though lean, and the "husky" child may be quite obese, awkward, weak, and subject to colds, and so on. Still the term "husky" is by far the more attractive word and less likely to damage the self-esteem of one so labeled.
3. We react in a particular way when told that something is *good* for us.
4. A public washroom labeled *sanitary* makes us feel better about using it, although as a matter of fact we may know nothing about its actual state of cleanliness.
5. We feel, somehow, better about a new bomb when told that it is *clean*—a *clean* bomb!
6. The nation reacted violently when *Asiatic flu* was said to have descended upon us. Cases broke out on the East Coast almost as soon as it allegedly arrived on the West Coast.
7. "It's time for your *shots*" is enough to drive many children into a near panic—in spite of the fact that ten times the pain is involved in playing a game of touch football or soccer.
8. The word *spinach* is enough to make many mothers contemplating serving it feel rather virtuous—and many children feel rather ill.
9. We have heard children, who were present, referred to by their parents as *brain-damaged, awkward, clumsy, skinny, slow learner, emotionally disturbed, nonverbal, fat,* or incapable of doing such and such; and we have wondered how these words made the children feel about themselves. Many parents do not fully realize that children tend to evaluate themselves on the basis of adult verbal evaluations.
10. To be called *a name* can be disturbing, enraging, or depressing, even though no one could possibly actually *be* what the word supposedly refers to. This calls to mind the observation that words are commonly used *not* as labels—which they are—but as things—which they are not.

The word *health* itself is loaded in curiously conflicting ways. On the one hand, it is a "good" word which can be used almost moralistically to justify activities, sell products, or force foods on children. Thus, people feel better about ducking out for an afternoon of golf if they can say it is good for their health; innumerable advertisements of such things as drugs, remedies, vitamins, sun lamps, and gadgets utilize health appeal much as many other advertisements utilize sex appeal; and certain foods, like milk, oranges, bread, and spinach bask in the glow of the word *health*. Our point is not whether these activities, products, and foods are beneficial or not, but that they are made to seem more attractive because of their association with a word, *health*. Conversely, to call something "bad for your health" places it in a poor light regardless of the actual effect of the thing or activity upon one's health. For example, heavy exercise, sexual self-stimulation, and drinking moderate amounts of alcoholic beverages have all been so-labeled without evidence that they are indeed "bad for your health."

On the other hand, health is also in some ways a "bad" word. Children, especially, are commonly so hammered with the word that it is often at best a bore and at worst something to rebel against. These effects are commonly apparent in the attitude of junior and senior high school pupils toward the commonly improvised "health course." It is noteworthy in this respect that adolescence is commonly regarded as being a rebellious period in life, and studies of the eating practices of youth suggest that they rebel against the "virtue" foods and virtually live on "bad" foods (colas, candies, pastries, coffee, fried chips, beer) or foods over which a real issue has not been made in the name of health (hamburgers, hot dogs, and ice cream concoctions). The cigarette serves as a common appetite appeaser.

To many parents and teachers the word *health* is a vague term used as a weapon to force cooperation: "If you want to be healthy, you'll . . ." People can feel quite good about forcing children to devour great piles of spinach and other greens or to bundle up to the point of being mummified in the name of health. Conversely, "If you don't eat such and such, don't go to bed at a certain time, don't put on a jacket, don't drink your milk, don't wash your hands, don't move your bowels regularly, don't put on clean underclothing—you'll be sick." Such threats are comparable to telling a child that if he goes into the basement or out in the dark "spooks or goblins will get you." To the youngster the words *health, sickness,* and *ghosts* and *spooks* share the quality that (1) they tend to have little or no meaning in the sense of referring to some tangible thing in reality, and (2) they gain meaning in the sense of the threatening context in which they are used. It is also noteworthy that in common usage the words *health* and *sickness* carry definite moralistic overtones which tend to confuse the issue of healthful living. "That's a good boy." "You're a bad girl."

A dynamic example of the influence of words upon behavior is provided by the subject of sex education. Sex education is an area within the health field that is full of loaded words. By way of illustration, these days it is recommended that "frankness" is the only way to present the subject honestly so as to avoid fears, guilt feelings, and confusions in children. But it has been our experience that numerous parents and teachers report an inability to use, especially in the presence of children, the words needed if one is to be frank. The society's traditional attitude is reflected in the fact that most sex-related terms are buried in a long-dead language— Latin. Thus one does not ordinarily refer to fingers as phalanges, but words like *vagina* and *penis* have never been translated into "acceptable" English. (What parent is able to point to any portion of the body below the abdomen and above the legs in the same manner as he does when pointing to his eyes, nose, or ears, saying "What is this?") From their early years people are conditioned to identify these and other sexual terms, and their English and Anglo-Saxon equivalents, as "dirty" words and with "dirty" jokes. It is little wonder that parents and teachers are uncomfortable when, suddenly, they are expected to use these "dirty" words or words closely associated with them in the process of being frank with their children.

In classes and Parent-Teacher Association meetings dealing with sex education, mothers and teachers frequently say that they do pretty well with their children until it comes to answering the question of how the baby got started. "I simply can't use these words in front of my child," is a common complaint. Many people find it difficult to talk about the facts of conception even though no one gets here without its having taken place. At such points as this, sex education tends to flounder, grow red-faced and slide over into terminology like "birds and bees," "the stork," "tinkle," "wee-wee," "little thing," "duty," and so on. Under circumstances in which loaded words play such an important part, it is not surprising that the subject is so confusing and hard to manage. Again, the spoken word.

When one adds to the basic sex terminology the really loaded words, barriers often grow insurmountable. Consider words like *intercourse, pervert, contraception* (in many schools teachers of world affairs would not consider discussing the world problem of overpopulation in relation to food supply because of the implications for birth control), *homosexual, masturbation,* and the four-letter Anglo-Saxon words—which, by the way, no publisher would permit in a book like this one. When such linguistic problems are taken into account it is possible to see how words can come to life and profoundly affect the educative process.

Persuasion Techniques and Health Advertising

Whatever else they may have been, the Nazi leaders were master public persuaders and propagandists. Their techniques of oral communication were extremely effective and these have been carefully studied and described.[6] They have since been widely adopted by advertisers and others interested in systematically influencing the behavior of the public.

A further step in public persuasion, the so-called "depth approach," has utilized findings of psychology and psychoanalysis in an effort to control the public's buying, voting, and other types of behavior. "The result is that many of us are being influenced and manipulated, far more than we realize, in the patterns of our everyday lives."[7] Health products, health-related programs, and health-

[6] The Institute for Propaganda Analysis in New York spelled out the propaganda techniques of the German fascists while they were in power.

[7] See Vance Packard, *The Hidden Persuaders,* New York, McKay, 1957. Packard quotes the head of a motivation research organization in summarizing the intent of such research: "Motivation research is the type of research that seeks to learn what motivates people in making choices. It employs techniques designed to reach the unconscious or subconscious mind because preferences generally are determined by factors of which the individual is not conscious . . . Actually in the buying situation the consumer generally acts emotionally and compulsively, unconsciously reacting to the images and designs which in the subconscious are associated with the product" (p. 50).

related organizations have, of course, made great use of the known persuasion techniques in recent years. The incomparable Lichty has commented on this situation in a cartoon showing a promotion counselor with Senator Snort (on whose office walls appear pictures showing, "Snort, your friend and mine," "Mom," and "Home"), saying, "We've popularized such dubious things as filter tips, vibrating machines and health diets, Senators . . . and with our know-how we can make a fad out of you, too . . ."[8]

It is of interest to note that the common techniques of persuasion. Some are presented here to the ends that (1) as popular awareness of the situation grows such things as health product advertising may eventually be brought and kept under control by a discerning public which is resistant to being misled or manipulated by cleverly chosen words or other persuasive tricks and (2) teachers of health, perhaps paradoxically, may be helped to utilize effective and appropriate persuasion techniques which will encourage pupils and the public at large to adopt sound health practices in the interests of healthful living. The thoughtful teacher will see that certain of these techniques are especially applicable in relation to the young child who is not yet sufficiently mature, informed, or experienced to make extensive self-directing choices. Needless to say, it is not recommended that health teaching be reduced to the extreme forms of persuasion that are so commonly seen in the advertising of the mass media, for these depend upon the *thoughtless* responding of people. (Packard refers to women going into a hypnoidal state when they enter a supermarket.) Healthful living is essentially *thoughtful* living—and not living in terms of a series of conditioned responses acquired through persuasion techniques. Nor, ideally, is it a matter of gratifying unconscious desires or compensating for frustrations.

Repetition. It was pointed out earlier that any speaker who is desirous of having his main points retained by his audience will reduce them to a minimum and repeat them. ("Tell them what you're going to say, say it, then tell them what you said.") The reader should make special note of the number of times key words are said in television and radio advertising. In an advertisement lasting only a few seconds the name of the product and perhaps some

[8] *Washington Post,* August 8, 1960.

exhorting words or a phrase like "buy it, buy it," or "buy it today," is repeated an almost incredible number of times.

In health education, repetition may be used by the judicious teacher to emphasize basic concepts of healthful and safe living. It is hoped, however, that this device will not be used to reduce healthful and safe living to some "health rules" or the excessive glorification of certain foods, habits, or health-related groups, or excessive preoccupation with being safe—a state of complete safety never being possible.

Transfer. This is a device by which one thing, for example, a particular connotation, that is generally accepted as "good," attractive, or virtuous is associated with or transferred to something else —a product being sold, a desired point of view, and the like. Thus, couples portrayed in attractive country scenes, engaging in water sports, enjoying youthful parties, eating Thanksgiving dinners with parents and children are, of course, pointedly associated with the product advertised. Toilet tissue has gained status by being portrayed on a pedestal surrounded by pleasant pastel veils and with a nice-looking woman in view.

Specific words with which people tend to have pleasant associations are used to transfer appeal to products or points of view. Words like *cool, refreshing, light,* somehow make beer and soft drinks taste better. *Young, fair,* and *debonair* could hurt almost no product in a society that glorifies youth and sex and social appeal. The word *togetherness* gilds products with the virtues of home (the modern, ranch-house type of course), mother (the "modern," "lovely," "fresh," obviously happy, married-to-a-young-executive type), children (the quite young, radiating health and happiness, and the less young, crew-cut, muscular or shapely, but obviously very "nice"). Father, in this scene, plays a role of happy outdoor cook, excellent provider, affluent, a youngish junior executive at home. How could a product to which such attractive words and things could be transferred fail to sell? Other much-used virtue words include: pure, smooth, white, rich, fresh, mild, imported, team, positive thinking, and right thinking. The interested reader may extend this list of virtue words by examining and listening to the daily advertising and political pronouncements.

Perhaps the basic thing to note about transfer is that when the individual buys or otherwise acts because word appeal has "gotten through to him," he is, in effect purchasing the *words* which have appealed to him. In point of fact he usually knows little or nothing about the actual content or merits of the product under consideration.

There is also a device that is popular with propagandists and politicians as well as advertisers which may be called reverse transfer or "name calling." In effect it asks or threatens, "Are you like *that?*" or "Are you guilty of that?" or "Do you want *this* to happen?" The listener almost instinctively has to say or think or hope, "No!" And thereby he aligns himself with the product advertised or the desired point of view. "Don't be half-safe," "Tattle-tale gray," "Are you sure?" "Women who care . . ." (you don't care?), "Are you a litterbug?" "Do you look *older* than you really are?" "Are you a wallflower?" Do you want to "get cavities? be sick? smell bad? get pimples?" These are examples of reverse transfer which have been used to turn people away from an unpleasant *word* or phrase and toward the desired purchase or behavior.

The teacher of health can make use of transfer (and reverse transfer) by associating favorable (or unfavorable) words with desirable (or undesirable) health practices. Young children aspire to escape from their helplessness and are attracted by words associated with their becoming more capable of adultlike achievement, of skilled movement and greater strength and size. Unfortunately, the desires of young children make them subject to exploitation by advertisers who help them distort reality by suggesting that certain foods or other products will make them equal to or superior to adults—super creatures.[9] A more wholesome approach might be to increase the chances that childhood might be more rewarding and less frustrating, something to be lived rather than escaped. At any rate the teacher may make use of transfer in a variety of ways. Following are some examples: "Protein foods build muscle." "Sleep rebuilds." "The canoer strokes and glides; we work and then we relax." "I make mistakes; often I learn by making mistakes." "A good winner is also a good sport."

Thus, transfer and reverse transfer can be used to encourage pupils to appreciate and wish to emulate the fitness, skill, health, maturity, self-understanding, and other traits of individuals sym-

[9] See Packard's discussion (*op. cit.*, pp. 135 f.) of the psycho-seduction of children.

bolized by certain words. However, it is necessary to point out that transfer, like the other persuasion techniques, is a powerful weapon that can easily be more harmful than constructive.

Testimonial. This is a means whereby an authority, or someone whose views we are prone to accept, is used to "sell us" on a product, or point of view. Individuals portrayed as physicians (in white jacket and with stethoscope draped around the neck) have been an excellent source of oral testimonial concerning health products. Others include "dentists," nurses, mothers, athletes and formerly fat, tired, and unhappy people.

A favorite technique of "quacks" is to produce the spoken or written testimonials of patients whom they have allegedly cured. It is not an easy matter to explain to the ill or the desperate that (1) in accepting a testimony at face value one can easily be falling prey to fakes, behind whose words there are no facts, and (2) almost every conceivable "cure" has actually cured *some* people. After all, many diseases have responded to faith healing and hypnosis. Cortisone, certain antibiotics, antihistamines, electrical and magnetic gadgets, and even aspirin have produced "miracles." But these treatments and many others have also failed miserably. No approach can guarantee successful therapy. In the present state of knowledge of the human personality, its susceptibility to disease, its potentialities for recovery and further growth, the "health-educated" person knows that spontaneous recovery is a well-known phenomenon in relation to virtually every known disease; that under certain conditions people can be inspired (usually verbally) to tap their own resources for self-healing (the so-called faith-healing and hypnotic literature are full of cases of this kind); that qualified physicians are aware of the limitations of their knowledge of "health" and "disease"; and that individuals who stand to profit by selling patients on miracle cures are automatically suspect.

A form of testimonial that seems especially unfortunate is that in which a person who makes his living by being "healthy" and fit goes on record as being enthusiastic for a given product. Professional athletes, for example, exercise enormous influence; and there is no doubt that their well-paid but thoughtless and uninformed testimonials concerning cigarettes and certain foods influence the behavior of the young far more than the teaching of large numbers of qualified coaches and physical educators.

Bandwagon. The theme of this device is "Everybody else is doing it, why don't you? or we?" There is a widespread tendency for people to feel more secure, more oriented, and less objectionable when doing what everyone else is doing. Advertisers, politicians, and propagandists prey upon this tendency with their arguments and statistics. To differ with the main body of the group, the norm, is to be abnormal. So and so outsells all its competitors; the people's choice; men who know . . . everybody knows. . . .

People who resent mob psychology and "keeping up with the Joneses" tend to find this technique especially disagreeable. They resent the lack of individuality in the glorification of keeping in step with everybody else. Nevertheless, the bandwagon technique can be used to help some pupils to break confining or unfortunate habits and try some possibilities which "the group" finds acceptable. Thus trying new foods may become praiseworthy, exercise programs or training regimens may become attractive, sportsmanlike behavior may become esteemed when the bandwagon approach is utilized and the individual finds himself at odds with the group if he clings to former behavior patterns.

Plain Folks. Politicians and advertisers often make a great point of identifying with "the common man," the working people. A true friend of the people, the advertiser as well as the politician "climbs the stump," behaving in any conceivable way to attract the unsophisticated. For the plain folks he will clown uproariously, kiss babies, and exude sentimentality and the "virtue" words. Obviously, the great majority of any population is the common man, and it cannot be ignored by the public persuader, vote seeker, or advertiser.

Let us consider some examples. Foods are better if they are "homemade." The sedentary office worker is likely to be attracted by associations which make him feel rugged and manly, and he-man advertising which features truck and tractor drivers, cowboys, builders, and lumberjacks are popular. Similarly, the activities of the farmer, hunter, fisherman, or sailor acquire a certain glamour because they imply vigor, solidness, and "down to earth" qualities not so readily associated with the business machine operator, lawyer, professor, or hairdresser. The tattoo on the hand or arm of the young executive implies an earlier life among the people.

The teacher of health may utilize the appeal of "plain folks" by associating healthful living with culturally esteemed personality types, activities, and careers. Thus the woodsman, farmer, hunter, fisherman, mountain climber, coach, athlete, telephone lineman, construction worker, truck driver, and so on, may readily be identified with, for example, the triangle of physical fitness or, perhaps, the triangle representing total personality health (see Chapter 3).

Card-Stacking. Card-stacking is a device by which the persuader employs all the arts of deception to win public support for his product, group, or organization, or nation, race, policy, practice, belief or ideal. He stacks the cards, usually without regard for the truth, for his purpose is not public education but control of behavior— his way. "He uses underemphasis and overemphasis to dodge issues and evade facts."[10]

It may seem unfair at this time to raise the issue of card-stacking in a book of this kind, when many sellers of health products have attempted to be responsible in their advertising and to align themselves with those endeavoring to improve the public health. For example, some baking concerns have tried hard to popularize breads which would be of such nutritional value that they could again be properly called "the staff of life." Moreover, in the Appendix of this book, which lists sources of free and inexpensive health education materials, it may be noted that the majority of free materials are provided by profit-making organizations, and many of these materials are excellent.

Still, the fact remains that card-stacking is commonly practiced by advertisers and others intent upon persuading the public in their own interests. For a dramatic but certainly not isolated example, large-scale collusion of certain pharmaceutical concern personnel and of some federal government officials led, finally, to congressional investigations in 1960.[11] Moreover, it would be superfluous to recount the advertised claims for patent medicines and certain foods, and the long history of quackery in health and medicine is legend.

Other card-stackers include single-minded enthusiasts who are so

10 From *"Propaganda Analysis,"* as quoted in R. E. Loomis and D. L. Clark, eds., *Modern English Readings,* 4th ed., New York, Farrar and Rinehart, 1942, p. 303.
11 See the series of articles in the *Saturday Review* by John Lear which appeared on this subject during that year.

convinced they are right in their point of view that any means of persuasion seems justified. Thus, for example, the present writers have heard Temperance League representatives "teach health" to high school students in such terms as: "If you take the first step—a cigarette—then the next step is a drink . . . and the next is prostitution!"

Now of course it is entirely possible that the advertiser is not only going to make a profit by selling his product, but as a matter of fact he may be going to encourage healthful behavior *if* he succeeds in selling his product. The consumer cannot count on this, and the burden of proof rests with the producer and advertiser of the product. If their claims are sound, they should be able to document them —just as any teacher or professor should be obligated to document his claims to his classes and not insist that they be accepted on faith or on the attractiveness of the argument.

The present authors see no way in which card-stacking as defined can be justified in health teaching—except as something to be forewarned against. (A basic defense against this technique that children can begin to utilize from an early age is to raise the simple question: "Why is he—or are they—so interested in *my* health, welfare, and happiness?") On the other hand, it should require no great ingenuity to stack the deck in favor of sound health and fitness attitudes and practices on the basis of what is known to be true about human needs, health, and vigorous living. It must be stressed, however, that enthusiastic but uninformed teachers, parents, and others run the risk of card-stacking in the negative sense of the term.

REFERENCES

Chaplin, J. P., *Rumor, Fear and the Madness of Crowds,* New York, Ballantine Books, 1959.

Doob, L. W., *Public Opinion and Propaganda,* New York, Holt, 1948.

Filbin, R., and S. Vogel, "Semantics for America's Schools," *Elementary English,* December, 1959.

Hayakawa, S. I., ed., *Our Language and Our World,* New York, Harper, 1959.

Hovland, C. I., I. L. Janis, and H. H. Kelly, *Communication and Persuasion,* New Haven, Yale University Press, 1953.

Katz, D., D. Cartwright, S. Eldersveld, and A. M. Lee, *Public Opinion and Propaganda,* New York, Dryden, 1954.

Lear, John, "The S-R Drug Reports and the United States Senate," *Saturday Review,* December 12, 1959 (and other reports in the 1959–1960 *Saturday Review*).

Lee, A., *How to Understand Propaganda,* New York, Rinehart, 1952.

Lee, I. J., *Language Habits in Human Affairs,* New York, Harper, 1941.

Linebarger, P. M., *Psychological Warfare,* Washington, D.C., Infantry Journal Press, 1948.

Lowell, B. J., *The Role of Television Health Advertising and Its Relationship to Health Attitudes as Measured by a Sentence Completion Test,* Doctoral Dissertation, College Park, University of Maryland, 1962.

McInerney, R., "You've Got to Sell Glamour," *Nation's Business,* June, 1953.

Miller, G. A., *Language and Communication,* New York, McGraw-Hill, 1951.

Packard, V., *Hidden Persuaders,* New York, McKay, 1958.

"Propaganda Techniques of the German Fascists," in R. E. Loomis and D. L. Clark, eds., *Modern English Readings,* 4th ed., New York, Farrar and Rinehart, 1942.

Schramm, W., *The Process and Effect of Mass Communication,* Urbana, University of Illinois, 1955.

Schubert, L., *A Guide for Oral Communication,* New York, Prentice-Hall, 1948.

Steinberg, C. S., *The Mass Communicators,* New York, Harper, 1958.

PLANNING FOR HEALTH TEACHING

7

1   *What are some of the factors which should be considered when planning for health teaching?*
2   *When planning a unit why should the activities selected to teach the content be considered in terms of the health concepts to be developed?*
3   *When evaluating health learnings in terms of behavioral changes, which aspects of the child's total growth and development should be considered?*
4   *What procedures are recommended for teaching pupils to read health textbooks and other materials?*
5   *What are the suggested procedures for health lessons involving the skills of scientific thinking?*

The great amount of time that teachers spend on schoolwork after school hours attests to the importance which teachers attach to planning or preparing for teaching in the days and weeks ahead. Planning is a technique by which teachers can keep a sense of direction while moving toward a specific goal. Much of the success pupils achieve in their learnings can be directly related to the quality of planning done by the teacher. Effective learning experiences for children are dependent to a large extent upon the teacher's well-defined purposes, appropriate content, effective planning, and effective execution of the plans. Consequently, in planning it is imperative that the teacher take into consideration such factors as (1) the nature of the learner—his stage in growth and development and how he as an individual learns, (2) the content or subject matter —its scope, sequence, and development, (3) educational experiences which can be offered so that the learner has the opportunity to progress mentally, socially, physically, and emotionally. In general, planning for health teaching should include the following:

1. Over-all plans for the year (resource units).
2. Long-term plans for units of work (teaching units).
3. Daily plans for areas of learning of specific lessons (daily lesson plan).

RESOURCE UNIT

The teacher usually has access to resource units which have been developed cooperatively by experienced teachers, principals, supervisors, and other educational consultants. These units are intended as a source of appropriate professional and scientific information to be used by the teacher in developing a teaching unit. Health resource units are usually characterized by certain features.

1. *A title or topic* suited to the needs, interests, and experiences of children at a particular grade level.

2. *Health concepts* to be developed. These valid health concepts become the teacher's objectives. The health concepts are the focus points of a unit around which the content is selected and organized. Concepts or understandings[1] represent the "why," or the objectives and reasons for the selection of content. Even though in later years specific facts about the subject matter may not be recalled easily, it appears that the concepts or understandings developed might still be evidenced in the behavior of the person and reflected in his health attitudes and practices. This premise seems to have merit in light of what some educators have suggested concerning how understandings are developed and extended. As an example Hanna, Potter, and Hagaman have pointed out that ". . . understanding comes from many varied experiences through which the child has opportunity to develop concepts and draw generalizations. Understanding does not come from the memorization of meaningless facts. Understanding comes only through experience; it occurs when a pupil is able to act, feel, or think intelligently with respect to a situation."[2]

[1] Lee and Lee suggest that there is little to distinguish between the two terms "concepts" and "understandings" and that they may be used interchangeably (J. Murray Lee and Dorris May Lee, *The Child and His Curriculum*, 3rd ed., New York, Appleton-Century-Crofts, 1960).
[2] Lavone A. Hanna, Gladys L. Potter, and Neva Hagaman, *Unit Teaching in the Elementary School*, New York, Rinehart, 1956, p. 338.

3. *Learning activities* or the experiences relating to the health concepts. Thus, the learning experiences in a resource unit indicate to the teacher "what" to teach (content), and "how" to teach it (activities).

The teacher needs to ask herself, "What content or subject matter must I teach to develop this concept?" Thus, her ultimate aim is the development of a particular health concept through the careful selection of content. Obviously, it is not possible or necessary to include all subject matter, so the teacher selects from such matter to develop concepts appropriate to the maturity level of her pupils. When the pupils have ample information from which to draw generalizations, this is the cue for the teacher to select the next segment of content. In so doing, pupils are provided the opportunity to develop new concepts as well as to strengthen and broaden previous concepts. Obviously, when this psychological organization of content is followed, a "ready-made" unit (resource unit) will not suffice.

Learning activities suggest the "how" or ways in which the content can be taught, to the end that the health concepts, or the purposes for teaching the unit, will be realized by the pupils. Health resource units usually list various types of activities—those suited for the immature child, the so-called "average" learner, and the fast learner. The teacher selects those activities best suited to the needs and abilities of her pupils. Activities list suggestions for initiating the unit; for gathering, organizing, and recording the information; for evaluating; for consolidating the unit as it proceeds (so pupils see interrelatedness in what they are doing); and for summarizing the unit.

Inherent in the activities are skills which the pupils use to acquire the information in question. The degree to which these skills function for the child is in direct relationship to the quality of learning. For example, misinformation can be acquired when the pupil does not have the skills needed to draw valid conclusions, or to interpret correctly what he hears, observes, or reads.

4. *Recommended resources.* Two separate lists of references, one for use of the teacher and one for the use of the pupils, are a part of the resource unit. These resources include a highly selected list of teaching aids, such as textbooks, reference sets, brochures, pamphlets, library books, pictures, films, filmstrips, graphs, charts, recordings,

display kits, exhibit items, stories, poems, songs, games, dances, and so on. In addition, resource people and places are included.

5. *Evaluation.* Evaluation for the teacher is an important aspect of health teaching. She must attempt to determine as accurately as possible the extent to which learning has occurred. Total evaluation concerns itself with health knowledge, attitudes, and practices which have resulted from the health teaching. In addition to objective tests, resource units suggest that the teacher use evaluation techniques which appraise behavioral changes in the pupils.

TEACHING UNIT

The resource unit is intended as a *source* of appropriate professional and scientific information to be used by the teacher in developing a detailed *teaching* unit for her particular class.

The various aspects of the teaching unit usually include: (1) planning it, (2) introducing it, (3) teaching it through daily lesson plans, and (4) summarizing it.

Planning the Teaching Unit

In planning the unit the teacher may refer to the following chart. This chart, based upon the previous discussion, indicates (1) the various aspects of a teaching unit, (2) the interrelatedness of each aspect, and (3) the importance of the concept as a focus point.

Certain considerations might prove helpful in planning a teaching unit. To begin with, it is important that the teacher develop a meaningful and functional form for recording the unit such as the following chart.

Time allotment for teaching a unit presents a real problem to most teachers, for there never seems to be enough time to teach all that has been included in the plans. In the interest of time, the teaching unit should be outlined prior to actual teaching. The next step consists of listing in sequence all the concepts to be developed during the entire unit. Since *all* concepts should be developed, a tentative schedule for teaching each concept should be indicated on the worksheet opposite the particular concept. Obviously, the same amount of time will not be required to develop each concept. It is conceivable that some might require three or four lessons, while

INTERRELATEDNESS OF PARTS OF A TEACHING UNIT WITH "CONCEPTS" AS A FOCUS POINT

Health Concepts	Learning Experiences			Resources
	Content	Activities	Skills	
Why unit is taught	What is taught to develop each "concept"	How the content is taught in order to develop each "concept"	Where skills are involved in the activities and are needed by the pupils to learn the content in order to develop each "concept"	Which information can be secured by the pupils who use skills involved in the activities to learn the content to develop each "concept"

HEALTH TEACHING UNIT FORM

Unit Title _____ Grade _____ No. of pupils _____ Teacher _____

Dates for teaching unit _____ to _____ School _____

Schedule	Health Concepts	Teaching Content	Learning Activities	Functional Skills	Resources

one or more of the others could be developed in a single one. At this point it seems quite practical to outline the specific content or subject matter opposite each health concept. Theoretically, the health concepts can be taken directly from a resource unit. However, much time can be saved for the teacher later on if she develops the content as problems to be solved and "spells out" the subject matter in detail.

As the teacher considers the various types of learning activities it would perhaps be helpful to study carefully all of those listed in a particular resource unit. Inherent in any learning activity are skills which need to be identified and charted for the teaching unit. As the teacher selects learning activities from a resource unit, or adds learning activities of her own, she should perhaps give consideration to such questions as the following:

Which learning activities are best suited for introducing the unit?

Which learning activities will serve as "on-going" experiences to tie the unit together, and give it wholeness and relatedness?

Which learning activities offer the most desirable experiences for the summarizing activity?

Which health concepts will a given activity help to develop?

Which skills are involved in the various activities?

Which of these skills have been reasonably mastered by the pupils?

Which skills should be taught as the pupils work on a given activity?

Which social skills should be planned for the unit?

How much variety in resources will be offered to the pupils, so that they have experience in skills needed to obtain information through various media?

It should be borne in mind that a health unit cuts across many areas of learning, and at the same time provides practice for needed skills in the child's physical, mental, social, and emotional development. This *integration* of health teaching with other curriculum areas involves planning for much more than teaching health content only to develop health concepts. (In subsequent chapters, which deal essentially with integration, these points will be developed further.) For instance, health teaching involves Reading, Arithmetic, Spelling, and so on. As the teacher cogitates in her planning of the health unit, she would certainly want to consider other areas of the curriculum, and ask herself questions concerning how each of these areas relates to the health unit she is planning. For example:

Reading

1. How can I teach the pupils to read health materials intelligently?
2. Which skills will I include so these pupils can grow in their ability to: grasp the total meaning of the selection, interpret critically what is read, reflect on information, build a meaningful vocabulary, organize ideas?

Handwriting

1. Have I examined the pupils' handwriting during the health lesson? In which skills are they the most proficient—the least proficient?
2. Is their writing functional, legible, and neat? What skills do they need to practice to meet the standards for cursive and manuscript writing?
3. Are my pupils doing needless copying of health material that could be duplicated for them?
4. How can I help my pupils improve margins, indentations, and the general appearance of their written work?

Spelling

1. How can I help these pupils to spell with ease and accuracy the new health words which they will use outside the classroom?
2. Which skills will I include to help them grow in their ability to use phonetic, structural, and semantic analyses in the spelling of new words in the health vocabulary?

Arithmetic

1. Which skills in arithmetic can these pupils gain through a study of this unit?
2. What functional experiences can I plan to have these pupils gain a deeper insight into the number system and its processes?

English—oral and written communication

1. How well can the pupils compose paragraphs, outlines, and stories?
2. How well can the pupils take notes?
3. How well can the pupils write an invitation, a business letter, or a thank-you note?
4. How well can the pupils conduct an interview?
5. How well are illustrated oral reports given?
6. What opportunities will be given the pupils to create poems, stories, plays, and songs?
7. What opportunities will be given for dramatizations or for the presentation of a health program?

Art

1. Which skills in art can be taught in this unit?
2. What construction activities should be carried on during this unit?

3. What improvement will there be in the art work displayed in the classroom during the unit?
4. How will I encourage creative art work?

Music
1. What songs should be included to give enrichment to this health unit?
2. Which skills can be practiced in a functional situation?

Literature
1. Which poems and stories should be included in this unit?
2. Which library books should be in my classroom for this unit?

Physical Education
1. Which games, stunts, and rhythmic activities should be included?
2. What skills (physical, social, mental, and emotional) will these physical activities provide for the pupils?

AN EXAMPLE OF A HEALTH TEACHING UNIT

Title: __Milk and Milk Products__ Grade __2__ No. of pupils _____

Teacher _____ School _____

Dates for teaching unit _____ to _____

(*Note:* This health teaching unit for the second grade is a part of the year's work on nutrition. Based upon the implications for teaching from the present knowledge of child growth and development, the recommended practice is a series of short health units for primary children, rather than the more lengthy units for the upper elementary children. In accordance with this practice, four short teaching units would be developed in order to teach the various aspects of nutrition involving (1) meats, (2) fruits and vegetables, and (3) bread and cereal, as well as the present unit on "Milk and Milk Products." The example of the health teaching unit on the ensuing pages shows how a teaching unit can be developed from a health resource unit. This example of a health teaching unit on "Milk and Milk Products" is based on the resource unit discussed previously in this chapter.)

AN EXAMPLE OF A HEALTH TEACHING UNIT (*Cont.*)

APPROXIMATE SCHEDULE	HEALTH CONCEPTS	TEACHING CONTENT
1 day	Dairy cows are the main source of our milk supply.	*A. Animals that Supply Milk for Us* 1. What animals' milk can we usually buy from the milkman or at the store? Cow's milk Goat's milk

LEARNING ACTIVITIES	FUNCTIONAL SKILLS
Activities to Teach the Content *Note:* Through the activities needed to teach the content, health teaching is integrated with other subjects.	*Note:* For the most part the general classification of skills is indicated here. As the teacher prepares the daily lesson, she plans to teach the specific skills which the pupils need in order to learn from the activity. For a treatment of the specific skills in each subject area, see Resources—"References for Teachers" accompanying this unit.
Discuss animals that the pupils think give us milk to drink.	Oral communication skills involving speaking clearly and correctly, and using correct enunciation and pronunciation.
Serve goat's milk to each pupil. Have pupils see, smell, feel, and taste goat's milk.	Thinking skills involving drawing conclusions.
Have the pupils describe the smell and taste of goat's milk. (*Note:* Help pupils express their opinions positively, as, "I haven't tasted goat's milk enough times to like it," or "I haven't learned as yet to like goat's milk.")	Vocabulary development skills involving selection of descriptive words.
Compare the taste and smell of goat's milk with cow's milk.	Vocabulary development skills involving words used to describe likenesses.
Tell pupils about the necessity of some persons having goat's milk in their daily diet.	Listening skills involving concentration.
Find the cost of goat's milk and compare with the cost of cow's milk.	Arithmetic skills involving concepts of "more" and "less."

APPROXIMATE SCHEDULE	HEALTH CONCEPTS	TEACHING CONTENT
1 day		2. What breeds of cows give us milk?
		Ayrshire cows are any shade of red, mahogany, or brown, and white. They give much milk.
		Guernsey cows are golden fawn color with white markings. They give milk rich with cream.
		Holstein cows are black-and-white. They give the most milk of the dairy cows.
		Jersey cows are fawn color, or gray, or brown, and sometimes spotted with white. They give the richest milk of the dairy cows.

LEARNING ACTIVITIES	FUNCTIONAL SKILLS
Activities to Teach the Content	
Read and discuss the poem, "The Friendly Cow" by Robert Louis Stevenson in M. II. Arbuthnot, *Time for Poetry,* p. 120.	Skills involving aesthetic listening.
Discuss colors of the cows the pupils have seen.	Oral communication skills involving correct usage, enunciation, pronunciation, and good sentences.
Study teacher's colored pictures of dairy cows to note distinguishing characteristics (size, color, horns).	Skills of observing involved in noting similarities and differences.
Check information by studying pictures in textbooks, such as M. L. Pierce *et al., The Community Where You Live,* p. 53.	Comprehension skills involving verifying conclusions.
Activities to Record the Content	
Color four life-size paper cows. Label "Ayrshire," "Guernsey," "Holstein," "Jersey." Stand them against wall in the classroom.	Principles of art involving color and emphasis.
Begin a vocabulary list for the unit called "Our Dictionary."	Vocabulary development skills involving definitions and/or descriptions.
Begin a frieze, "The Story of Milk." Show four breeds of dairy cows.	Principles of creative art involving line, form, color, and balance.

AN EXAMPLE OF A HEALTH TEACHING UNIT (*Cont.*)

APPROXIMATE SCHEDULE	HEALTH CONCEPTS	TEACHING CONTENT
2 days	Dairy cows require special care at milking time.	*B. The Story of Milk from the Dairy Farm to Us* *Note:* It is suggested that the milking-time routine of the dairy farm to be visited be taught here. 1. What is the usual routine at milking time on the modern dairy farm? Cows are brought into barn and washed. Disinfectant is used on udder and teats. Cows are brought into milking barn and put in stanchions. Cows are fed hay during morning milking, and mixed grains during afternoon milking. Each cow has her own water fountain. A cow drinks about 8 gallons of water a day. Milking machine is attached to each cow's teats or cow is milked by hand. Cow is milked in from three to four minutes. Scales beside each cow indicate correct weight of milk given by cow. Pounds of milk are recorded on a chart beside each cow's name. Cow is "stripped" by hand after milking tubes have been detached. Cows are released from stanchion, and returned to corral, barn, or pasture.

LEARNING ACTIVITIES	FUNCTIONAL SKILLS
Activities to Teach the Content	Skills of writing a letter of request.
Write a class letter requesting a visit to a dairy farm at milking time.	Skills of handwriting involving slant, size, line, spacing, alignment, and letter formation.
Study and discuss pictures in multiple texts to learn routine at milking time. Use the following books:	Skills involved in studying pictures for information.
Goodspeed, J. M., *Let's Go to a Dairy*—Feed troughs, drinking cups, stanchions, p. 4; weighing milk, p. 8.	Skills of oral communication involving correct usage, relevant ideas, and sharing information with others.
Letton, M. C., *et al., Maybe I'll Be a Dairy Farmer*—Washing cow's udder, p. 4; stanchions, p. 4, 10, 14; teat cups, p. 5.	
McIntire, A., *et al., How We Get Our Food*—Chart showing cows' names and amount of milk given, p. 59.	
Activities to Record the Content	
List the various jobs done at milking time. Organize the dairy farm routine in the sequence which it seems to occur.	Organizational skills involving sequence, association, and relationships.
Role-play the part of various dairy farm workers.	Skills of creative dramatics.
Plan with pupils to check milking-time routine which they have recorded with milking time which they will observe on their visit to the dairy farm.	Skills involved in defining a problem. Skills involving group planning.
Add frames to frieze on the story of milk. Such frames might be cows coming to stalls, cows in stanchions, cows being milked.	Principles of creative art involving line, form, color, balance, emphasis, and contrast.

APPROXIMATE SCHEDULE	HEALTH CONCEPTS	TEACHING CONTENT
1 day	Milk goes through various processes at the dairy farm to keep it clean and pure.	2. What processes does the milk go through at the dairy farm?
		Milk is taken immediately to milk room.
	Milk must be kept clean at all times.	Milk is strained into large sterilized cans and kept cool.
		Refrigerated trucks transport milk in large cans to the dairy.

LEARNING ACTIVITIES	FUNCTIONAL SKILLS
Activities to Teach the Content	
Study and discuss pictures in multiple texts to learn processes milk goes through at dairy farm. Use the following books:	Skills involving observing pictures for specific information.
	Skills of oral communication involving usage, enunciation, pronunciation, and good sentences.
Hallock, G. T., *et al.*, *Health in Work and Play*—Milk cans on truck, p. 83.	
Hunnicutt, C. W., *et al.*, *I Have Friends*—Milk cooler, p. 52.	
Letton, M. C., *et al.*, *Maybe I'll Be a Dairy Farmer*—Milkroom, p. 8, 10, 14, 15; cooler, p. 6, 10, 14, 15.	
Schloat, Jr., G. W., *Milk for You*—Straining milk, p. 26; cooling milk, p. 27; loading milk cans on truck, p. 27.	
Activities to Record the Content	
Write a class story telling the process milk goes through on the dairy farm; title might be: "What Happens to Milk at the Dairy Farm." (*Note:* Copy on a chart.)	Skills of paragraph writing involving topic sentence, sequence, closing sentence, title, grammar, punctuation and capitalization.
Plan with the pupils to check these processes on their visit to the dairy farm.	Skills involving defining a problem. Skills involving group planning.
Role-play the part of the various farm workers.	Skills of creative dramatics.
Add new words and their meaning to the vocabulary chart. Such words might be *milkroom, sterilizer, cooler, refrigerated trucks.*	Vocabulary skills involving description and/or definition of terms.

AN EXAMPLE OF A HEALTH TEACHING UNIT (*Cont.*)

APPROXIMATE SCHEDULE	HEALTH CONCEPTS	TEACHING CONTENT
1 day		
1 day		
1 day		

LEARNING ACTIVITIES	FUNCTIONAL SKILLS
Activities to Teach the Content	
Plan a visit to the dairy farm.	Skills involved in planning and group discussion.
Set up standards for behavior on bus and at farm. Practice standards.	Skills involving safety practices.
List things to observe and check at dairy farm, such as routine at milking time; processing of milk at farm; different kinds of work being done by dairy farm workers.	Thinking skills involving recall, retention, and association.
Learn to play game, "Cow Poker" in E. B. Salt *et al., Teaching Physical Education in the Elementary School,* p. 318, to play with partner on bus en route to dairy.	Skills involving physical education.
Visit the dairy farm.	Skills involving group participation, listening, observing, recall, and retention.
	Social skills involving good manners.
Evaluate the visit to the dairy farm in terms of (1) information received about topics listed above; (2) behavior; (3) what pupils learned; (4) what pupils enjoyed most.	Skills involving critical evaluation.
Write a class thank-you letter to the dairy farmer.	Skills involving handwriting. Letter-writing skills involving form, punctuation, spelling, and capitalization.

APPROXIMATE SCHEDULE	HEALTH CONCEPTS	TEACHING CONTENT
3 days	Milk goes through many processes at the dairy.	3. How is milk processed at the dairy?
		Lid of can is removed and milk is smelled (pure, fresh milk has a sweet odor).
	Processing of milk at the dairy requires the skill and cooperation of many people.	Milk is weighed. Farmer is paid by pounds of milk he sends to the dairy.
		Samples of milk are tested for butterfat and purity.
		Milk is filtered as it flows into vats where it is chilled.
	Pasteurized milk is considered safer to drink than raw milk.	Milk is pasteurized.
		Milk is then processed according to use.
		Milk that is made ready for home use flows into machine for bottling.
	Cleanliness is one of the most important factors in the modern dairy.	Milk is bottled, capped, inspected, packed in containers, and stored in refrigerated rooms.
		Delivery trucks are loaded with milk from the refrigerated room.
	Milk is distributed by many people.	Milkman brings milk to our homes, the stores, and eating places.

LEARNING ACTIVITIES	FUNCTIONAL SKILLS
Activities to Teach the Content	
Show film, *They Bring Us Milk* (Golden State Company, Ltd.) to find out how milk is processed at the dairy. Discuss how a modern dairy operates.	Skills of observing, listening, and thinking. Skills involving oral communications.
Have a directed reading activity about a dairy. (*Note:* See subsequent discussion in this chapter, "Suggested Procedures for Teaching Pupils to Read Health Materials Intelligently.") Read and discuss the information from these two books:	Reading comprehension skills involving grasping meaning, organizing ideas, building meaningful vocabulary, and locating information.
Hunnicutt, C. W., *et al.,* in "At the Dairy," *I Have Friends,* pp. 58–63.	Word-recognition skills involving visual and auditory discrimination, phonetic and structural analysis.
McIntire, A., *et al.,* "The City Dairy," in *How We Get Our Food,* pp. 60–62.	
Enjoying the following poems through choral speaking:	Skills involving aesthetic listening and choral speaking.
"Frozen Milk Bottles"; "Milk in Winter"; "The Milkman's Horse"; from H. A. Brown, *et al., Let's Read Together Poems—Primary.* Discuss the milkman and his work.	
Learn the song, "The Milkman," from O. McConathy, *et al., The New Music Horizon*—Grade I, p. 136.	Skills involving singing for enjoyment.
Activities to Record the Content	
Write a class story telling the processes milk goes through at the city dairy.	Skills of paragraph writing involving title, topic sentence, sequence, closing sentence, grammar, punctuation, and capitalization.

AN EXAMPLE OF A HEALTH TEACHING UNIT (*Cont.*)

APPROXIMATE SCHEDULE	HEALTH CONCEPTS	TEACHING CONTENT
1 day	Milk can be consumed in many ways.	C. *Milk—Kinds, Products, Uses* 1. What are the different kinds of milk? Certified milk is raw milk produced with extreme attention to the nutrition of the cow, and to sanitary production. Cream is the butterfat in milk. Enriched milk has vitamins added. Evaporated milk is homogenized whole milk with about half the water removed. Homogenized milk has been treated so that the cream is mixed evenly with the rest of the milk. Pasteurized milk has been processed to destroy bacteria. Powdered milk has the liquid substance removed. Only the dry minerals remain. Raw milk is milk as it comes from the cow.

LEARNING ACTIVITIES	FUNCTIONAL SKILLS
Activities to Teach the Content	
Discuss and list different kinds of milk the pupils know about.	Skills involving oral communication.
Bring in different kinds of milk containers and bottle caps to read for information on the kinds of milk. Label and display on exhibit table.	Skills involving spelling and handwriting.
Prepare liquid milk for lunch from powdered milk.	Skills of following directions.
Activities to Record the Content	
Add the following words and their meanings to the vocabulary list: certified milk, cream, enriched milk, evaporated milk, homogenized milk, pasteurized milk, powdered milk, raw milk.	Vocabulary development skills involving word recognition, and skills needed to define and/or describe.

APPROXIMATE SCHEDULE	HEALTH CONCEPTS	TEACHING CONTENT
2 days	Many by-products can be made from milk.	2. What other foods are made from milk at the dairy? Butter

LEARNING ACTIVITIES	FUNCTIONAL SKILLS
Activities to Teach the Content	
Show certain frames of curriculum filmstrip, *Dairy Products,* to note the process for making butter at the dairy. Discuss steps in process.	Skills involving silent and oral reading.
	Discussion skills involving speech.
Have a directed reading activity. Read E. Thomas, *et al.,* in "The Town Club Makes Butter," in *Your Town and Mine,* pp. 113, 114 to list steps to use in making butter in the classroom.	Reading comprehension skills involved in grasping meaning, organizing ideas, building a meaningful vocabulary.
List what will be needed to make butter in the classroom.	Skills involved in defining a problem.
	Arithmetic skills involving liquid measurement.
Decide upon procedures to be followed when making butter, such as (1) tasks to be accomplished; (2) designation of specific jobs to certain groups of pupils; (3) group behavior.	Skills involving organization.
	Skills involving group participation, such as following directions, assuming responsibilities, taking turns, respecting the rights of others.
Make butter; serve butter on crackers; drink buttermilk.	Skills involving group participation.
	Science skills involving observing, experimenting, and following directions.
Activities to Record the Content	
Evaluate the making of butter in terms of (1) information acquired; (2) group behavior; (3) what pupils like about making butter.	Skills involving objective evaluation.
Write a class recipe for making butter. Begin a class recipe book, *Our Favorite Milk Recipe Book,* by placing this recipe in it.	Skills involving handwriting and spelling.
	Arithmetic skills involving liquid measurement.

APPROXIMATE SCHEDULE	HEALTH CONCEPTS	TEACHING CONTENT
2 days		Cheese

LEARNING ACTIVITIES	FUNCTIONAL SKILLS
Activities to Teach the Content	
Collect and study labels from cheeses to note kinds and places where cheeses are made. Label and add to exhibit.	Reading comprehension skills involving silent, oral reading and word recognition skills. Beginning map skills involving geography.
Have a directed reading activity. Read E. Thomas, *et al.,* "The Town Club Makes Cottage Cheese," in *Your Town and Mine,* pp. 112, 113 to list steps in making cottage cheese.	Reading comprehension skills involving grasping meaning, organizing ideas, and critically interpreting the information.
List what is needed to make cottage cheese in classroom.	Skills involving recall and organization. Arithmetic skills involving liquid measurement.
Make cottage cheese. Use the demonstration method. (*Note:* Some pupils assist teacher to make cheese while others observe.)	Skills involving group participation. Science skills involved in observing, following directions, and drawing conclusions.
Serve cottage cheese salad and crackers for lunch.	Social skills involving good table manners.
Learn dramatized rhythmic activity for "Little Miss Muffett" in G. Fiedler, *The Rhythmic Program in the Elementary School,* p. 96.	Skills involving creative rhythms.
Activities to Record the Content	
Write class recipes for serving cottage cheese as a salad. Add recipes to class recipe book.	Skills involving handwriting, spelling, and paragraph writing.

AN EXAMPLE OF A HEALTH TEACHING UNIT (*Cont.*)

APPROXIMATE SCHEDULE	HEALTH CONCEPTS	TEACHING CONTENT
1 day		Ice cream
1 day		3. What foods usually have milk as a basic ingredient?
		Custards and puddings are usually made with milk.
		Creamed soups are made with milk and sometimes cream.
		Ice cream contains milk and sometimes cream.
		Milk drinks and milk shakes contain milk.
		Cream sauces usually contain milk and cream.

LEARNING ACTIVITIES	FUNCTIONAL SKILLS
Activities to Teach the Content	
Show certain frames of curriculum filmstrip, *Dairy Products* to note process for making ice cream.	Skills involving recall and retention. Skills involving observation, reading comprehension, and discussion.
Learn song, "The Ice Cream Man," in L. B. Pitts, *et al. Singing on Our Way*, p. 64.	Music skills involved in singing for enjoyment.
Activities to Record the Content	
Write class story about how ice cream is made.	Skill of paragraph-writing involving title, topic sentence, sequence, closing sentence, grammar, punctuation, and capitalization.
Activities to Teach the Content	
Discuss foods that have milk as a basic ingredient.	Skills involving discussion, listening, and observing.
Read ingredients given on food packages.	Skills involving silent and oral reading.
Activities to Record the Content	
Add, to class recipe book, recipes which have milk as a basic ingredient. (*Note:* Each child asks his mother to help him write a favorite recipe using milk. Have pupils write names on recipes before placing in class recipe book.)	Skills involving handwriting. Skills involving form, organization, sequence, spelling, punctuation, and capitalization.

APPROXIMATE SCHEDULE	HEALTH CONCEPTS	TEACHING CONTENT
2 days	Milk is considered one of the most nutritive foods.	D. *Milk—an Essential Health Food*
	Milk helps us grow strong and healthy.	1. Why do we need to drink milk?
		Milk builds strong bones, teeth, and muscles.
		Milk supplies energy.
		Milk contains many of the basic elements in other foods.
		Milk tastes good.
		Milk is excellent to drink and to use with other foods.
		2. When should we drink milk?
		We should drink milk for breakfast, lunch, and dinner.
		We should drink milk between meals when we are hungry or thirsty.
		We drink milk at parties.

LEARNING ACTIVITIES	FUNCTIONAL SKILLS
Activities to Teach the Content	
Discuss why milk and milk products are important in our daily diet.	Skills involving reflective thinking.
Invite the health nurse to discuss (1) the importance of milk in daily diet; (2) when we should drink milk.	Skills involving interviewing, interrogative, and concentrative listening.
	Skills involving group participation.
Have directed reading activity to find out why and when we should drink milk. Use the following books:	Reading comprehension skills involving location of information, skim reading, and careful reading.
Bauer, W. W., *et al.*, *Seven Or So,* pp. 28, 29, 45, 46, 118, 121.	
Brownell, C. L., *et al.*, *Blue Skies,* pp. 25–27.	
Byrd, O. E., *et al.*, *Learning About Health,* pp. 38, 39.	
Hallock, G. T., *et al.*, *Health in Work and Play,* pp. 10, 11, 88, 96, 102, 107.	
Irwin, L. W., *et al.*, *Growing Day by Day,* pp. 16, 52, 53.	
O'Keefe, P. R., *et al.*, *Side by Side,* pp. 21, 103, 151.	
Activities to Record the Content	
List when and why we should drink milk. (*Note:* Copy on a chart.)	Thinking skills involving organization, association, and application.
Write individual stories, "What I Like Best About Our Story of Milk."	Skills involved in writing a story, such as selecting content, organizing content, spelling, punctuation, grammar, and capitalization.

SUMMARIZING THE UNIT

The major summarizing activity, in the form of a program, will evolve from the way the unit unfolds as it is taught. Every pupil should participate in the planning and presentation of the program. About three days will be needed to summarize this unit—one day for planning the program, one day for practicing it, and another day for presentation. Parents may be invited. Below is a program which could evolve from this unit.

PROGRAM—MILK AND MILK PRODUCTS

Greetings	Announcer
Song, "The Milkman"	Class
Illustrated Talk, "Breeds of Cows That Give Us Milk" (Four large paper cows)	Four pupils
Role play, "Milking Time on the Dairy Farm"	Four pupils
Choral Reading, "The Cow"	Class
Illustrated Talk, "Our Exhibit"	
Cow Feed	One pupil
Milk Containers	One pupil
Cheese Labels	One pupil
Poem, "Ice Cream Man"	One pupil
Reading, "Our Dictionary" (Words and meaning from vocabulary chart)	One pupil
Role play, "The Milkman Delivering Milk"	One pupil
Reading, Correspondence	
Letter sent to dairy farmer	One pupil
Letter received from dairy farmer	One pupil
Poem, "Come, Butter, Come"	Class
Reading, "Our Favorite Milk Recipes" (Class recipe book)	
"How We Made Butter"	One pupil
"How We Made Cottage Cheese"	One pupil
Illustrated Talk, "The Story of Milk" (Frieze)	One pupil
Original Song	Class
Expression of Appreciation	Announcer

Refreshments

Milk   Cookies

EVALUATING THE UNIT IN TERMS OF OBSERVABLE CHANGES IN BEHAVIOR

OBSERVABLE CHANGES IN HEALTH PRACTICES AND ATTITUDES

1. Do the pupils understand that milk is essential in their daily diet?
2. Do they understand that milk is one of the most nutritive foods?
3. Have they developed the practice of drinking milk with every meal?
4. Do they understand that milk should be kept clean and cold?
5. Do they understand that milk can be consumed in many different ways?

OBSERVABLE CHANGES IN PHYSICAL GROWTH

6. Are they looking very well and happy, and growing at a reasonable, expected rate?

OBSERVABLE CHANGES IN SOCIAL AND EMOTIONAL GROWTH

7. Are they learning to live, work, and play together harmoniously?
8. Are they learning to control themselves in unsupervised situations?
9. Are they becoming concerned for the rights of group members?

OBSERVABLE CHANGE IN LANGUAGE ARTS SKILLS

10. Do they listen to others courteously and attentively?
11. Are they growing in their ability to speak correctly, clearly, and forcefully?
12. Are they finding out how to obtain information, and to use it?
13. Are they selecting and reading more books independently?
14. Are they learning to express themselves through writing?

RESOURCES

REFERENCE BOOKS FOR TEACHERS

Association for Supervision and Curriculum Development, *Learning and the Teacher,* Yearbook, Washington, D.C., National Education Association, 1959.

Bauer, W. W., D. W. Baruch, E. R. Montgomery, E. T. Rounds, *et al., The Basic Health and Safety Program,* Fair Lawn, N.J., Scott, Foresman, 1957–1960.

Primer, *Just Like Me,* pp. 25, 27, 40.

Grade 1, *Being Six,* pp. 11, 13, 22, 47, 62, 64.

Grade 2, *Seven or So,* pp. 28, 29, 45, 46, 118–121.

Grade 3, *From Eight to Nine,* pp. 154, 165.

Grade 4, *Going on Ten,* pp. 13, 30, 31, 45, 188, 189.

Grade 5, *About Yourself,* pp. 120, 181, 183, 187.

Brownell, C. L., R. Evans, and L. B. Hobson, *ABC Health Series,* New York, American, 1959.

Grade 1, *All Day, Every Day,* pp. 15, 16, 36, 64, 95, 96.

Grade 2, *Blue Sky,* pp. 25, 27, 44–46, 139–146.

Grade 3, *Come Rain, Come Shine,* pp. 87, 88, 91, 182, 183.

Grade 4, *Among Friends,* pp. 24, 114–118.

Grade 5, *Broad Street,* pp. 47, 52–57, 109, 112, 242.

Grade 6, *Crossroads,* pp. 50, 55, 172–179, 191, 214, 215, 290.

Burger, I. B., *Creative Play Acting,* New York, Barnes, 1950.

Byrd, Oliver E., Edwina Jones, Paul E. Landis, Edna Morgan, and Thelma Shaw, *The New Road to Health Series,* Summit, N.J., Laidlaw, 1960.

Grade 1, *First Steps to Health,* pp. 58–63.

Grade 2, *Learning About Health,* pp. 28, 30, 33, 38, 39.

Grade 3, *Habits for Health,* pp. 56, 58, 61, 117, 118.

Grade 4, *Building for Health,* pp. 121, 170.

Grade 6, *Growing in Health,* pp. 93, 99, 117, 118, 145–148.

Clark, J. R., and L. K. Eads, *Guiding Arithmetic Learning,* New York, World, 1954.

Commission on the English Curriculum of the National Council of Teachers of English, *Language Arts for Today's Children,* New York, Appleton-Century-Crofts, 1954.

Compton's Picture Encyclopedia, Chicago, Compton, 1957.

Articles on "Butter," "Cheese," "Dairying," "Ice Cream," "Milk."

Dawson, M. A., and M. Zollinger, *Guiding Language Learning,* New York, World, 1957.

Freeman, F. N., *Handwriting Aids for Primary Teachers,* Columbus, Zaner-Bloser, 1948.

Hallock, G. T., R. L. Allen, and E. Thomas, *Health for Better Living Series,* Boston, Ginn, 1958.

Grade 1, *Awake and Away,* pp. 8, 17, 24, 42, 57, 58.

Grade 2, *Growing Day by Day,* pp. 16, 52, 53, 145.

Grade 3, *Keeping Fit for Fun,* pp. 13, 38, 74, 77, 130, 141.

Grade 4, *All Aboard for Health,* pp. 54, 55, 58, 99, 179.

Grade 5, *Better Health for You,* pp. 16, 17, 81, 167.

Grade 6, *Safeguard Your Health,* pp. 28, 88, 212, 213.

Kainz, L. C., and O. L. Riley, *Exploring Art,* New York, Harcourt, Brace, 1947.

Lowenfeld, Victor, *Creative and Mental Growth,* New York, Macmillan, 1952.

Miel, A., *et al., Cooperative Procedures in Learning,* New York, Columbia University, 1952.

Oftedal, L., *Milk,* Chicago, Laboratory School, University of Chicago, 1952.

O'Keefe, P. R., C. H. Maxwell, *et al., Winston Health Series,* Philadelphia, Winston, 1960.

Grade 1, *From Head to Toe,* pp. 6, 7, 10, 14, 15, 42, 43, 49, 50, 88.

Grade 2, *Side by Side,* pp. 21, 105, 151.

Grade 3, *How We Grow,* pp. 37, 57, 96, 102, 105, 107, 109, 118.

Grade 4, *Bigger and Bigger,* pp. 5, 19, 24, 38, 103, 123, 124, 135, 158, 168, 197, 210, 218.

Grade 5, *Getting Acquainted,* pp. 41, 66–70, 72, 88, 89, 123, 130, 137, 149, 231, 233, 234.

Rudomin, E., *Let's Cook Without Cooking,* New York, Crowell, 1955.

Buttermilk Banana Cooler, p. 79;

Cottage Cheese and Pineapple Salad, p. 30;

Cream of Chicken Soup, p. 10;

Milk Shakes, pp. 77, 83;

Puddings, p. 66;

Tomato Sour Cream Soup, p. 14.

World Book Encyclopedia, Chicago, Field Enterprises, 1955.

Articles on "Butter," "Buttermilk," "Cheese," "Churn," "Cow," "Creamery," "Dairying," "Ice Cream," "Milk," "Nutrition," "Pasture," "Separator," "Vitamins."

AUDIO-VISUAL MATERIALS

FILM

Golden State Company, Ltd.
1120 Towne Street
Los Angeles, California
They Bring Us Milk, 20 minutes, color, sound.

FILMSTRIP

Curriculum Films
Distributed by Educational Projections, Inc.
10 East 40th Street
New York 16, New York
No. 37, *Janet Visits a Dairy Farm.*
No. 510, *Milk.*
No. 511, *Dairy Products.*

PICTURES AND POSTERS

National Dairy Council
111 North Canal Street
Chicago 6, Illinois
  "Dairy Cows" (posters); "Milk Makes the Difference" (pictures).

Informative Classroom Picture Publishers
31 Ottawa Avenue, N.W.
Grand Rapids 2, Michigan
  "The Dairy Farm," "Milking Time."

GAMES AND RHYTHMS

Fielder, G., *The Rhythmic Program for Elementary Schools*, St. Louis,
  Mosby, 1952, "Little Miss Muffet," p. 96 (dramatized rhythm).
Geri, F. H., *Games and Rhythms for Children*, New York, Prentice-Hall,
  1955, "Farmer in the Dell," p. 35 (singing games).
Salt, E. B., G. I. Fox, E. Douthett, and B. K. Stevens, *Teaching Physica*
  Education in the Elementary School, New York, Barnes, 1960, "Cov
  Poker," p. 318 (number game).

LITERATURE

Arbuthnot, May H., *Time for Poetry*, New York, Scott, Foresman, 195?
  "The Cow," p. 120; "The Pasture," p. 123.
Brown, Helen A., *et al.*, *Let's Read Together Poems—Primary*, Whit
  Plains, N.Y., Row, Peterson, 1949, "Frozen Milk Bottles," p. 98; "Milk i
  Winter," p. 101; "Milking Time," p. 41; "The Milkman's Horse," p. 7.
Huber, Miriam B., *Story and Verse for Children*, New York, Macmilla
  1955, "Come, Butter, Come," p. 54; "The Cow," p. 96; "The Milkmai
  and Her Pail," p. 307.
McConathy, Osbourne, *et al.*, *The New Music Horizons, Grade 1*, Ne
  York, Silver Burdett, 1949, "The Milkman," p. 136.
Pitts, Lilla Belle, Mabelle Glenn, L. E. Watters, and L. G. Wersen, *Sin*
  ing on Our Way, Boston, Ginn, 1959, "Ice Cream Man," p. 64.

REFERENCE BOOKS FOR CHILDREN

Barr, Jane, *Mike, the Milkman*, illus. by Chauncey Maltman, Chicag
  Whitman, 1953.
Bauer, W. W., D. W. Baruch, E. R. Montgomery, and E. T. Pounds, *Sev*
  or So, Chicago, Scott, Foresman, 1957, "A Good Breakfast," pp. 28, ?
  "Things You Can Do," pp. 45, 46; "Why Is Milk Good for Us?" pp. 11
  121.

Brownell, C. L., R. Evans, and L. Hobson, *Blue Skies,* New York, American, 1959, "The Blue Ribbon Cow," pp. 139–142; "Clean Milk," pp. 143–146; "Food from the Farm," pp. 44–46; "How to Be Strong," pp. 25–27.

Byrd, Oliver E., *et al., Learning About Health,* Summit, N.J., Laidlaw, 1960, "Good to Eat," pp. 28, 30, 33, 38, 39.

Goodspeed, J. M., *Let's Go to a Dairy,* illus. by Raymond Abel, New York, Putnam, 1957.

Greene, C., *I Want to Be a Dairy Farmer,* illus. by Frances Eckart, New York, Children's Press, 1957.

Hallock, G. T., R. L. Allen, and E. Thomas, *Health in Work and Play,* Boston, Ginn, 1958, "Breakfast Time," pp. 10, 11; "The Dairy Farm," pp. 82–87; "Drink Milk Every Day," p. 88; "What Do You Eat Every Day?" p. 96; "Three Good Meals a Day," p. 102; "Who Can Tell?" p. 107.

Hanna, P. R., G. A. Hoyt, and C. F. Kohn, *In City, Town, and Country,* Chicago, Scott, Foresman, 1959, "Dairy Business in the City," pp. 150–153; "Dairy Business on the Farm," pp. 146–149; "Planning a New Dairy Barn," pp. 142–145.

Hunnicutt, C. W., and J. D. Grambs, *I Have Friends,* Syracuse, Singer, 1957, "At the Dairy," pp. 58–65; "Milking Time," pp. 51–57.

Irwin, L. W., W. W. Tuttle, and C. De Kelver, *Growing Day by Day,* Chicago, Lyons and Carnahan, 1958, "Dinner Time," pp. 52, 53; "The Farm Animals," p. 145; "Time for Lunch," p. 16.

Leaf, Munro, *Health Can Be Fun,* illus. by the author, Philadelphia, Lippincott, 1943.

Letton, M. C., and B. K. Meyer, *Maybe I'll Be a Dairy Farmer,* Chicago, National Dairy Council, 1955.

Letton, M. C., and B. K. Meyer, *Maybe I'll Be an Ice Cream Maker,* Chicago, National Dairy Council, 1956.

Letton, M. C., and B. K. Meyer, *Maybe I'll Be a Milkman,* Chicago, National Dairy Council, 1957.

McCrory, M., *The Story of Milk,* Columbus, Merrill, 1956.

McIntire, A., and W. Hill, *How We Get Our Food,* Chicago, Follett, 1954, "The City Dairy," pp. 60–63; "Uncle George's Dairy Farm," pp. 57–60.

O'Keefe, P. R., C. H. Maxwell, and M. S. White, *Side by Side,* Philadelphia, Winston, 1960, "Strong Teeth," p. 103; "Things to Do," p. 21; "Things to Do Each Day," p. 151.

Pierce, M. L., and E. Georgas, *The Community Where You Live,* Boston, Allyn and Bacon, 1959, "Care of Milk," p. 50; "Do You Drink Milk?" pp. 51–53; "On a Dairy Farm," pp. 48, 49.

Schloat, G. W., Jr., *Milk for You,* New York, Scribner, 1951.

Smith, M. E., *Mother's Story of Dairying*, illus. by Gladys Peck, New York, Scribner, 1951.

Thomas, E., E. W. Tiegs, and F. Adams, *Your Town and Mine*, Boston, Ginn, 1954, "Mr. Hill Buys Cheese for His Store," pp. 106, 107; "Parties Are Fun," p. 115; "Sunny Brook Dairy Farm Sells Milk," pp. 110–112; "Table Talk Can Be Fun," p. 115; "The Town Club Makes Butter," pp. 113, 114; "The Town Club Makes Cottage Cheese," pp. 112, 113; "Where We Get Our Milk and Butter," pp. 109, 110.

INTRODUCING THE UNIT

The planning for teaching a health unit includes collecting, assembling, and organizing materials of instruction for the particular unit. Some successful teachers report that it is helpful to have a special labeled container for each unit. Whether it is a drawer in a filing cabinet or a discarded suit box, it serves the need for a designated place for illustrative materials. Appropriate pictures and many free and inexpensive materials can be added to the collection from time to time.

In selecting activities to begin the unit, consideration should be given to the purposes of the introductory phase. Some of these purposes are (1) to arouse the curiosity of the pupils, (2) to stimulate interest, (3) to raise questions (not to answer them), (4) to provide for creative thought, and (5) to set purposeful goals. This procedure involves teacher-pupil planning.

Preparatory to introducing the unit, it is most important that the teacher provide for an arranged environment to stimulate interest. For example, to introduce the teaching unit, "Milk and Milk Products," certain materials seem essential for the classroom setting to capitalize upon the pupils' urge to explore, to try new experiences, and to ask questions. Some of the following aspects might be considered for a classroom environment conducive to learning:

1. *Bulletin Board Arrangement*

2. *Exhibit Table.* Several items can be placed on an exhibit table with the following question lettered on tagboard: "What do you want to find out about these things?" Some of the items might be:

> box containing powdered milk
> miniature butter churn
> feed trough

jars with samples of feed for cows
toy milk truck
several different milk bottle caps
silo
different cheese wrappers

3. *Library Table.* Books such as the following can be placed on the library table with the question: "What do you want to find out after looking at these books?"

Barr, Jane, *Mike, the Milkman.*
Greene, Carl, *I Want To Be a Dairy Farmer.*
Schloat, Jr., G. W., *Milk for You.*

Also on the library table, several photographs can be placed with the question: "Where would you go to see these things?" The photographs should show such things as:

barns
cows grazing in a pasture
field of corn
milk truck
silo

4. *Construction Materials.* Materials to be used for construction are assembled in a corner of the room. These materials might include:

crayons
drawing paper

easel paper and paints
orange crates which could be used for a miniature milking barn
nails
paper boxes
scissors
tool cart with hammers, saws, files, clamps, pounding board
wood of various sizes

Even though this list is suggestive of the more important essentials for the classroom on the day the unit is introduced, it is by no means exhaustive. The classroom reflects the enthusiasm of the teacher for the unit she is teaching, and to a degree determines the success of the future learning that is to take place.

An arranged environment constitutes an important part in successfully introducing a unit. However, because of the individual differences in abilities and interests, a variety of other stimuli are needed to develop an interest and a desire on the part of the pupils to study a prescribed unit of work. Some specific ways of introducing the unit "Milk and Milk Products" might include (1) looking at colored pictures of cows flashed on a screen from an opaque projector, (2) preparing milk to drink by mixing powdered milk and water, or (3) interviewing the milkman who delivers milk to the school.

It is during the introductory phase of the unit that teacher-pupil planning might well take place. The pupils, under teacher guidance, can formulate and organize pertinent questions and problems. In so doing, the pupils establish their own purposes for studying, and perhaps because of their curiosity assume responsibility for finding information to satisfy their inquiries. For instance, while browsing in the arranged environment and mixing powdered milk or talking with the milkman, typical pupils' questions might be:

How do cows sleep?	Why do cows chew so much?
Will cows hurt us?	Why is milk good for us?
Where do cows stay at night?	How old are cows?
Do cows do any work?	How does the farmer tie the cow
How do people get powdered milk?	to be milked?

Such pupils' questions as these serve as leads for the teacher to proceed in a way that would be most beneficial to the learning needs of the pupils.

TEACHING THE UNIT

At the outset of this discussion it seems pertinent to consider some of the conditions under which health lesson planning might take place. It should be clearly understood that the present discussion of lesson planning is oriented to the individual lessons of a teaching unit. However, the suggested procedures are applicable to situations where the unit procedure is not used. Experience indicates that the procedures discussed might be effective for teaching the scientific method, developmental procedures, and intelligent comprehension of reading materials in other subjects and areas of the curriculum.

After the unit has been introduced, the teacher turns to more detailed daily planning. The effectiveness of daily planning is closely related to the individual teacher's ability to use, from her plans, those techniques which will bring the pupil and the subject matter together, so that the most desirable learning will take place. Plans can be considered as a means of structuring techniques for effective learning. Since teaching is a profession, the successful teacher might well be considered an artist, who takes her flexible plans and, on the scene of the lesson, adjusts and adapts procedures to meet the needs of the individuals.

Most successful teachers no longer consider lesson plans as a way of recording subject matter which becomes educational diet to be digested by the pupils. In the modern elementary school, the teacher tends to consider lesson plans as techniques through which the pupils acquire and practice skills needed for living in a democracy at the same time that they are developing understandings and concepts from the prescribed subject matter. For example, while the pupils are studying health content they are also involved in a process which gives practice to such skills as:

Arriving at solutions to problems through the process of scientific thinking
Reading health materials intelligently
Following specific directions
Doing research
Operating effectively as a group
Acquiring productive work-study habits
Developing powers of observation
Giving reports

Conducting discussions
Recording pertinent information in numerous ways

These skills, as well as numerous others, could be inherent in practically any structured daily lesson plan. The following procedures are examples of lesson plans, which involve these processes and skills.

Suggested Procedure for a Lesson Involving Skills of Scientific Thinking

STEP 1.   Recognize Problem to be Solved

Problem solving is a realistic approach to learning. To know when one is faced with a problem and to be able to state the problem in clear terms are basic to any problem-solving situation. Pupils tend to accept a problem as their own when they participate in stating and defining it. For the most part, learning is more likely to be assured when pupils are faced with a problem for which the solution matters to them.

The problem or question for the daily lesson arises from various sources, such as (1) introductory experiences when the unit was introduced, (2) problems not solved during a previous lesson, (3) problems growing out of former real life experiences, (4) inquiries from children based on specific interests related to the unit, (5) pupils' needs as seen by the teacher, and (6) prescribed content for the unit.

STEP 2.   Analyze the Problem, and Form Tentative Hypothesis or Formulate Sensible Opinions

Under teacher guidance, the pupils discuss what is involved in the problem, and what they *think* they know as possible answers to the question to be answered or problem to be solved.

STEP 3.   Gather Pertinent Information

At this point, the pupils are ready to participate in appropriate activities to gather data. It is the teacher who must decide upon the expediency of having the pupils work as a total group or in small groups. The nature of the problem, needs of the pupils, availability and variety of resources, and the importance of any specific source of information tend to determine whether or not the teacher will have the class engage in one activity, such as all pupils studying the same textbook, or engage in a variety of activities concurrently.

Some activities for obtaining pertinent information might include:

Reading textbooks, reference books, library books, newspapers, magazines, encyclopedias, pamphlets, charts, graphs
Taking trips
Interviewing qualified people
Studying pictures, films, filmstrips
Listening to recordings
Seeing demonstrations
Performing experiments

STEP 4. Filter out Facts That Do Not Fit the Problem; Appraise and Verify Information

Under the skillful guidance of the teacher, the pupils practice skills involving critical thinking as they appraise, verify, and select only that information which is pertinent to the problem. For instance, children should read to:

Evaluate the source of information
Distinguish fact from opinion
Note what is stated and what is inferred
Compare writings that state different points of view (copyright dates, authorities)
Note discrepancies in the information

This is the step where pupils are taught "not only to answer questions, but to question answers."

STEP 5. Organize and Summarize the Information

Unrelated bits of information tend to be of little or no use. These facts must be related and organized around large general ideas. Children in the elementary school need much practice, under teacher guidance, in organizing information in many different ways. As a summary to the lesson, the teacher assists the pupils in organizing and refining statements of what was learned. (Suggested ways of summarizing information with accompanying skills are identified in English textbooks for the grade level.)

Information for a single lesson is sometimes recorded in more than one way, such as (1) writing a summary for the diary being kept for the unit, (2) adding new words to the vocabulary list, and (3) making a pictorial graph.

STEP 6.   Interpret Information and Draw Valid Conclusions; Use the Information

As the pupils draw conclusions, these are checked against tentative opinions made at the beginning of the lesson. Further interpretation and use of the information leads to new and unanswered questions. Plans for the next lesson arise as to "what do we need to learn and to do next?"

STEP 7.   Evaluate Group Processes of Learning Together

Continuous evaluations of the effectiveness of group processes are carried on by discussion, check lists of standards, and other techniques of individual and group self-evaluation.

One of the greatest responsibilities of the modern elementary school is to teach children how to solve problems through the *steps of scientific thinking.* The emphasis is on the pupils' acquiring proficiency in the skills of *how to think,* rather than *what to think.*

The lifetime importance of critical thinking in relation to all aspects of one's total health cannot be overlooked. Practices involving good thinking need to be established in the elementary school. Only as ability in critical thinking is developed throughout the child's education can the schools help to produce clear-thinking citizenry so necessary to a democracy. Such procedures for solving problems can be used by elementary school children as well as by scientists at Cape Canaveral or diplomats around a conference table. Solving problems scientifically is a way of working together which is vital to democracy, and to the establishment and maintenance of world peace.

Suggested Procedures for a Lesson Involving Skills Needed to Read Health Materials Intelligently

STEP 1.   Developing Readiness

The purpose of this initial step is preparing pupils to read the selection. As the teacher studies the selection to be read, she should ask herself: "Which concepts in this selection do these pupils have?" "Which new concept(s) will this selection help to develop?" (teacher's purposes). To introduce the new concept, the teacher should plan how to present the new words or ideas orally in a setting familiar to the readers. Throughout the discussion preceding the silent reading, the teacher should try to create an interest on the part of the pupils in reading the selection. Motivation of pupils to read health materials should be relatively easy, since most pupils are naturally interested in learning more about themselves and their health. (This is a theoretical postulation which does not always prevail in practical situations.) As the pupils become interested in the selection, they begin to ask questions concerning things they should like to find out while reading the selection. Consequently, the pupils establish their own purposes for reading.

STEP 2.   Guiding the Silent Reading

The first reading of a selection is *always* done silently. In so doing, the pupil reads to find the answer to his own questions (his purpose for reading). Silent reading of a selection approximates a normal reading situation and at the same time allows the child to (1) develop keener interpretation, (2) develop independence in word recognition, (3) use versatility, and (4) adjust his rate of reading to meet his purposes. As the pupils read silently, the teacher diagnoses the word-recognition skills, comprehension skills, and silent reading habits.

STEP 3.   Developing Comprehension Skills

This step involves the *art of questioning,* since asking good questions is a part of good teaching. Through her purposeful questions, the teacher attempts to *teach, practice,* or *maintain* those skills which the pupils need for intelligent comprehension of the selection. It is suggested that the teacher list the comprehension skills needed to understand the particular selection. It is also suggested that after each skill the teacher record the type of question(s) that involves the skill. As the teacher asks each question to stimulate spontaneous discussion, a diagnosis of the individual pupil's responses is made in terms of the comprehension skills in which he is the most proficient, or the least proficient. For instance, the pupil who has more difficulty with questions involving the ability to read "between the lines" than with questions involving chronology of events, will need to be asked more questions involving *inference* than *sequence*. The successful teacher knows the individual needs of her pupils and differentiates teaching in terms of those needs.

Among the comprehension skills needed for intelligent reading of health materials are those concerning fact, main ideas, subordinate ideas, cause and effect, sequence, inference, vocabulary, organization, conclusion, prediction of outcome, reflective thinking, and critical evaluation.

STEP 4.   Developing Word-Recognition Skills

During the silent reading it is expected that the teacher will assist individual pupils with word problems by guiding them in the use of picture clues, context clues, word analysis, or by actually telling the word. For those pupils requesting teacher help, and for others who have difficulty in oral reading, a period is suggested for word study under teacher guidance.

In the development of functional skills for independence in word recognition, it is imperative that the following categories of skills be taught: (1) auditory discrimination, (2) concept development, (3) basic sight vocabulary, (4) visual discrimination, (5) phonetic analysis, (6) structural analysis, (7) semantic analysis, and (8) dictionary.

Drill can be an effective technique for acquiring speed and accuracy in word recognition. The criteria for effective drill on health words are the same as for drill in arithmetic or other subjects. In this regard it is important to remember:

That the purposes of the drill are known to the pupils
That drill is given only after word meanings have been established, and
    word recognition skills have been taught
That drill should be interesting, varied, and of short duration
That the number of words should be limited

STEP 5.   Rereading

Rereading can be oral or silent. It can be done during the comprehension check to compare statements, to prove a point, or for any other reason involving a better understanding of the selection. The need for rereading of a part or a complete selection, is a decision to be made by the teacher and is dependent upon whether or not the purposes for which the selection was intended have been accomplished.

STEP 6. Following up the Reading

Follow-up activities are sometimes needed to strengthen the health concepts presented in the selection, or to find additional information for pupils' questions that remain unanswered.

Children should be taught to read health materials intelligently. A good basal reading program does not insure effective reading of health materials. Reading of the latter involves concept development, thinking, and learnings peculiar to its specialized content. The intelligent reading of health materials needs no further justification in the light of the public's concern for, and interest in, the physical, social, mental, and emotional health of its constituents.

Suggested Procedures for a Developmental Lesson Involving Effective Learning Techniques

Note: It is assumed that in a democracy one of the most effective techniques for working with people, whether pupils in school or adults in the community, is that of having the process evolve step by step as the group moves toward accomplishing its common goals or objectives. This evolving method is known as the developmental process. Its steps are rather sequential and logical, yet at the same time flexible and adaptable. Various terminology is used in the current educational literature to define and describe the steps; however, the procedure usually includes (1) purpose(s), (2) presentation of a topic for study, (3) participation in assembling information relating to the topic, (4) evaluation of information and processes, and (5) summary.

STEP 1. Purposes

At the beginning of the preparation the teacher needs to record the specific health concept to be developed during a lesson. The teacher must decide the developmental procedure for the lesson. The nature of the concept; maturity, needs, and abilities of the pupils; and the materials on hand are factors influencing the *thought* process used. Since the process of thought involves induction and deduction, one method or the other or a combination of both might be needed in a single lesson.

The inductive method, sometimes termed "the discovery method," involves the development of conclusions or generalizations from the accumulation of facts. This method has special interest appeal to elementary school children, working diligently to make a "discovery" of an accepted fact. For instance, "Are there carbohydrates in fruits?" might be the problem. After a due number of experiments with various fruits, each showing to some degree the same results, the pupils arrive at the conclusion by inductive procedures that "fruits contain carbohydrates."

When pupils are ready to do abstract thinking, the deductive method has definite appeal and educational value. As an example, the pupils might take the concept, "The basic four foods provide elements needed for the body's maintenance, growth, and repair," and through study and reasoning deduct a series of related facts inherent in the concept and needed to understand its meaning.

STEP 2. Presentation

Two points are of major concern in planning the presentation of the topic or question for study. These are:

How is the topic or question to be stated to assure the development of the concept

For optimum learning how will the pupils become interested in and see a purpose for this study

STEP 3. Participation

Participation deals with the "planning" and "doing" phases of learning. It appears essential that teacher planning precede pupil-teacher planning. In general, the teacher must decide upon the most effective ways for the pupils to acquire information. During planning sessions with pupils, various ways might be discussed and decisions made. Emphasis should be placed upon a variety of activities rather than on one or two, such as "reading" and "question and answer" lessons.

The teacher should take into account the facts that children learn in different ways and that children learn by doing. Firsthand experiences usually lead to a high degree of learning, since the pupils use the five senses concurrently to acquire information. These experiences, such as demonstrations and experiments, can be used to clarify concepts, to provide knowledge, and to sharpen the powers of observation, as well as to give practice in the skills of listening and following directions.

Firsthand experiences also stimulate reading and related research. Once conclusions and generalizations have been made, the pupils then should be guided to check their findings against the material in health textbooks and related health materials. At this point in the lesson the teacher needs to plan for the specific research skills and work-study skills that the pupils will use to do this type of reading effectively. Thus, the teacher has planned to have the pupils go from the concrete (firsthand experiences) to the abstract (vicarious experiences). When the pupil has had a wide background of firsthand experiences from which to develop concepts, he becomes more and more adept in doing abstract thinking and drawing conclusions from vicarious experiences. The skillful teacher must know when the child can or cannot get the desired concepts from vicarious experiences, and plan the work accordingly.

This step in the teacher's plan is aptly termed "participation" for the pupils participate in gathering information as individuals, as small groups, or as a total class group. Again the teacher must decide which type of participation will bring the most desirable results for the particular lesson.

There are frequently times when the teacher prefers to teach the class as a group. This procedure is recommended when (1) a unit is introduced, (2) common understandings basic to the unit are being developed, (3) the subject matter must be supplemented by the teacher, (4) the skills needed to study the content have not been previously taught, and (5) a unit is concluded.

Small-group participation provides for maximum participation by affording every child the opportunity to make a worthwhile contribution and to be successful at work which he himself helped plan and carry out. For the class to be successful in carrying out activities in small groups, there must be much long-term planning by the teacher, so that the small-group work is an outgrowth of the way the class operates as a complete group. Prior to working in small groups it is advisable to work out with the class well-functioning patterns of behavior, standards for oral and written work, and plans for improvement. Then, too, the teacher should continually build independence on the part of the pupils. When the teacher is familiar with the abilities of the class and sees an opportunity for productive small-group work, the idea is introduced and its advantages are cited.

The next step is usually to set up the purposes of small-group work with the whole class. The purposes might be:

To discover certain information and share it with the whole class
To develop more varied and interesting ways of presenting information
To economize on time and cover more materials thoroughly
To be an "authority" for the class on one topic
To learn to work productively in a cooperative manner
To assume a fair share of the responsibilities
To learn how to organize within a small group to work effectively with a chairman and secretary

When the purposes have been established, the *procedures* for working in a group are considered. Included among these are:

To meet as a class for general planning before going into small groups
To convene, secure materials, and move furniture in a quiet manner
To define specific assignments in the small group before starting to work
To talk in a low tone and only when necessary
To discuss progress and future plans as a small group before the end of each period
To meet as a class group for general progress report and evaluation

The teacher should plan to circulate among the class members during the work period to give help and check on progress, as well as to encourage and assist the groups to find diverse means of making their presentation. When the groups present their reports, it is imperative that the information be summarized by the class as a whole. A thorough evaluation, following each group report, reassures pupils as to the value of their work. Small-group participation is reassuring to the teacher who discovers the creativeness and ingenuity displayed by the pupils when given incentive and opportunity.

STEP 4.   Evaluation

Evaluation can be one of the most important phases of learning for the pupils. The quality of evaluation is in direct relationship to the quantity and quality of the evaluative experiences of the pupils from the start of their formal schooling. It is conceivable that a group of primary children might be as skillful in objective and constructive evaluation as an upper elementary group just beginning such experiences. Well-planned, purposeful evaluations can provide much of educational worth for the pupils. When children are given the opportunity to discuss the lesson and to suggest ways in which improvement might be effected, desirable learning is likely to take place. In so doing, the pupils see themselves and their work in perspective. This requires a high level of thinking and reasoning under teacher guidance. In planning for the evaluation step in the lesson, the teacher should not fall into a stereotyped procedure; however, her plan should be logical and inclusive. Depending upon what was planned for the participation phase of the lesson, the teacher should plan the evaluation phase accordingly. For instance, the following general questions might serve as a guide for beginning the evaluation:

Content:
   What are some of the things we learned today?
   What will we study tomorrow?

Participation:
   What did you like about the way we worked together?
   Can you suggest some things which might improve our working together?

Questions such as these place the children in situations which require thinking, and thus tend to provide for satisfactory learning situations. The evaluation phase of the lesson is the time for effective pupil-teacher appraisal of accomplishments, and pupil-teacher planning for next steps. Learning makes sense to the pupil when he knows what he is doing, sees a purpose for doing it, and has a part in the planning.

In the daily plan, the teacher notes the facts or generalizations she expects to have the pupils arrive at by the conclusion of the lesson. She also lists the ways the learnings will be recorded. Ways of recording information should be appropriate to the content to be recorded, and to the needs and abilities of the pupils. The teacher plans for the pupils to learn from the varied experiences which come from recording information in *numerous* ways. This procedure is much preferred to recording information in the same manner from lesson to lesson or unit to unit, such as the traditional summary in the pupils' notebooks. Every lesson needs a summary as part of the evaluation, to bring together in a succinct way the important learnings of the lesson.

In consideration of appropriate ways for the pupils to record health information, the following are submitted as suggestive procedures: (1) summary paragraphs; (2) diary records; (3) outlines; (4) vocabulary lists; (5) graphs; (6) pictorial charts; (7) original dramatizations; (8) stories; (9) poems; (10) songs; (11) riddles; (12) murals; (13) puppets; (14) models; (15) dioramas.

Suggested Procedure for Lessons Involving Skills for Preparing and Presenting an Oral Report

Note: This procedure suggests the sequence of steps for the teacher to use in teaching pupils the research skills and work-study skills needed to prepare a report, as well as skills needed for the effective presentation of an oral report.

STEP 1. Limit the Problem

Under teacher guidance, practice is given in the skills needed to arrive at the problem to be solved.

STEP 2. Discuss and List Possible Sources of Information

When developing the skills needed to exercise good judgment in turning to authentic sources for information, consideration might be given to (1) consulting numerous materials, (2) visiting places, and (3) consulting people.

STEP 3. Locate and Assemble Various Materials

Under teacher guidance, practice is given in skills needed to locate information. These skills include use of (1) table of contents, (2) chapter headings, (3) titles of books or articles, (4) unit titles of a book, (5) topic sentences, (6) glossary, (7) keys, (8) index, (9) cross references, and (10) footnotes.

STEP 4. Prepare a Simple Bibliography and Resource List

Practice is given in the skills needed to record a bibliography.

STEP 5. Obtain Pertinent Information

The teacher observes how effectively the pupils function when using these skills. She teaches the pupils according to the needs shown. Included are the skills needed:

For using materials:
   Appropriate reading skills
      Careful reading
      Rapid reading
      Skim reading
   Interpretation of maps, graphs, globe, charts, pictures, tables
   Location skills
   Social skills

For studying places:
   Inquiry skills
   Listening skills
   Observation skills
   Social skills

For consulting persons:
   Interviewing skills
   Listening skills
   Social skills

STEP 6.   Take Notes

Since these skills are introduced in the upper elementary grades, pupils need much practice, under teacher guidance, before they become proficient enough to take notes independently. Some important skills to be acquired are:

Comprehending the whole selection
Selecting information pertinent to the problem to be solved
Deciding upon form to use in recording notes:
   Phrases or sentences
   Lists
   Quotations
   Outline
Putting the information in one's own words for the notes
Using the proper method for copying a quotation verbatim
Listing properly the sources of information

STEP 7.   Organize the Information

The pupils practice such skills as:

Checking, comparing, and verifying the information
Arranging the information in some logical order:
  Sequence
  Chronological
  Importance
  Cause and effect
  Psychological
Defining new words and phrases
Giving credit to sources of information
Drawing conclusions
Remembering important learnings for the report

(Pupils in the elementary schools learn much more from research than they are able to organize in written form.)

STEP 8.   Adapt the Material to the Audience

The teacher stimulates the pupils to use their initiative, creativeness, and ingenuity in selecting the most appropriate way to report the information. Under the teacher's guidance, the pupils *practice* and refine the report to meet the standards set by the class for giving a report.

STEP 9.   Present the Oral Report

This procedure involves an audience situation. The steps include:

Setting up certain standards for giving a report (teacher directed)
Setting up standards for the audience (teacher directed)
Presenting the report
Mentioning sources of information
Discussing the information with the audience following each report

STEP 10.   Evaluate the Report

Under teacher guidance the pupils evaluate: (1) the content of the report, (2) the presentation of the report, (3) audience participation, and (4) further interests or information desired. Before leaving the report, the entire class is responsible for summarizing the most important learnings.

SUMMARIZING THE UNIT

The concluding phase of the teaching unit is referred to frequently in current education literature as the culminating activity.

The word *culminating* tends to imply too much finality to be used in relation to health teaching. Based on the concept that education is dynamic and on-going, the term "summarizing" will be used to identify this phase of the teaching unit.

Just as every lesson needs a summary, so every teaching unit needs concluding, summarizing activities. Through these, the pupils review, summarize, and bring the unit to a climax. The summarizing activity should be broad enough in scope to (1) include all phases of the unit, (2) utilize the basic academic and social skills involved, (3) provide for maximum application of the learning, (4) provide for appraisal of outcomes, and (5) sustain interest in the unit. In addition to the various types of testing, most units can be summarized through a review of the activities carried on. For example, the activities can be arranged into a program about the health unit. Such a program might include original skits, stories, songs, dances, and poems interspersed with explanations of charts, murals, booklets, exhibits of construction items, bulletin board displays, and reports on interviews and trips. The preparation of such a program is rarely time-consuming, since it evolves from the way the unit developed. The values derived for children in presenting such a program to other pupils or parents cannot be overlooked. These include (1) working together with peers, (2) being responsible for one's part, (3) assisting when and where needed, (4) participating before an audience, (5) taking turns, (6) having something worthwhile to do, (7) feeling worthy, and (8) meeting success as an individual and as a member of a group. They are but a few of the intangibles that bring feelings of satisfaction to pupils and teacher alike.

In summary, unit teaching of health content involves ways of learning and living together productively and effectively while studying a prescribed unit. It is the classroom teacher who knows what to teach (content), why she is teaching it (objectives), to whom she is teaching it (pupils), and how to teach it (methods), to the end that learning has been stimulated and guided for the individual pupils assigned to her.

REFERENCES

Association for Supervision and Curriculum Development, *Research for Curriculum Improvement,* 1957 Yearbook, Washington, D.C., National Education Association, 1957.

Betts, Emmett A., *Foundations of Reading Instruction*, New York, American, 1957.

Hanna, Lavonne A., Gladys L. Potter, and Neva Hagaman, *Unit Teaching in the Elementary School*, New York, Rinehart, 1956.

Irwin, Leslie W., James H. Humphrey, and Warren R. Johnson, *Methods and Materials in School Health Education*, St. Louis, Mosby, 1956, chap. 8.

Lane, Howard, and Mary Beauchamp, *Understanding Human Development*, New York, Prentice-Hall, 1959.

Lee, J. Murray, and Dorris May Lee, *The Child and His Curriculum*, 2nd ed., New York, Appleton-Century-Crofts, 1950.

Preston, Ralph C., *Teaching Social Studies in the Elementary School*, New York, Rinehart, 1955.

Russell, David R., *Children's Thinking*, Boston, Ginn, 1956.

CRITERIA FOR THE SELECTION OF HEALTH TEACHING CONTENT

1 *What is the relationship between health needs and health interests?*
2 *What are some of the important health needs of children?*
3 *What are some of the procedures for determining health needs of children?*
4 *What are some factors which should be taken into account when health interests are to be considered as criteria for the selection of health teaching content?*
5 *What are some of the procedures for determining health interests of children?*

The three preceding chapters have been essentially concerned with methods and procedures of planning and providing health learning experiences, or "how" health might be taught. The present chapter and the one following will deal largely with health curriculum content, or "what" might be taught. Discussions in this chapter will focus upon the general bases for selection of health teaching content, while the succeeding one will deal with the scope, sequence, and grade placement of "what" might be taught.

Although various valid criteria might be considered as bases for selecting health teaching content it appears sufficient here to deal only with the two broad general criteria of health *needs* and health *interests* of children.

RELATIONSHIP OF HEALTH NEEDS AND HEALTH INTERESTS

The terms "needs" and "interests" of children have been used together so often that there is a strong likelihood that their meanings have become confused. For this reason it appears important that the ensuing discussions be prefaced by a few comments about the relationship of needs and interests.

In thinking in terms of their relationship one must also consider how they differ. While health needs and interests of children may be closely related and highly interdependent, there are nevertheless certain important differences which should be taken into account when these criteria are used as bases for the selection of health teaching content.

Needs of children, particularly those of an individual nature, are likely to be innate. On the other hand, interests for the most part may be acquired as products of the environment. Herein lies a difference of paramount importance in the selection of health teaching content for children of elementary school age. For example, it is possible that a child may demonstrate an interest in a certain unsafe practice that is obviously not compatible with his needs at a certain age level. The 2-year-old youngster may be interested in running into the street, but this practice might result in injury. Acquisition of a particular interest because of environmental conditions is further illustrated in the case of children coming from families who might be superstitious about certain kinds of foods, or of certain foods eaten in combination. In such cases the acquisition of such an interest from other family members might build up a lifetime resistance to a certain kind of food that might be very nutritious and beneficial to the child's physical needs.

Perhaps one of the most important aspects involved in the relationship between health needs and health interests as criteria for selection of health teaching content is that of obtaining a proper ratio between the two. Indeed, arriving at a happy medium between needs and interests is at best a very difficult problem. We should think first in terms of meeting the child's health needs, but we need his interest in order for the most desirable learning to take place. Consequently, when health needs and interests are combined in proper ratio, a near-ideal situation exists for desirable and worthwhile learning in health education.

In determining the degree of health needs and interests as criteria for teaching content, teachers might well be guided by the age levels of children. In this regard a general principle is that the lower the age level of children the more we can depend upon health needs as a valid criterion. This is based on the assumption that the younger the child the less experience he has had, and consequently there is less opportunity to develop certain interests. In other words, a lack of interest at an early age level might possibly be synonymous with ignorance. To illustrate, a first-grade child might not be interested in a certain kind of food that has a high nutritional value, because he has not had the opportunity to eat it and thus become "interested" in it. Conversely we could assume that the higher the age level the more we might depend on the criterion of health interest of pupils. This of course is based on the idea that the older the child the better the understanding he should have of his needs. Similarly, the older child has had more experience and this is apt to result in a greater range of interest.

SOME BASIC CONSIDERATIONS OF HEALTH NEEDS AS CRITERIA FOR CURRICULUM CONTENT

Basing the selection of health teaching content on health needs implies essentially that learning experiences are provided in accordance with certain fundamental requirements of children. The use of needs as a criterion for the selection of elementary school curriculum content is not necessarily a recent innovation. In fact it is a matter of record that this procedure was in effect over half a century ago, when the elementary school at the University of Missouri was established in 1904. It has been reported that this school "abandoned the conventional curriculum and developed methods of teaching required to make child needs and growth the dominant purpose of the school."[1]

In considering children's needs as a basis for health teaching certain basic considerations should be taken into account. For one thing it should be recognized that it is not necessarily an easy matter to arrive at entirely satisfactory procedures for discovering children's needs. Moreover, a problem is sometimes posed when attempts are made to determine what the implications of these needs are for curriculum content. In this particular regard, although there is some degree of general agreement that health teaching might

1 Harold G. Shane, ed., *The American Elementary School*, Thirteenth Yearbook of the John Dewey Society, New York, Harper, 1953, p. 415.

well be based on the health needs of children, there is also some difference of opinion with respect to what the needs may be, and what their implications are for the curriculum.

Another important factor is the question as to how much the demands of society should be taken into account as related to the needs of the individual. Various points of view have been expressed in this particular connection. One school of thought tends to hold that, because the schools are publicly supported to serve the needs of society, the curriculum content should be based primarily on factors oriented in a direction to meet these societal needs. A second point of view suggests that, inasmuch as it is the purpose of schools to educate the individual, the curriculum should be based upon the needs of individuals. A rather obvious third point of view involves some sort of happy medium between the first two. This is based on the fact that the individual is a part of society and that he should be educated with the idea in mind that he will interact with it.

As important as the needs of the child are, these needs should not be considered as separate and unrelated entities as far as the culture is concerned. Certainly, demands of the culture should be taken into account. Such factors as the requirements for social acceptance and the fluid character of American culture might serve as guideposts for proper adjustment between cultural demands and individual needs.

Kinds of Health Needs

It is a well-known fact that children's needs have been classified in many ways. However, it should be borne in mind that any classification of human needs is usually an arbitrary one made for a specific purpose. For example, when one speaks of biological needs and psychological needs it should be understood that each of these, although classified separately, are interdependent.

The classifications of health needs used here should be thought of in terms of the preceding frame of reference, that is, for purposes of discussing the use of health needs as a basis for health teaching content.

Two broad classifications of needs are suggested here: (1) those needs that are innate to the individual, and (2) those needs which are based on certain aspects of the environment. It should be remembered that much overlapping is likely to occur in these two broad categories.

Inherent Health Needs of the Individual. One aspect of inherent health needs involves the basic anatomical structure and the basic physiological function of the human organism. Included here, of course, are the need for food, rest, and activity, proper care of eyes, ears, and teeth, and the like. Another aspect is concerned with the necessity of meeting social, mental, and emotional needs. This is sometimes expressed in terms of the need for a sense of personal achievement and worth and the need for emotional maturity. It is apparent that an important function of the elementary school is to guide the health learning experiences of children so that these needs may be satisfied in acceptable ways.

Health Needs That Are Products of the Environment. Many of the health needs in this category might be subclassified as *immediate* and *prospective* and as *general* and *specific*. Many of the *immediate* needs are likely to be reflected in the growth and developmental traits and characteristics of children at the various age levels. As such, these are perhaps better classified as innate needs; however, they may also be concerned with some sort of interaction of the environment. *Prospective* needs are those which might be considered in terms of some of the present family and community health problems existing at the adult level. *General* health needs involve those which are reflected in health and safety hazards which prevail on a nationwide basis. On the other hand, *specific* needs might be considered as related to the health status of pupils in their local or nearby surroundings. As an illustration, general health needs may be indicated from a standpoint of national mortality and morbidity statistics, while specific needs might be determined from sources of information about these statistics at the local or community level, as well as other local information pertaining to the health status of children.

In some cases it might be well to combine the immediate and specific needs and refer to them as *immediate specific* health needs. The following list suggests sources of some of these.

1. Health problems of a local nature which are considered as such by the local board of health
2. Major causes of death in the various age levels at the local level

3. Extent of communicable diseases and infections at the local level
4. Examination of local school medical records
5. Records of local school absenteeism
6. Results of local tuberculin testing and X-ray programs
7. Results of local school screening tests for vision and hearing
8. Anecdotal records of teachers resulting from observations

Procedures for Determining Health Needs

The literature suggests various general ways in which the needs of children might be determined. However, it should be mentioned that the determination of needs of children is a complex and varied problem. An overview of the various conclusions reported could possibly be more confusing than informing. Consequently, it appears important to examine some of the procedures for determining needs and some further approaches and resultant differences in conclusions. Two of these approaches, the *inferential* or *rational* approach and the *quantitative* approach, will be discussed.

The inferential or rational approach, which tends to lack objectivity, is based primarily on reflection of personal experiences with children, and may be subject to the influences of their background interests and purposes. On the other hand, this approach has the advantage of not being encumbered with possible misinterpretations which may be based on a mass of statistical data. Moreover, it tends to allow for analysis in the light of the broad background of an expert or group of experts who have had years of experience in a specific area.

The quantitative approach is found quite frequently in studies involving personal adjustment problems, interests, and other concerns of children. The differences in results obtained usually depends upon the kinds of instruments and research tools employed, and the slanting of statements by individuals making the studies.

Mention has been made that studies of needs may be undertaken by individual persons or groups. This may need clarification with regard to the results obtained. The *statement of needs* formulated by groups may perhaps have some advantage over those by individuals, inasmuch as some of the limitations of individual preparation, past experience, insight, and adjustment might be counteracted by group judgments. However, the value of the statements, whether formulated by a group or an individual, in the final analysis depends upon the abilities of the members of the group or the individual.

The following list of procedures is submitted as a possible guide for determining health needs of the individual.

1. Use an outline of needs to aid in understanding behavior
2. Make use of the results of school medical examinations
3. Analyze personal-adjustment needs
4. Analyze social-adjustment needs

The following procedures may be valuable for determining the needs of the group:

1. Make use of the reports of studies of children
2. Make one's own studies of children
3. Make use of the reports of the studies of the activities and problems of people in the community
4. Make one's own studies of the activities and problems of people in the community
5. Make use of the reports of studies of the activities and problems in our society
6. Explore the ideas of teachers regarding pupil needs
7. Explore the ideas of pupils regarding their needs

How Classroom Teachers Can Discover Immediate Health Needs

Although teachers may recognize what the general health needs of children are, there still remains the necessity for attempting to meet immediate needs at the local classroom level. This is important from a standpoint of generating pupil interest in the study of a given health topic.

There are a variety of ways which teachers might use to study particular health needs of children in their own classrooms. The two illustrative cases which follow, one for the third grade and one for the sixth grade, are suggestive of such procedures.

CASE 1

In X elementary school, lunches are served in the school cafeteria, but about three-fourths of the children bring their lunches. These children usually buy cookies, ice cream, or fruit for dessert. A balanced lunch is served, but it has been observed that green vegetables and much of the other food goes into the waste disposal.

One of the third-grade teachers had planned to teach about nutrition in connection with one of the social studies units on "Peoples of the Earth." However, upon recognizing the situation described she decided to develop a teaching unit on "Foods for Growth." She hoped to develop the following ideas: (1) that children need to learn why certain foods are valuable to their bodies, (2) that more children should be taking advantage of the school lunch program, (3) that food should not be wasted, and (4) that an interest in eating a variety of foods and of tasting new foods should be developed by children.

The need was apparent to many of the teachers as well as the lunchroom workers. The PTA was so concerned that the supervisor of the lunch program was invited to explain why certain types of lunches were served. A change in the lunchroom personnel, with new methods of food preparation, resulted in some improvement in the sale of lunches.

The third-grade teacher decided to use a menu for the week as a questionnaire to help determine the needs of her 34 children as far as learnings in the unit on "Foods for Growth" were concerned. The following data was obtained from this questionnaire:

MENU FOR THE WEEK	LIKE	SOMETIMES EAT	NEVER EAT	NEVER TASTED
Hamburger on roll	32	—	2	—
Potato salad	23	5	5	1
Kale	12	13	6	3
Orange	34	—	—	—
Milk*	25	8	1	—
Ham sandwich	29	3	2	—
Baked potato	30	3	1	—
Carrot stick	33	—	1	—
Cupcake	34	—	—	—
Grilled luncheon meat	6	10	8	10
Baked beans	21	10	3	—
Bread and butter	27	—	7	—
Orange and grapefruit	27	—	—	7
Vegetable beef soup	23	9	2	—
Toasted cheese sandwich	25	4	3	2
Crackers	32	—	2	—
Jello	33	—	1	—
Fish cakes	5	8	14	7
Buttered beets	6	6	13	9
Cole slaw	25	4	4	1
Peanut butter cookies	20	—	—	14

*18 did not like milk served at school.

On the basis of these results the following questions were formulated:

1. What foods do most of the children like?
2. Do you know what these foods do for our bodies?
3. Do you know why we eat food?
4. Do you know why we should eat enough of certain foods?

A teacher-pupil planning session developed, and many worthwhile learning experiences resulted from the selected learning activities. The latter were based on the questionnaire which the teacher used as a technique for determining the needs of her class in this particular situation.

CASE 2

In Y elementary school a sixth-grade teacher observed that many in her class of 30 pupils seemed to neglect the care of their teeth. In addition, children were often absent from school because of toothache.

One day two children showed the teacher cards on which were written the times for their appointment with the local dentist. The teacher used this opportunity to mention to the class what a fine thing it was to have nice-looking teeth. She then told them that she had asked the local health nurse to visit the room and examine the teeth of the members of the class.

The nurse examined the teeth of the 30 children, and her examination revealed that 7 pupils with clean teeth had previously had some dental work done, and that 23 pupils had stained teeth and were in need of dental work.

A few days later the teacher told the class that she was interested in doing some work concerning the dental health of the class, and that in order to do this she wanted their help in answering a list of questions. They were told not to sign their names on the papers because the teacher was not concerned with names, but with facts.

A list of the questions which the 30 members of the class were asked to answer revealed the following information:

1. Do you have a toothbrush?   Yes 30   No 0
2. Have you ever had a toothache?   Yes 26   No 4
3. Have you ever had a tooth pulled?   Yes 30   No 0
4. How many teeth have you had pulled?

NUMBER OF CHILDREN	NUMBER OF TEETH PULLED
1	0
1	1
3	2
1	3
6	4

NUMBER OF CHILDREN	NUMBER OF TEETH PULLED
4	5
5	6
0	7
3	8
0	9
1	10
0	11
0	12
0	13
1	14
1	15
0	16
1	17
1	18
0	19
1	20

5. Have you ever had a tooth filled?   Yes 15   No 15
6. How many teeth have you had filled?

NUMBER OF CHILDREN	NUMBER OF TEETH FILLED
15	0
1	1
4	2
3	3
1	4
3	5
1	6
1	7
1	8

7. How often do you brush your teeth?

NUMBER OF CHILDREN	FREQUENCY OF BRUSHING
10	Once daily
15	Twice daily
2	Three times daily
1	Four times weekly
1	Once weekly
1	Twice monthly

8. Are you having, or have you had, your teeth straightened?   Yes 2
No 28

9. Do you ever have bleeding gums?   Yes 15   No 13   Sometimes 2
10. Do your parents have false teeth?   Yes 18   No 12
11. Have you ever been to a dentist?   Yes 24   No 6

After the teacher made the above tabulations from the questionnaire, she made a further attempt to learn more about the dental health needs of her class by sending the following letter and inquiry form to their parents:

Dear Parent:

I am doing some work concerning the dental health among your children who are in my sixth-grade class. In connection with this would you help by answering the following questions:

1. Do you have regular dental care? _____
2. Do you have any cavities? _____
3. Do you have any fillings? _____
4. Have you had any extractions?_____
5. Do you have dental plates? _____
6. Do your children have regular dental checkups? _____

You need not sign your name because I am interested only in the answers to the questions. Thank you for your cooperation,

Sincerely yours,

Nineteen of the thirty inquiry forms returned revealed the following information:

	YES	NO
1. Do you have regular dental care?	4	15
2. Do you have any cavities?	4	15
3. Do you have any fillings?	6	13
4. Have you had any extractions?	9	10
5. Do you have dental plates?	9	10
6. Do your children have regular dental checkups?	3	16

Although the teacher questioned some of the responses that she received, she felt that as a result of the information from the children and their parents she had a better understanding of the dental health needs of her class. The data she collected helped her to plan a dental health teaching unit which was designed particularly for her sixth-grade class.

SOME BASIC CONSIDERATIONS OF HEALTH INTERESTS AS CRITERIA FOR CURRICULUM CONTENT

It is important that the teacher have an understanding of the meaning of interest as well as an appreciation of how interests function as an adjunct to learning. As far as the meaning of the term is concerned the following description given by Lee and Lee expresses in a relatively simple manner what is meant by the terms "interest" and "interests." *"Interest* is a state of being, a way of reacting to a certain situation. *Interests* are those fields or areas to which a child reacts with interest consistently over an extended period of time."[2]

The same authors also suggest certain concepts of interest which have important value for teachers and others who might consider interest as a criterion. These concepts, listed below, might well serve as a guide to a better understanding of the place of interest as it relates to the learning process.

1. Interest is developed through utilizing the child's experience, ability, and needs.
2. The development of interests is greatly influenced by the child's environment, his ability, and his concept of himself and his role.
3. Interests change with age and become more stable during the teens.
4. Interests of adults have their beginnings in childhood.
5. The child continues with those interests that are satisfying and drops those which are not satisfying.
6. Interests can be expanded through utilizing already existing interests.
7. There seems to be a persistence of interests related somewhat to the pattern of personality.
8. Interests give valuable leads as to what children and adolescents would like to learn.[3]

The fact that pupil interest is a very important aspect of learning offers evidence that health interests of children should be given serious consideration in health education curriculum construction. Nevertheless, there are certain basic factors which should be taken into account when health interests are used as a basis for selection.

Certainly, interest should not be the only foundation for the selection of teaching content in health education. Indeed, there are a number of factors which might seriously militate against its exclusive use as the sole basis for curriculum construction. For instance, it could be very likely that there might be a lack of interest because of a lack of information. In cases where this situation pre-

[2] J. Murray Lee and Dorris May Lee, *The Child and His Development,* New York, Appleton-Century-Crofts, 1958, p. 382.
[3] *Ibid.,* pp. 383–388.

vails it would be necessary for teachers to attempt to motivate pupil interest in some of the health problems of the school and local community. Another factor that should be considered, particularly at the elementary school level, is that interest may be focused on insignificant health problems. In addition, it may be difficult to provide suitable learning activities and experiences for pupils at certain age levels in the elementary school even though these children may have a specific interest in a certain area of health.

As stressed, the near-ideal situation probably prevails when health *needs* and health *interests* are in proper balance, and certainly all persons concerned with curriculum construction should be aware of this. As stated previously, the older the pupils, the greater the emphasis that might be placed on health interests as a basis for health teaching content.

Procedures for Determining Health Interests

It is generally known that growing children are interested in the health aspects of their own bodies, as well as in some of the various health phenomena in the surrounding environment. However, health interests need to be explored more extensively by various kinds of techniques. These devices include the following, among others.

1. *Observation of children.* Teachers should be alert to the things that children say and do which might indicate some of their present health interests. Sometimes conversations and discussions of children provide the teacher with clues indicative of health interests. The kinds of questions children ask about various factors which pertain to health can serve as a good guide to their current interests.

2. *Questionnaires and inventories.* This type of inquiry form has been used with varying degrees of success as a means of determining health interests of children. It is a procedure which can be used by the individual teacher as a way of determining health interests of a particular class, or it can be a satisfactory device for ascertaining a general understanding of the health interests of children in an entire school system. An example of the latter is the study of health interests of some 3600 pupils from kindergarten through the twelfth grade conducted in the Denver Public Schools.[4] This study

4 *Health Interest of Children,* Denver, Denver Public Schools, 1947.

tended to reflect relative degrees of interest in such health topics as dental hygiene, nutrition, personal appearance, and social acceptability.

3. *Free-writing and check-list techniques.* This procedure is satisfactory when the classroom teacher wishes to discern the health interests of her particular group. Children can be asked to write (free-writing) three or more aspects of health that they would be interested in exploring. The results of this free writing of interests may be tabulated, and the teacher can use it as necessary.

An important value of the free-writing technique is that it lends itself well to the integration of health education and writing—one of the expressive phases of language arts. With first-grade children, who may not be proficient in manuscript writing, the technique may be used in a different manner. For example, their health interests can be "dictated" to the teacher, who in turn writes them on the chalkboard, or on an "experience chart." This procedure can be used to integrate health education and reading when the children read the material as it is placed on the experience chart.[5]

Sometimes the teacher may decide to take the free-writing material, particularly that of upper elementary children, and compile it into a check list. The list can then be submitted to children for checking of those items which are of greatest interest to them. This procedure helps to eliminate having the children resort entirely to recalling items of interest.

4. *Health counseling.* In those elementary schools where there is an organized guidance program, a fine opportunity is available for determining health interests of children. The periodic personal interviews with pupils by teachers and other counselors are apt to yield many health interests that might not be as accessible through other sources. This is particularly true because the child is contacted on a rather informal basis through this medium. As a consequence, some children might be more likely to feel free to express given health interests during the privacy of a personal interview, especially if the teacher or counselor has the child's confidence.

Information in the way of health interests derived by the counselor can be channeled to teachers so that they can make proper use of the results of these individual conferences.

[5] The reader is referred to Chapter 13 for a detailed discussion of the integration of health education and language arts.

REFERENCES

Fleming, Robert S., "Building an Effective Health Program," *The National Elementary Principal*, February, 1960.

Harsh, Richard, "Critical Needs in Human Development," *The Journal of School Health*, June, 1960.

Shane, Harold G., "Children's Interests," *NEA Journal*, April, 1957.

Shaw, John H., "Evaluation of the School Health Instruction Program," *American Journal of Public Health*, May, 1957.

"Sub-Committee on Guidelines for Curriculum Development in Elementary School Health Education," *The Journal of School Health*, April, 1960.

HEALTH TEACHING CONTENT FOR THE VARIOUS GRADE LEVELS[1]

9

1 *What are some of the factors which influence the selection of the health teaching content for the various grade levels of the elementary school?*

2 *What are some of the major categories into which the health content can be organized?*

3 *What constitutes the scope and sequence of the health content for the elementary school?*

4 *What is the recommended health content for each grade level?*

5 *How can the interrelationship of health concepts within a grade level enhance learning?*

HEALTH TEACHING CONTENT

A major consideration in curriculum development for the elementary school is the teaching content for any area of learning. All areas of the curriculum deal with relating the content to the interests, needs, and abilities of the individual. These considerations apply equally well to the selection of health teaching content. The factors influencing the selection of health content are similar to those used in other areas; yet by its very nature health teaching is unique and different. Health is personal and is concerned with the state of being of the individual as a dynamic living organism. It is a natural corollary then that health content is focused upon the basic needs of the individual as he relates himself to his environment and others relate themselves to him.

[1] The authors are grateful to Mary P. Warner, M.D., Director of Child Health Services, Anne Arundel County Health Department, Annapolis, Maryland, for her critical reading of this chapter.

The selection of health teaching content for the various grade levels should be the joint responsibilities of such key people as experienced classroom teachers, curriculum experts, and specialists in health education, physical education, and child growth and development.

Based upon a thorough analysis of the most recent textbooks, a study of current research and literature, participation in child study programs, years of experience in the classroom, personal observations, and other intensive study, certain conclusions concerning elementary health teaching content seem warranted.

Scope

In general, the health teaching content as organized under various areas, can be classified by topics of emphasis. Ten different ones have been arbitrarily selected to include the scope of the content for children from kindergarten through Grade 6.

The major topics of emphasis at all grade levels center around the three basic needs of the human organism, namely, (1) foods and nutrition; (2) exercise and physical activity; and (3) sleep, rest, and relaxation. The seven secondary topics of emphasis relate to the human organism as it functions in its environment. These should include subject matter on (1) safety; (2) first aid; (3) stimulants and narcotic drugs; (4) clothing; (5) the human organism—its structure, function, and care; (6) health services; and (7) mental, social, and emotional health.

Grade Placement

On the basis of the present knowledge of the growth processes and the psychology of learning, subject matter should be appropriate to the developmental level of the child and the degree to which he can ingest the concepts. For instance, the emphasis at the primary level needs to center around practices which will lead to the formation of good health practices in the *care* of the body; at the upper elementary level the pupils are mature enough to understand the reasons for good health practices through a study of the structure and function of the body. Other examples could be cited from any area of topical emphasis. In the study of clothing, primary children should have practice in wearing clothes appropriate to the weather;

at the upper elementary level, the pupils study clothing in relation to regulation of body temperature.

Development

For the most part a positive approach should be emphasized in concept development, to the end that the pupils acquire wholesome attitudes toward good health. An approach that capitalizes on the importance of proper diet as a basic need for the body cells to produce radiant health is much preferred to an approach that might cause a fear of rickets or tooth decay.

In the development of content, consideration should be given to the continuity of learning experiences from one grade to another. Concepts that are introduced in the first grade should be extended and made increasingly more difficult at each succeeding grade level. The following example of concept development relates to an understanding of the *daily diet,* and is intended to illustrate this point.

GRADE LEVEL	CONCEPTS	LEARNING SEQUENCE
Kindergarten	We choose a good breakfast.	Eating.
Grade 1	To be healthy we need to eat regularly every day.	Regular meals for good health.
Grade 2	Some foods that help us grow strong and healthy are meats, fruits, vegetables, milk and milk products, and bread and cereals.	Foods for good health.
Grade 3	Proper foods give us energy; they build strong muscles, teeth, and bones.	Value of food to the body.
Grade 4	The body needs a daily supply of foods from each of the four food groups for good nutrition.	Four food groups.
Grade 5	The cells in our body get their nourishment from the materials in foods called food elements.	Food elements.

Grade 6   The amount of food required   Food and body energy.
                 daily depends upon how ac-
                 tive the person is and the
                 energy used by the body.

A considerable amount of integration of concepts is needed so that specific concepts extend, support, and strengthen other concepts at each of the grade levels. Moreover, concepts developed in certain topical areas should be closely related to those in other areas. The following example indicates how certain concepts involving digestion appear also in such other topical areas as exercise; foods and nutrition; mental, social, and emotional health; and sleep, rest, and relaxation. (These concepts might be developed at the fifth-grade level.)

TOPICAL AREA	CONCEPTS INVOLVING DIGESTION
Exercise and physical activity	Exercise stimulates and aids *digestion*.
Foods and nutrition	Vitamin B helps steady the nerves and aids in *digestion*.
Mental, social, and emotional health	Control of emotions is important for maintenance of proper bodily functions (*digestion*).
Sleep, rest, and relaxation	Rest aids *digestion*.

Sequence

Thus far, consideration has been given to the scope, grade placement, and development of health teaching content. Another dimension involved in health teaching is the pattern for the sequence of content from kindergarten to first grade, from first grade to second grade, and so on, through the elementary school.

This discussion of sequence of content will deal with the major emphasis at each grade level and the corresponding health concepts. The list of concepts appearing in the following pages should not be assumed to be theoretically complete. They should be considered representative examples of concepts which might be developed with children at the various grade levels.

Foods and Nutrition.   In kindergarten the emphasis is upon the practice of starting the day with a good breakfast and eating a good lunch and dinner. Stress in the first grade is on good eating practices and the importance of foods. The second-grade content carries the emphasis of the kindergarten and first grade, with the addition of selection and variety of foods. General foods such as meats, fruits and vegetables, milk and milk products, and bread and cereals are introduced. Third-grade content deepens the previous concepts, adds care and handling of foods, and introduces the idea of what foods do for the body. At the upper elementary level the subject matter should be much more structured. The four food groups are introduced in the fourth grade; elements of food, in the fifth grade; and the body's dependence upon foods, in the sixth grade.

SUGGESTED HEALTH CONCEPTS TO BE DEVELOPED

KINDERGARTEN

We choose a good breakfast.
We drink milk every day.
We drink water every day.
We eat a good lunch.
We eat a good dinner.
We eat a snack.

GRADE 1

The food we eat helps us to grow big and strong and to keep well.
To be healthy we need to eat breakfast, lunch, and dinner every day.
Milk helps us grow.
We need to drink water every day.
Fruit makes a good after-school snack.
Breakfast is an important meal; it can help to keep us happy and wide awake.

GRADE 2

Some foods that help us grow strong and healthy are meats, fruits and vegetables, milk and milk products, and bread and cereals.
Food from breakfast helps give us energy to work and play in the morning.
As healthy children we need to eat well-balanced meals each day.
We need to select and eat a variety of foods every day.
Milk helps us grow strong and be healthy.
Good food helps our teeth grow.
Our bodies need water every day.
We need to eat slowly and chew our food well.

GRADE 3

Proper food gives us energy, and builds strong muscles, teeth, and bones.

Good food helps the body keep well and fights diseases.

We need to eat regular meals and to select a variety of foods to be healthy.

Sweets between meals can take away our appetite.

Milk helps our teeth to grow strong.

Unless proper care is taken food will spoil and become unfit to eat.

Special care is needed in the handling of food at the store and in the home to keep it clean, fresh, and free from germs.

Pasteurization kills germs in milk and makes it safe to drink.

People who handle food should be clean; their hands should be especially clean.

Clean food is best for good health.

We need to drink only safe, pure water.

GRADE 4

There are four groups of foods important to good health.

The body needs a daily supply of foods from each of the four food groups for good nutrition.

Fruits and vegetables help our bodies to grow and maintain good health.

Milk and milk products give us energy, make good teeth and bones, and help our bodies to grow.

Meat, fish, and eggs give our bodies the materials needed for muscles and blood.

Bread, cereal, butter and margarine give our body heat and energy.

Our bodies need and use the water we drink.

Food supplies energy; a lack of proper foods can make us tired.

GRADE 5

The cells in our body get their nourishment from the materials in foods called food elements.

Food keeps us well, helps us grow, gives heat and energy to the body, and protects us from disease.

The food elements are carbohydrates, fats, proteins, minerals, and vitamins.

Almost all foods are a mixture of several different elements.

Carbohydrates (starch and sugar) and fats (vegetable and animal) furnish heat and energy.

Proteins (primarily from meat, milk, eggs, and fish) are essential for the building, repair, and maintenance of body cells.

Minerals (from plant-eating animals) help regulate certain body functions and furnish the calcium necessary for bone formation.

Vitamins help our bodies use all the other elements in foods.

Vitamins help to regulate body functions and to protect our health.

Vitamins A and B help strengthen the eyes and keep the skin healthy and the hair glossy.

Vitamin B helps steady nerves and aids in digestion.

Vitamin C helps to make the walls of the blood vessels strong.

Vitamin D (sunshine vitamin) helps calcium and phosphorus to build bones and teeth.

Our body uses water for carrying on body functions.

When we eat properly, we show we are learning to care for our bodies.

GRADE 6

Body cells are dependent upon the wise choice of food at mealtimes.

Since no single food contains all essentials, the cells of the body require a supply of the four basic food elements daily.

The amount of food required daily depends upon how active a person is and the quantity of energy used by the body.

Water helps carry food to the cells and to carry waste away from them.

Bacteria, which decays food, is destroyed or its growth is prevented by methods used to preserve foods (canning, pasteurization, refrigeration, drying).

Careful methods of production, handling, purchasing, and storage should be used to keep foods free from harmful bacteria.

Families can protect their food supply by refrigeration, clean utensils, and sanitary surroundings.

Good nutrition depends upon adequate digestion as well as an ample supply of basic food elements.

As food is used in the body, it provides necessary heat and energy.

The need for energy is constant because the body never stops working.

The body receives the most benefit from food when meals are well planned and served at regular times.

We can help one another to make mealtime more enjoyable by being punctual and by using good table manners.

Eating with others can be an enjoyable social experience.

Exercise and Physical Activity. Effective health teaching is adapted to the day-by-day experiences of boys and girls. Experiences relating to the child's natural urge to play or exercise the body should include indoor and outdoor activities at home and school, on the farm, at parks and playgrounds, at the beaches and seashores, and on hikes. Giving the pupils opportunities to develop the physical and social skills needed for game participation is the responsibility of the kindergarten and primary teachers. The emphasis at the upper elementary level should be on *why* the body needs exercise and activity, and *how* activity aids growth, development, and bodily functions. Physical education activities appropriate to the growth and developmental level of each child should be an integral part of the health teaching content.

SUGGESTED HEALTH CONCEPTS TO BE DEVELOPED

KINDERGARTEN

"Duck Walk," "Rabbit Hop," "Bear Walk," and "Elephant Walk" are good exercises.
We play games inside on rainy days.
We play out-of-doors after school.

GRADE 1

Play helps us grow strong and healthy.
We need to play out-of-doors in the fresh air and sunshine all during the year.
Running and jumping help us grow big and strong.
Toys and pets make indoor play more fun.
Play can be more fun when we take turns and share.
We are a good sport when we play fair and follow the rules of the game.

GRADE 2

Playing and exercising in the fresh air and sunshine help us grow strong and healthy.
Stunts, hopping, galloping, and throwing and catching a ball provide good exercise.
Summer offers many chances for healthful living because there is more time to play out-of-doors.
Out-of-doors play helps us look well, feel well, and sleep well.

GRADE 3

Out-of-door play is important to good health.
Active out-of-door play gives us a healthy appetite.
Camping, hiking, and swimming help us build strong, healthy bodies.
When we climb on playground apparatus, we help ourselves to grow bigger and stronger.
Races and relays give us needed exercise.
Exercise helps your body to develop different skills.

GRADE 4

Daily out-of-door exercise helps to produce strong muscles and a healthy body.

Exercise strengthens the body's defense against disease.
Games and stunts exercise our muscles and help them grow strong.
Bicycling and roller skating are healthful out-of-door activities.
Picnic and outdoor swimming are healthful activities.

GRADE 5

Active out-of-door exercise helps us to sleep, eat, and feel better.
Active play contributes to lung and bone development.
Physical activity is necessary for the development of muscles.
Sunshine and fresh air are helpful to all parts of the body.
Exercise stimulates and aids digestion.

GRADE 6

There are many ways to get good physical activity.
Physical activity increases the respiration rate.
Physical activity increases the rate of the heart.
Physical activity stimulates the heat production of the body.
Physical activity helps one to keep fit.
Physical activity helps the blood circulate properly.
Physical activity aids body functions.
Physical activity conditions the body and adds to its strength, endurance, and agility.

Sleep, Rest, and Relaxation.   For effective learning, concepts related to sleep, rest, and relaxation can be integrated successfully with other areas of emphasis, such as (1) rest before and after meals, (2) rest and digestion, (3) balance of exercise and rest, (4) rest and body functions, (5) rest in the prevention and cure of diseases, and (6) rest and emotional health. Again the emphasis at the kindergarten and primary levels is on the development of practices regarding regular hours for sleep and ways of resting and relaxing. Fourth-grade pupils learn about the *value* of sleep. At the fifth-grade level the emphasis is on sleep and *body growth and development*. Sixth-grade content deals with sleep and *bodily function*.

SUGGESTED HEALTH CONCEPTS TO BE DEVELOPED

KINDERGARTEN

We rest after we play.
We rest when we are tired.
Story time is a quiet, restful time.

GRADE 1

We grow when we sleep.

Regular hours for going to bed and for getting up help us get the sleep we need.

A bath before bedtime can help us sleep better.

GRADE 2

To prepare for sleep it is helpful to take a bath, brush our hair, and clean our teeth.

Rest before dinner can help us to enjoy our meal.

Listening to a story or to music is a good way to relax after play.

Lack of sleep can make us irritable, tired, and quarrelsome.

GRADE 3

Our bodies need a balance between rest and exercise.

Relaxing activities before bedtime can help us to sleep well.

Sleep helps the body get ready for the next day's work or play.

A regular amount of sleep every night can make us lively and happy.

GRADE 4

Sufficient sleep aids growth, stimulates alertness, and can improve our disposition.

A warm bath or shower at bedtime is a good way to relax.

Balance between work and play activities can help to prevent fatigue.

Sleep helps our bodies build defense against disease.

Sleep is a time well suited for the body to grow.

GRADE 5

Regular sleeping hours are essential to healthful living.

Sleep and rest give the body a chance to rebuild cells and get rid of waste.

Sleep and rest are important to improve the strength of muscles, especially the muscles of the heart.

Sleep relaxes tired nerves.

Rest aids digestion.

Sleep and rest are an aid to proper body mechanics.

GRADE 6

Sleep is a basic need which helps the body function properly.

During sleep the circulatory system carries off the waste stored in muscle tissues.

During sleep the body refreshes itself as the processes slow down.

Sleep gives rest to the nerve cells.

Rest in bed when ill helps the white blood cells fight germs.
Doing things that interest us help us to relax.

Safety. "Safety-conscious pupils in a safe environment" might sum up the purposes of safety teaching in the elementary school. Generally speaking, there seems to be complete agreement among authorities in the field of health education that safety is an important and essential facet of elementary education at all grade levels. Safety might well be a functional aspect of health teaching related to the child's ability to assume responsibility for his own safety and that of others. In general, the teaching content of safety education can be rather specific and structured, since it involves the well-being of the child wherever he finds himself.

In the kindergarten the major emphasis is on safety while en route to and from school. At the first-grade level it is important to stress safety to and from school, safety on the school bus, safety with toys and sharp objects, and safety during fire drills. The safety patrol and policeman are introduced as safety helpers.

Safety practices in the second grade include those from previous levels, plus safety on the bicycle and safety measures with strange animals. The fireman is introduced as a safety helper. Subject matter for the third grade centers around safety and strangers, the use of the sense organs for safety, and seasonal safety. Assuming more responsibility for safety at home and for fire prevention is appropriate for third-grade pupils.

By the fourth grade emphasis is on doing things the safe way and assuming more responsibility for one's own safety and the safety of others at home, on a picnic, on a hike, or in the water. The lifeguard is introduced as a person concerned with the safety of people around the water. Bicycle clubs provide worthwhile experiences for this age pupil who is seeking group belongingness. At the fifth-grade level pupils should be participating members of classroom and/or school safety councils. Since they are now mature enough to go away from home with groups of children under adult supervision, safety in the woods includes concepts based upon a knowledge of poisonous reptiles, such as snakes, and plants, like poison ivy and poison sumac. In the sixth grade the effect of one's feelings and emotions on personal safety should be developed.

Suggested Health Concepts to Be Developed

KINDERGARTEN

We look both ways before crossing the street.
We do not go with strangers.
We stay seated when we ride on a bus or in a car.

GRADE 1

Policeman and safety patrols help children get to and from school safely.
We need to cooperate with the policeman, safety patrol, and bus driver.
To be safe, we need to know and obey the safety rules on the way to and from school, and on the bus.
At unguarded street crossings we must be our own policeman.
Traffic lights and signs tell us how to cross streets safely.
Careful boys and girls play in safe places.
We need to know and obey the safety rules for our classroom, for the school building, and for the playground.
Fire drills are held for our safety.
We should know our name, address, and telephone number.
When we put our toys away we are helping to make our home safe.
We should use school scissors in a safe way.

GRADE 2

The policeman is a friend who helps children to be safe.
Traffic lights are placed at dangerous crossings to protect people.
When we cooperate with the safety patrol we help ourselves and others.
Bus rules are for our safety and need to be obeyed.
There are safe ways to ride a bicycle.
We need to recognize when a place is safe for play.
It is not safe to pet strange animals.
The fireman is interested in our safety.
Fire drills need to be carried on quickly and quietly for the safety of everyone.

GRADE 3

The senses protect us by helping us to see, hear, feel, and smell things that may be dangerous.
There are safety signs along the road that help keep us safe when we are walking on the highway, riding in a car, or riding a bicycle.
Even in safe places we need to play safely.
Playing with electricity and matches is an unsafe practice.
It is best not to walk or ride with strangers.

Certain safety rules need to be followed when we are playing on the snow or ice.

When we are in a hurry we should follow safety rules and regulations.

Labels tell us when and how to take medicine safely.

GRADE 4

Each child needs to accept responsibility for his own safety at all times.

Policemen help to guard our health by enforcing laws.

It is necessary to know and practice right ways of crossing streets.

It is necessary to know and practice safe ways of walking when there are no sidewalks.

Bicycle clubs can help us to be a good bicycle rider.

Many accidents can be prevented by being careful—not hurrying, not pushing, and not getting angry or upset.

It is important to think about our own safety and the safety of others when playing or doing stunts.

To keep fire safe, it is necessary to know the rules for building, tending, and putting out a fire.

We should know how to call the fire department in case of an emergency.

Campers and picnickers should not leave without putting out their fires.

We should stay with the group on a picnic or hike or at camp.

On hikes or picnics, we should follow the rules and cooperate with the leader.

We should abide by "drinking water" signs at camping sites and other public places.

The lifeguard works for the protection and safety of people.

It is safest to go in bathing where a lifeguard is on duty.

GRADE 5

A careful bicycle rider checks his bicycle for safety and observes the traffic rules.

The danger of fire at home can be minimized by safety precautions.

Much can be done to avoid accidents from falls in the home by the careful arrangement of things.

Older children can assume some responsibility for the safety of younger children.

We should keep swimming a safe and healthful sport by observing certain regulations.

Precautions should be taken in the home when handling flammable materials such as cleaning fluids.

Certain safety precautions are always necessary in the woods.

It is necessary to take certain precautions to prevent infection from poison ivy.

A careful camper is on the lookout for poison ivy and poisonous snakes.
Safety councils consist of safety patrol workers who are mature enough to care for their own safety and the safety of others.

GRADE 6

Safety is based upon an awareness of danger and a determination to exercise care.
Some children have more accidents than others because of their feelings about themselves.
It is normal to experience fear in the presence of danger.
Where panic may endanger the safety of others it is important to control the expression of such fears.
Parents can organize safety projects for the betterment of the community.

First Aid.   An objective approach to health teaching implies that pupils should develop a respect for first aid through a knowledge of its purposes and its limitations. At the primary level the pupils learn that personal cuts, scratches, and "hurts" are reported to adults. This practice should be maintained throughout the elementary school level, but with the idea in mind that children should become more self-reliant in this particular regard. In the fourth grade the first-aid kit is introduced, with definite instructions concerning *when* and *by whom* first aid is administered. Fifth-grade pupils should be aware that first aid is different for different types of accidents. Sixth graders should learn first-aid precautions concerning what *not* to do. Also they should have learning experiences involving certain first-aid procedures.

SUGGESTED HEALTH CONCEPTS TO BE DEVELOPED

KINDERGARTEN

Mother and father and the teacher take care of our "hurts."

GRADE 1

We need to tell our parents, or the teacher, immediately about cuts, scratches, and hurts.

GRADE 2

Germs can enter our skin when it is scratched or cut.
Our teacher, the school nurse, or our parents can clean our cuts and scratches to keep germs away.

GRADE 3

We need to avoid staying in the sun until it burns us.

Our parents can treat our sunburn so it will not make us sick.

All cuts, scratches, and hurts should be cared for immediately by adults.

It is important to report a dog bite to our parents or the teacher.

Germs from a dog bite could enter our body through the broken skin and make us sick.

GRADE 4

First aid for slight injuries is given by the teacher, an adult, or our parents.

Burns, blisters and open wounds require first aid to remove possible causes of infection.

A first-aid kit contains such supplies as adhesive tape, sterile gauze, disinfectant, and scissors.

First-aid supplies and all medicines must be kept in a special cabinet and out of reach of younger children.

GRADE 5

First aid is safest when the person knows how to use it.

First aid is different for different types of accidents.

Wounds should be cleaned and protected by sterile gauze.

Bleeding can be stopped by direct pressure.

GRADE 6

First aid can make the patient more comfortable and lessen serious defects of injury.

People who administer first aid should know what *not* to do, as well as what to do.

After giving first aid it is important to discuss the treatment immediately with parents or adults.

Washing with soap and water immediately after contact with poison ivy serves as a possible precautionary measure against poisoning.

Certain kinds of antiseptics are used for cleaning wounds or for insect bites and stings.

Sore muscles can be relieved by rest, massage, and the proper use of heat application.

Stimulants and Narcotic Drugs.   Little or no mention of harmful stimulants or drugs seems warranted until the third grade or the upper elementary level. Fourth- and fifth-grade pupils should learn the reasons why stimulants can be harmful under certain conditions. In the sixth grade, in learning something about the human organism, pupils can begin to develop an understanding of the effects of harmful stimulants and narcotic drugs on bodily functions.

SUGGESTED HEALTH CONCEPTS TO BE DEVELOPED

GRADE 3

When children drink tea and coffee they might neglect to drink milk.

GRADE 4

Tea and coffee are not considered to have food values.
Tobacco can reduce appetite.
Alcohol can interfere with the way the brain works.

GRADE 5

Tea and coffee contain a drug that could have harmful effects on our bodies.
Alcohol can weaken the body's resistance to disease.
Alcohol can slow up the mental processes.

GRADE 6

Stimulants and narcotics can be injurious to the proper functioning of the body.
Caffeine from tea and coffee may cause sleeplessness, and thus interfere with a basic need of the body.
Smoking is a habit that is easy to form and hard to break.
Alcohol can affect a person's judgment, self-control, and physical condition.
The drinking of alcohol can become habit-forming.
Laws regulate the sale and use of alcohol in some communities.
Narcotic drugs can be habit-forming and extremely dangerous.
The government tries to control by laws the manufacture and sale of harmful drugs.

Clothing.   From the standpoint of health the study of clothing should be concerned with body comfort and protection, appearance and personality. In kindergarten the pupils need an awareness that weather influences the kind of clothes they wear. In the first grade practice needs to be established for the care of clothes. Attention should be focused on knowing when to wear play clothes, warm clothes, and/or dry clothes. Second-grade pupils should assume some responsibility for keeping their own clothes clean and neat and caring for their shoes. In addition, they need to learn the importance of wearing clothes appropriate to the occasion and the weather. Third-grade pupils are ready to learn about clothes for protection, comfort, and good health. The content for the fourth grade should include the importance of clothing in the regulation of body temperature and in the prevention of illness. The ability to assume more responsibility for the care and selection of clothing becomes more evident among fifth-grade pupils. Therefore, consideration should be given to the color and material of clothing in relation to grooming and appearance. Consideration at the sixth-grade level centers around clothing as it relates to age, durability, economy, and bodily functions.

Suggested Health Concepts to Be Developed

KINDERGARTEN

We wear rain clothes on a rainy day.
We wear snowsuits on a cold day.
We wear clean clothes.

GRADE 1

Warm clothes are best for cold weather and for playing in the snow.
Play clothes are the right clothes for playing at home, at a picnic, or on the farm.
Our school clothes will look better and last longer if we hang them up when we take them off.
We change to play clothes after school.
We should change to dry clothes after being caught in the rain.

GRADE 2

It is a good idea to select appropriate clothes for school, for a party, and for church.
We need to wear clothes suited to the weather.
Raincoat, rain hat, and rubbers are appropriate rainy day wraps.
Outdoor wraps should be taken off and hung up when we come indoors.
Our shoes should fit properly.

GRADE 3

Coats protect us from cold and wet weather.
Sweaters keep us warm in cool weather.
Shoes protect our feet from sticks and stones.
Hats protect our heads from the very hot, cold, or wet weather.

Being appropriately dressed for the weather protects our health and helps us feel comfortable.

We can keep our own shoes clean so they will look better and last longer.

We change our clothes when we play, go to school, or go to bed.

GRADE 4

Clothes protect us from cold, heat, and moisture.

Clothes help the body maintain its normal temperature.

Dressing properly for the weather can help us to keep well and to avoid illness.

Clean and neat clothes improve our appearance.

Different kinds of activities determine the type of clothes we wear.

We need to choose our clothes wisely so they can be useful, appropriate, and suitable.

We can help to care for our own clothes.

GRADE 5

Wearing clothes suitable for season and weather indicates that we are learning to protect and care for our health.

A neat, well-groomed appearance helps us to feel more comfortable, and helps others to see us at our best.

We should assume some of the responsibility for the cleanliness and care of our clothes.

When choosing clothes wisely, we should consider characteristics of the materials as well as the selection of proper colors.

GRADE 6

Clothes that fit properly are the most becoming and comfortable.

Sex, age, durability, economy, and attractiveness are points to be considered when purchasing suitable clothes.

Clothes should fit well enough to provide for comfortable body movements.

It is our responsibility to select shoes that provide protection and comfort to the feet.

We can assume more and more responsibility for care of our clothes, seeing that they are clean, well brushed, and well pressed.

The Human Organism—Its Structure, Function, and Care. Health teaching fundamentally is concerned with the basic needs of the body. In the primary grades the areas of emphasis consist of (1) establishing routines and practices conducive to the maintenance of good health; (2) understanding the importance of body cleanliness, including clean hair, nails, skin, and teeth; (3) learning about growth; (4) caring for teeth, eyes, and ears.

In general, the subject matter for the upper elementary level can be classified under structure and function of the body. The fourth-grade teaching content includes such topics as (1) structure and function of eyes and ears; (2) identification of the framework and organs of the body; and (3) control of certain communicable diseases. At the fifth-grade level the various systems of the body should be studied. Other health content areas include (1) structure and function of the skeleton, muscles, nerves, and sense organs; and (2) defense against disease. Sixth grade concepts center around the interdependence of the systems of the body (circulatory, digestive, nervous, respiratory), and glandular functions.

Suggested Health Concepts to Be Developed

(It should be noted that the concepts in this category have been grouped with respect to the body's structure and/or function.)

KINDERGARTEN

Cleanliness
We wash our hands before we eat.
We wash our hands after going to the toilet.
We take a bath every night.

Growth
We are growing up.
We get weighed and measured to see how much we grow.

Teeth
We brush our teeth after eating.

GRADE 1

Cleanliness
We should take a bath, clean our teeth, and brush our hair before going to bed.
When we get up in the morning it is important to wash our face and hands.
We should wash our hands before and after eating, after going to the toilet, and after blowing our nose.

Growth
Our body grows during the night as well as during the day.

When weighed and measured regularly we can check on how much we
are growing.

Teeth

We can care for our teeth by eating proper foods.

We can care for our teeth by visiting the dentist regularly.

We can care for our teeth by brushing them or rinsing our mouth after
meals.

Eyes

Sufficient light on our book helps us protect our eyes.

Sunglasses can protect our eyes from strong sunlight.

Ears

Healthy, clean ears are needed for good hearing.

We need to tell a grownup when our ears hurt.

Common Colds

When we have a cold we can try to prevent it from spreading to others.

We use a paper handkerchief and dispose of it.

We cover our nose and mouth when we cough or sneeze.

Elimination

We should go to the toilet before we go to bed at night and when we get
up in the morning.

GRADE 2

Cleanliness

The morning routine should include washing face and hands, cleaning
teeth, cleaning fingernails, brushing hair, and dressing in clean clothes.

The evening routine should include bathing, brushing hair, cleaning teeth,
and putting on clean night clothes.

Growth

When we walk, stand, and sit correctly we help our bodies grow.

Each boy and girl grows in his or her own way.

Height and weight are measures of growth.

Teeth

We should take care of our baby teeth so that our permanent teeth will
be strong and healthy.

Eyes

We can care for our eyes by using a good reading light, keeping our hands
away from our eyes, and telling grownups when our eyes hurt.

If we wear glasses we need to keep them clean.

Ears

We should try to avoid being hit on the ear.

Loud noises can hurt our ears.

Our ears can be tested with a machine called an audiometer.

Common Colds

Good health practices, such as eating proper food, getting enough sleep
and rest, and playing in the fresh air and sunshine, help keep us free
of colds.

We can help ourselves to keep well by keeping fingers away from our
nose and mouth.

When we have a cold we need to rest, eat proper food, and stay away from
others.

Elimination

The practice of going to the toilet regularly can help keep us well.

GRADE 3

Cleanliness

We need to assume responsibility for the cleanliness of our bodies.

Baths are important to wash away dirt and germs from our skin.

Baths help us relax and can help make us feel clean and rested.

We use only our own toothbrush, comb, and towel to protect our own
health and that of others.

We help to keep our hair healthy and attractive by brushing it daily and
shampooing it regularly.

Growth

The body needs food, rest, and activity in the fresh air and sunshine.

The body is growing constantly.

We each have our own "timetable" for growth.

Teeth

If our teeth are to grow straight and strong, they require good care.

Eating proper foods can help prevent tooth decay.

Cavities can form in neglected teeth.

We should use the teeth only for that which they are intended.

Eyes

In caring for our eyes we should hold a book a comfortable distance away
from our eyes for reading.

We should have regular eye examinations and wear glasses when needed.

Ears

We can care for our ears by blowing the nose gently.

It is best to see a doctor when we have earache.

Illness and Disease

We can build body resistance to common colds by diet, activity, and sleep.

When we get a cold we need to observe health practices to prevent its spread.

Some illnesses require isolation because they are contagious.

Elimination

Our body rids itself of waste through perspiration, bowel movements, and urination.

Senses

We have five senses which help us to know about and enjoy life.

Skin

It is the purpose of the skin to keep our body at the right temperature.

The skin prevents germs from entering the body.

The skin carries off waste through its pores.

Nose

The hairs in our nose help to keep the dirt and germs out of our body.

Lungs

We can get fresh air in our lungs when we play outside.

Heart

When we feel our pulse we feel the pressure of the blood as the heart sends it through the tubes of the body.

GRADE 4

Cleanliness

Children should accept responsibility for their own cleanliness.

Growth

Changes in the body size are an important aspect of physical growth.

We grow at different rates in different ways at different times.

Teeth

We have four kinds of teeth, each useful in a different way.

Cavities may grow until the whole tooth is endangered, unless it receives dental care.

Each tooth has a crown protected by a hard coating of enamel, the neck, and roots.

The pulp in the center of the tooth contains nerves and also blood vessels through which nourishment is brought to the tooth.

Teeth help digest our food through chewing, thus mixing it with saliva.

Teeth help the tongue and lips make speech sounds.

Eyes

The iris of the eyes regulates the amount of light that enters the eye.

Our eyes are protected by the bones of the skull, the eyelids, eyebrows, eyelashes, and by tears.

We can help to care for our eyes by eating proper foods.

We can help to care for our eyes by sitting a proper distance from a television or movie screen.

We can help our eyes by having the proper amount of light around us.

Ears

The special structure of the ear catches sounds and carries them to nerves, which in turn carry messages to the brain.

We can do much to care for our ears by washing them thoroughly but carefully.

Cold and some illnesses can cause loss of hearing.

It is important to have our ears examined after illness so loss of hearing can be quickly discovered.

Illness and Disease

Disease can be spread by fingers, flies, foods, and air.

Infection involves a fight between the body and the germs that enter it.

Rheumatic fever is an infection which can damage the heart.

We can protect ourselves against infectious diseases by avoiding the germs or by being immunized.

When we are immunized we receive medication administered by a doctor as a protection from infections such as whooping cough, diphtheria, smallpox, poliomyelitis, and tetanus.

Digestion and Elimination

Digestion is the process of changing food so that the materials can pass into the blood and be used by the body.

Various parts (teeth, stomach, intestines) of the body aid in the digestion of food.

Saliva and other juices in the digestive system aid in the digestive process.

The materials in food which cannot be digested are moved out of the body by way of the large intestines during a bowel movement.

We can aid digestion by resting after eating.

We can aid digestion by eating proper foods.

We can aid digestion by chewing food properly.

Parts of the Body

Our body is like an engine that never stops.

Some of the parts of the body which carry on its functions are the outer covering of skin, hair, and nails; the fat; the skeletal muscles; and the framework of backbone, ribs, skull, and bones of the legs and arms.

The important organs that carry on specific functions are the brain, heart, liver, lungs, kidneys, bladder, and intestines.

GRADE 5

Growth

Our body grows because cells divide to make new cells.

Individual differences in height, weight, and body build among children of the same age are to be expected.

The age at which a person begins to grow tall, the way he grows, and the time he stops growing, are individual matters.

Mouth and Teeth

The lips, teeth, tongue, taste buds, and salivary glands perform important bodily functions in the sense of taste.

In the mouth food is tasted, ground, and moistened for digestion.

Proper care of the mouth and teeth should be a well-established health practice.

Eyes

The eyeball, iris, pupil, lens, retina, optic nerve, cornea, and tear glands each serve a unique function in helping us to see.

Light, passing through the pupil and lens, throws a picture on the retina, and stimulates the optic nerve, which carries the message to the brain, causing us to see.

Ears

The outer ear, middle ear, and inner ear each serve a unique function in helping us to hear.

Sounds (vibrations in the air) travel through the ear to the auditory nerve, which reports them to the brain.

The brain tells us the kind of sound and from where it came.

Illness and Disease

The body forms chemicals in the blood stream to fight infection.

The prevention and cure of communicable disease can be based upon what is known about germs, how they spread, and how they are controlled.

Most communicable diseases spread through the harmful bacteria found in the waste given off by the body through the bowels, in the urine, and in discharge from the nose and mouth.

Immunization, vaccination, and quarantine are measures used to control disease.

Elimination

The blood, bowels, lungs, kidneys, and skin function to eliminate the body of its waste.

Regularity of elimination by bowels and kidneys indicates that the body is functioning to eliminate its waste.

Digestive System

Digestion begins in the mouth, is continued in the stomach, and is completed in the small intestines.

Saliva in the mouth changes the starch in food to sugar.

Proteins begin to dissolve in the stomach.

Digestive juices from the liver that are stored in the gall bladder break fats into tiny drops in the small intestines.

Pancreatic juices and digestive juices from the walls of the small intestines complete the job of digesting carbohydrates, proteins, and fats.

If there is more food than cells need, it is stored in the liver and muscles or changed to fat and stored under the skin.

Food which cannot be digested passes to the large intestines for elimination.

Skin

The skin is the body covering through which touch and feeling are experienced.

The skin helps protect the body from heat, cold, dirt, disease, and injury.

The skin admits sunlight, helps to regulate body temperature and eliminates waste.

The skin is composed of three layers each of which serves a specific purpose.

The epidermis (outer layer of skin) varies in thickness and contains pigments that give the skin color.

The dermis (underlayer of skin) contains blood vessels, nerves, sweat glands, oil glands, and hair and nails, which perform necessary bodily functions.

Below the dermis is a layer of fat cells which cushion the skin.

Nose

The nose is the organ in which the sense of smell begins.

The nose cleans and warms the air before it goes to the lungs.

The parts of the nose which perform important bodily functions are the two nostrils, membranes, hairs, and opening to the Eustachian tube.

Respiratory System

The oxygen in the air is used by the body to convert food into heat and energy.

The lungs breathe in oxygen.

Carbon dioxide is the waste from the blood as it comes in contact with the air spaces of the lungs.

The lungs expel carbon dioxide.

Circulatory System

The circulatory system supplies the body with food and oxygen.

The circulatory system aids the body in getting rid of waste.

Structure

The smallest part of our body is a cell.

The body is made up of millions of living cells which require food to grow, to repair themselves, and to produce energy and heat.

The blood carries digested food to body cells.

The framework of our body consists of the head, neck, trunk, arms, and legs.

The backbone is the supporting center for the framework of the body.

The bones help to give the body its shape.

The bones support and protect the organs.

The trunk consists of the chest and abdomen, which contain vital organs.

The chest holds and protects the heart and lungs.

The abdomen holds and protects such vital organs as the stomach, intestines, liver, bladder, and kidneys.

Bones, joints, muscles, and nerves work together to help permit our body to move.

Voluntary muscles working in pairs bring about the movements made under our own direction.

Involuntary muscles automatically bring about movements of organs in the trunk, such as work of the heart, lungs, and intestines.

Throat

The throat is an opening through which food passes from the mouth to the stomach.

Air passes through the nose, mouth, and throat to the lungs.

The parts of the throat which perform important bodily functions are the open chamber, trachea, larynx, esophagus, tonsils, and adenoids.

The epiglottis keeps food out of the larynx when we swallow.

Vibrations of the vocal cords in the larynx make us able to speak.

The lips, tongue, palate, and teeth help to formulate speech sounds.

Body Temperature

Our body makes heat by burning the fuel in food we consume.

Vigorous exercise uses more body heat than normal exercise.

More heat than usual passes into the air from the skin when we are too warm.

More heat than usual is held when we are too cold.

When we are well, oral temperature remains at approximately 98.6° and 99.6° by rectum.

Brain and Nerves

Our brain is made up of millions of nerve cells which have branches called fibers.

Our nerves help us to see, hear, taste, smell, touch, and move.

Through the senses things are stored in the brain and become a part of our memory.

Nerves are made of specialized cells.

Each part of the brain receives messages from different parts of the body.

One set of nerves carries messages to the brain and another set carries messages away.

Both sets of nerves must be used to make the body move.

GRADE 6

Glandular System

The lymph glands constitute one important defense against infection.

The pituitary gland, located at the base of the brain, regulates the body's growth in height.

Endocrine glands have an important role in regulating growth.

The thyroid gland, located in the neck, affects the body's weight and the nervous system.

Sex glands are important glands used to reproduce the human race.

Growth

Everyone grows in spurts, but not everyone spurts ahead at the same time.

Good diet, proper rest, and exercise help us reach our potential in growth.

Teeth

Chewing is the job of the teeth.

Teeth require specific nutrients from food.

Tooth decay can be prevented and controlled.

Healthy gums are important to good health.

Eyes

Light rays enter the pupil of the eye and form a picture on the retina at the back of the eye.

A special nerve from the retina carries the picture to the brain, where it is recognized and interpreted.

The eye is protected by bones around it, by the eyelids and the eyelashes, by tears, and by its ability to adjust itself to light.

Periodic eye examination by an eye specialist is one means of maintaining good eyesight.

Most visual defects can be corrected by glasses.

Ears

Sound waves are channeled from the outer ear to the canal leading to the eardrum.

The vibrations of the eardrum set in motion the three small bones in the inner ear.

The inner ear is filled with liquid and lined with tiny threads of nerve cells.

When the liquid of the inner ear is disturbed by the vibration of the bones, the nerve ends transmit messages to the brain, and hearing takes place.

A change in air pressure causes a new sensation in the ear due to changes in pressure on the eardrums.

Conservation of hearing is our personal responsibility.

Illness and Disease

Ways of keeping well and preventing disease are based on scientific research.

The cure of a disease is seldom discovered by one person working alone, but is the result of cooperative efforts.

Much research is being conducted today on the causes and cures of diseases.

Tiny organisms called germs and viruses cause many diseases.

White blood cells fight germs and viruses.

The body can build antibodies against certain communicable diseases, thereby making itself immune to the disease.

The part of the blood which carries antibodies is a protein substance in blood plasma called gamma globulin.

Diseases can be caused by lack of certain vitamins in the diet.

Disease can be caused by harmful bacteria in food, water, milk, and air.

Unsanitary conditions, where harmful bacteria can spread and grow, can contribute to disease.

Digestive System

Digestion changes food so it can be used by the cells of the body.

Digested food is delivered by the blood to the tissues in the form which the cells can use it.

Skin

The skin and mucous membranes act as a protective covering for our body.

Proper care of the skin is important for good grooming and good health.

Respiratory System

The nose, throat, and lungs are the chief parts of the respiratory system which supply oxygen to all body cells.

Our body needs oxygen from the air to burn the fuel in food to produce energy.

Circulatory System

The circulatory system carries blood to all parts of the body.

The heart is a nonstop pump which helps circulate the blood through the body.

Arteries carry blood away from the heart, and veins carry blood back to the heart.

It is through the very thin walls of the capillaries that oxygen, food, water, heat, and waste pass into and out of the blood.

Cells

The organs of the body consist of many cells.

Skeleton

The spine is made up of many small bones separated from each other by firm, tough cushions.

There are three kinds of bones in the body, each shaped to perform its work efficiently.

Bones are held together by muscles and ligaments.

The muscles move the bones at the joints.

Muscles are arranged in pairs and, when a bone moves, one muscle shortens and the other lengthens.

Control of Body Temperature

Blood circulation helps our body to maintain proper temperature.

The blood gets rid of heat by radiation as it flows through the tiny blood vessels in the dermis layer of the skin.

If not enough heat is lost in radiation the extra heat is lost by evaporation of perspiration in the skin.

Neuromuscular Coordination

The brain sends nerve impulses to the voluntary muscles which cause them to act.

Voluntary muscles working in pairs and controlled by the brain permit us to move as we wish.

Bodily movements which we cannot control are carried on by involuntary muscles.

Nervous System

The nervous system controls the various actions of the body.

The nervous system enables us to think and act as we wish.

Nerves take messages from the sense organs to the brain.

Nerves take orders for action from the brain to the muscles and organs.

Information which constantly comes into the brain from the sense organs helps us to think.

The kind of thinking we do to express feelings, ideas, and opinions is a most important function of our mind.

Touch and pressure spots on the skin send messages to the brain, which helps us feel the things we touch.

Messages sent to the brain from taste buds on the tongue make us able to taste.

Odors cause cells in the nose to send messages to the brain, and we can smell.

Health Services. During his elementary school experiences the child extends his environment from the home to the school and into the community. Thus, he learns about the importance which his community attaches to the health of its citizens. He observes the various health services available. He avails himself of the services and develops feelings and attitudes toward the importance and responsibility of the community for the health and welfare of its citizens. The kindergarten pupil needs to learn about the importance of the school nurse and doctor. The first-grade pupil adds the dentist to his list of professional personnel. The importance of using the available health services for a complete physical examination needs to be emphasized in the second grade. The hospital can be introduced as a health service. Third-grade content centers around a study of the services of the health department, with emphasis on the need for immunization. During the fourth grade, the pupils should be introduced to community health through a study of the services rendered by the health officers. Emphasis, too, needs to be placed on the responsibility of the individual in the prevention of illness. The topics for the fifth grade should include health laws, health agencies, Junior Red Cross, and pioneers in public health. At the sixth-grade level, subject matter should include a study of community sanitation, health department services, hospital services, and the results of some of the current medical research.

SUGGESTED HEALTH CONCEPTS TO BE DEVELOPED

KINDERGARTEN

The school nurse helps us keep well.

The doctor is our friend.

GRADE 1

Regular physical examination by the doctor can help us to stay well.

The eye doctor can find out how good our vision is and whether or not we need glasses to help us see better.

The dentist can help us by examining our teeth, filling cavities, and caring in general for our teeth.

We can help the doctor, dentist, and nurse by being considerate and by cooperating with them.

GRADE 2

Regular examinations by the doctor and dentist can help us stay well.

The doctor uses a stethoscope to listen to the sounds our heart and lungs make.

The sounds the doctor hears from the stethoscope help him find out about our health.

The hospital is a place where doctors and nurses help sick people get well.

GRADE 3

Hospitals have doctors, nurses, and equipment to take care of us when we need special care to get well.

Doctors can help us stay well by giving us "shots" to help prevent some diseases.

The health department protects our health by inspections to insure a safe supply of milk and drinking water.

The dentist can give our teeth the professional care they need.

GRADE 4

Doctors are interested in the prevention as well as cure of disease.

A dental hygienist is trained to examine and to clean teeth.

The dentist can straighten irregular teeth by putting braces on them.

The school nurse is prepared to give boys and girls friendly advice and help.

We can help to keep our schoolroom healthful by proper lighting, ventilation, and by maintaining a room temperature of about 70° F.

Public health officers protect the health of the people in the community.

Under the supervision of the health department storage places for food and also restaurants are inspected.

The health department tests drinking water.

Everyone can have a part in providing a safe, healthful community in which to live.

GRADE 5

The school nurse can give advice to boys and girls about their growth and development.

The community organizes many departments that work to protect the health of its citizens.

Government health agencies such as the health department, Red Cross, clinics, and hospitals are health agencies which operate for the benefit of all.

We can help ourselves and others to have better health through the Junior Red Cross.

Certain medical discoveries have contributed to better health for us.

GRADE 6

The services of many people are required to keep a community safe and healthful.

Many government and private agencies work for health and safety.

Community sanitation includes the collection and disposal of garbage and trash, sewage disposal, insect control, filtering of water, and milk inspection.

Research today continues to play an important role in the improvement of community and personal health.

Mental, Social, and Emotional Health.   The human organism is an indivisible unity. One cannot look at any facet of growth and development without observing the interaction and interrelatedness of one facet upon another. How the child feels emotionally affects his social, physical, and mental health, and conversely how he acts socially is reflected in his mental, physical, and emotional health. Any discussion of mental, social, and emotional health must be relative to the individual at the particular moment. The effectiveness of this aspect of health weighs heavily upon the teacher and the professional knowledge which he brings to the situation. From this point of view, the personal development of each child as a complete unity is a matter of degree in development, as observed in the way he feels about himself, the way he acts toward and with others, how he learns to understand and control his emotions, how he assumes responsibility, and how he acquires proficiencies in academic skills. All teaching situations, whether during lessons devoted to health or not, should be such that the child has the opportunity to grow and to develop to a higher degree of emotional stability, social adjustment, and mental alertness. The following concepts might serve as examples of some of the more significant aspects of mental, social, and emotional health.

Suggested Health Concepts to Be Developed

KINDERGARTEN

We learn to listen in school.
We share in school.
We wait and take turns.
We feel more comfortable when we know what is expected of us.
We can work alone.
It is fun to play together.
Everyone is different.
Everyone makes mistakes.
We talk things over with our parents.

GRADE 1

It is important to be considerate of the wishes of others in our family.
Getting ready and being on time at home and at school are two ways to show we are growing up.
When we amuse ourselves and do some things on our own we show people we are growing up.
If we have fears we should talk about them with our parents.
People live differently and like to do different things.
Differences help to make life more interesting.
School is a good place to make friends.
We are polite when we express our thanks for the kind things people do for us.
If we make mistakes we should learn from these mistakes.
It is better to control our feelings and to find other things to do than to quarrel.

GRADE 2

We help our family when we are considerate, kind, and cooperative.
When we do our share at home and school, we show we are growing up.
We are responsible for what we do.
When we make others happy we make ourselves happy.
As we grow up, we can think of different ways to do things and different things to do.
It is fun to discover how many things we can do well.
Adults can help us to make wise choices.

It helps when we are considerate of the mistakes of others.

When something goes wrong it helps to try to be cheerful and to find something else to do.

GRADE 3

We can each do some things well.

It helps us to know what we can do well.

Each person can contribute something of interest to the group.

We help ourselves and others when we are good followers and good leaders.

Time can be saved by doing things together.

A sense of humor can often make things better for everyone.

When we plan we make things easier for ourselves and others.

We need to assume our share of the responsibility for carrying out the plans we help to make.

It helps to make the best of a situation we cannot change.

GRADE 4

A happy family is one in which each member makes contributions to the happiness of others.

Family life goes more smoothly and happily when all members share responsibilities.

Planning can help us spend our time wisely and happily.

Whether we earn money or are given an allowance, it is wise to save some each week for unexpected occasions.

Working in groups can make it easy to accomplish tasks that are hard to accomplish alone.

For happy group living one needs to respect the rights and wishes of others.

Having a friend and being a friend are important to happy group living.

Thoughtfulness and consideration make for pleasant relationships with others.

Hobbies can bring us relaxation and recreation.

Everyone should have confidence in his own ability and be willing to try new experiences.

Almost everyone has unpleasant feelings sometimes.

Ways of handling disturbed feelings is something each of us must learn.

GRADE 5

A mature person assumes responsibility for his own health, safety, and behavior, as well as the health and safety of younger children.

Being able to plan ahead is a sign of increasing maturity.

People already living in a community can welcome or give help to new-comers.

Vacation time affords opportunities to develop new interests.

We need to meet our problems and to solve them without anger, jealousy, or unhappiness to ourselves or others.

A responsible person completes a task when it needs to be done.

A responsible person knows when to ask for help.

Mental ability is shown in the way we learn, make choices, and solve problems.

Control of emotions is important for maintenance of proper bodily function.

GRADE 6

We grow physically, socially, mentally, and emotionally.

Growing up emotionally means growing up in an understanding of our own feelings, and in the ways we handle our feelings.

Control of emotions helps us accomplish our tasks and enjoy life.

Mature people understand and respect their families, friends and other people.

An awareness of and respect for the feelings of others is evidence of growing up emotionally.

Growing up socially means growing in the ability to get along with others.

The ability to meet others graciously and to operate as a worthy group member help to make the individual pleasant company for others and add to his own happiness.

Self-confidence is gained by setting worthwhile goals for ourselves and working toward their attainment.

A good sport thinks of others as well as himself.

Talking over our problems and feelings with someone we trust helps to get rid of the problem.

Handling an allowance can help us develop a sense of responsibility.

REFERENCES

American Association of School Administrators, *Health in Schools,* Twentieth Yearbook, rev. ed., Washington, D.C., National Educational Association, 1951.

Bauer, W. W. *et al., The Basic Health and Safety Program,* Fair Lawn, N.J., Scott, Foresman, 1957–1960.

Brownell, Clifford, *et al., ABC Health Series,* New York, American, 1959.

Byrd, Oliver E., "The Health Curriculum: 500 Topics," *Journal of School Health,* March, 1958.

Byrd, Oliver E., *et al.*, *The New Road to Health Series*, Summit, N.J., Laidlaw, 1960.

Foster, Roy A., *An Analysis of the Types and Quantity of Health Information in Selected Health Education Textbooks for Grades One Through Six*, Unpublished Doctoral Dissertation, Bloomington, Indiana University, 1952.

Hallock, Grace T., *et al.*, *Health for Better Living Series*, Boston, Ginn, 1958.

Hicks, Dora, "Scope of Health Instruction, Grades 1 to 12," *Journal of School Health*, June, 1953.

Irwin, Leslie W., *et al.*, *Health, Happiness and Success Series*, Wilkes-Barre, Pa., Lyons and Carnahan, 1958.

Moore, Virginia D., and James H. Humphrey, "An Analysis of Elementary School Health Textbooks Indicating Recommended Grade Placement of Health Concepts," (Research of Interest) *Journal of School Health*, September, 1960.

O'Keefe, Pattric Ruth, *et al.*, *Winston Health Series*, Philadelphia, Winston, 1960.

TEACHING AIDS
AND MATERIALS

10

1 *What is the essential difference between a "teaching aid" and a "teacher substitute"?*
2 *What are some basic considerations which should be taken into account in the proper utilization of teaching aids?*
3 *What are some important aspects to be considered in the "follow-up" of teaching aids?*
4 *What are some of the ways in which "reading materials" may be successfully used as teaching aids?*
5 *What are some of the factors to be considered in the use of various types of mass media as teaching aids?*

Education has traditionally been regarded as predominantly symbol-centered and more or less isolated from the realities represented by the symbols. In effect, most teaching aids amount to an effort to bring the realities themselves—or more or less direct representations of them—into the classroom to facilitate understanding and learning. The psychology of perception in relation to learning is of primary importance in this connection. (Discussions of this subject may be found in most recent books dealing with audio-visual aids listed in the references at the end of the chapter.)

The discussion which follows deals with two major types of teaching aids; these will be discussed separately even though they have many things in common—including most of the principles which should control their use. Admittedly the distinction to be made between the two is in some respects arbitrary and not entirely clear cut. However, the first type to be considered, in effect, amounts to temporarily introducing a second "teacher"—upon which the pupil's attention is focused for appreciable periods of time—into the classroom; this second "teacher" is represented by a variety of aids, including books, recordings, films, radio and television—all of which may actually take over the burden of teaching individuals or groups as the classroom teacher moves temporarily into the background.

The second type of aid to be considered is merely used by the teacher while actively engaged in teaching. This type does not take over temporarily as a second "teacher." Aids of this kind are of such diverse nature as models, exhibits, charts, flash cards, specimens, and adhering boards—none of which in any real sense involves bringing a second "teacher" into the classroom. Thus, the teacher may use flash cards to help pupils discriminate among poisonous plants and reptiles but of course does not depend exclusively on the flash cards.

Although aids of the second type are numerous and can be used by virtually all teachers, the less widely available teaching aids of the first type are discussed first, because the role of the former in instruction may be more clearly defined and fully appreciated when considered in relation to aids like films and television, which are sometimes conceived as teacher substitutes.

TEACHING AID VS. TEACHER SUBSTITUTE

Occasionally, a communication medium appears which is heralded not only as a teaching aid but as a teacher substitute as well. The enormous expense of mass education, coupled with the need for high-quality teaching, has given rise to the wish that somehow a relatively few master teachers could direct the learning of large numbers of persons. In this way, it has been reasoned, both quantitative and qualitative problems of American education could be solved or at least minimized.

Several of the mass media of communication have been proposed with varying degrees of enthusiasm as the answer to this problem of educating large numbers of people well. Books, recordings, radio, films, television, and recently teaching machines have all been experimented with and widely used. For example, at the university level, it has been suggested that the reading of certain "great" books would bring the essence of an education. Recordings played over radios have been proposed as educational tools which would reduce the need for teachers. Resources available to the military during World War II made possible extensive utilization of experimentation with motion pictures as training devices. For certain purposes, including assisting in visualizing mechanisms, grasping techniques of mechanical operations and certain training and work procedures to be followed, films were doubtless of great value in facilitating learning on the part of large numbers of men. Quite naturally, this military experience affected the thinking of educators in peacetime and evidence has since been presented in support of the claim that films facilitate learning by pupils of varying intelligence levels.[1]

The swelling of school enrollments at all grade levels since World War II, and the somewhat parallel development of television as a mass medium of communication, have led to a quite logical hope, based to a considerable extent on impressions gained from the military experience with tailor-made training films, that a new era of teaching is at hand. There has been a widespread interest in and experimentation with educational television as not only a teaching aid but also as a promising teacher substitute.

In spite of their great value in education generally, as well as in health education, all the mass media of communication have been found wanting when tried as teacher substitutes rather than as teaching aids, perhaps especially at the elementary school level. It is interesting to consider why.

In brief, the answer probably lies in the fact that although a teacher usually deals with a group of children, he or she must remain sensitive to the *individual*. The qualified teacher is aware that every child is almost incredibly unique and that he approaches all of his learning tasks with his own levels of motivation, capacity, experience, and vitality. Moreover, such a teacher is aware that the individuals in a class must be *prepared* for a learning experience so that the experience may, in some way, be recognized by them as having meaning for them. Preparation of any class must be in terms of the particular individuals in that class. The teacher must then, by a combination of emotional and logical appeal, help each individual find his way through the experience at his own rate and, to some extent, in his own way. The teacher must also help the individual "nail down" the meaning of the experience to himself—

[1] See W. A. Wittich and C. F. Schuller, *Audio-Visual Materials,* 2nd ed., New York, Harper, 1957.

help him to incorporate it and its use into his own life. Even very bright children are dependent to a very considerable extent upon the quality of the teacher-pupil relationship for their inspiration to pursue their interests and develop their potentialities.

The mass media and the other teaching aids to be considered are concerned with (1) a subject and (2) a hypothetical group and age level for whom they are designed. A teacher is needed to adapt them to individual learning programs. Now, of course, by chance, an individual may be ready for just the information in the form utilized by a mass medium or other aid, and he will, therefore, benefit from it to one degree or another. For example, a sixth-grade boy who is learning canoeing may benefit from happening to see a film on boating, hydrodynamics, or water safety. However, the film, as an isolated experience, may be entirely irrelevant or, at best, nothing more than a passing curiosity to the majority of this boy's fellow sixth graders. Similarly, the extraordinary films on health, science, and biology that some large companies have presented on television have usually passed from the entertainment to the educational level only when individual teachers obtained them or in some way incorporated them into the learning experience pattern of a particular group.

The point of view reflected in this chapter on teaching aids and materials may be summarized as follows:

1. There is no substitute for a competent teacher who, while necessarily teaching a *group*, is highly sensitive to the *individual* pupils involved.
2. Any elementary school teacher can utilize a wide variety of aids and materials to great advantage in the teaching of health.[2]

SOME GENERAL CONSIDERATIONS

The proper utilization of teaching aids presupposes an awareness of certain principles which should govern their use. Beginning teachers and others who have had little experience using teaching aids need to make a special point of observing these principles. On the

[2] The National Defense Education Act of 1958 emphasizes the importance of audio-visual aids in education and directs the Commissioner of Education to increase and improve techniques for their use. Government grants have become available to assist states and localities with experiments concerned with such media as "educational television."

other hand, teachers who are experienced in such matters are usually able to observe them almost automatically because they have been found to produce desirable results—just as one drives a car on the right-hand side of the street or selects well-balanced meals.

The list of factors which follow are suggestive of those which should govern the use of teaching aids and materials.

Selection

There are several considerations to be taken into account in regard to the selection of teaching aids and materials. In the first place, they should be selected on the basis of the Gestalt of the learning experience. In other words, no matter how good they are, their value is greatest if they fit in an appropriate manner into, and thus contribute to, the total learning experience that is in progress. For example, posters concerned with dental health are of less value if displayed without regard to the lessons in progress than if displayed as a meaningful part of a lesson on dental health. Secondly, teaching aids should be selected on the basis of their quality. This, of course, makes it necessary for the teacher to have a complete knowledge of the particular aid in advance of using it. In this connection, questions such as the following need to be taken into account. Is the health information technically correct? Is advertising intruded in such a way as to detract from the value of the aid? Does the aid convey significant concepts or is it essentially entertaining and amusing? In approach, vocabulary, and technicality, is it appropriate for the particular group for which it is being considered? And, thirdly, the selection of the teaching aid may, in itself, be an important learning experience in that it may be sought out or made as a result of pupil as well as teacher planning, investigating, and evaluating. Thus, for example, individual pupils and/or committees may be made responsible for making, obtaining, or selecting suitable aids or materials.

Selection of appropriate health teaching aids implies familiarity with all the audio-visual resources that are available to the teacher. Unfortunately, indications are that a large percentage of teachers do not utilize resources that are provided, or are at least accessible.[3]

[3] W. R. Fulton and A. W. White, "What Constitutes Teacher Competence in Audio-Visual Communication?" *Phi Delta Kappan*, January, 1959, p. 158.

Preparation

After the health teaching aid has been selected and obtained, certain preparation is needed if the greatest value is to be derived from it. The message of the aid should be clearly noted so that the pupils may, if necessary, be helped to distinguish it. With some aids such as good posters, this is a simple matter because these are concerned with a single message and the point is generally easily understood. With others, such as motion pictures, this may be a problem of importance because, of several dozen points made, six or fewer may be critical and should be highlighted. Even more mature pupils commonly need help in distinguishing the essential from the, perhaps, not so essential; and the teacher's preparation should include getting these important points clearly in mind. In this connection, some experienced teachers have found it useful to draw a target, the "bull's eye" of which represents the *essential* information, the next ring of which represents relatively less important information, the next ring still less important information, and so on. Such a technique can be very helpful to the teacher and can also make a valuable form of pupil-teacher analysis of a book, film, television program, or other relatively complex teaching aid.

The teacher's preparation should also include noting such details as new vocabulary (as in books or moving pictures) and the operation of mechanisms or physiological functions, as in films, charts, demonstrations, and models.

A further aspect of preparation has to do, not with the teaching aid itself, but with the preparation of the class for the aid. This consideration is especially important in relation to such aids as films, radio, television programs, and demonstrations, because these ordinarily are not prepared for the particular group or the precise lesson the teacher is dealing with. A state of readiness to learn must be established if the health teaching aid is to make a maximum contribution to the learning experience in progress. Unless the teacher is deliberately presenting the aid to the class "cold" in order to test the pupils' spontaneous reaction to it, the pupils should be alerted as to what to look for, what new terms mean, and so on. Key questions may be raised which will draw attention to important points to be discussed later.

Mechanical aspects of preparation include doing whatever needs to be done to obtain the teaching aid at the desired time and planning the best way of using it. In the case of films, it may be necessary to schedule their use several weeks or even months in advance (state, city, and county education and health departments and other film resources differ considerably in their scheduling policies). In the case of radio and television programs, advanced planning is also necessary if the aid is to complement the learning experiences in progress in the classroom.

Presentation

Clearly the teaching aid must be ready and functional when it is needed, and thus presentation depends to a great extent upon the thoroughness and care of preparation. For example, the effectiveness of a teaching aid frequently depends upon its visibility and/or audibility, as the case may be. Excellent models and demonstrations are often only partially successful in contributing to learning because they are presented without sufficient regard for the importance of clear and full visibility or satisfactory audibility.

The presentation of even such "simple" aids as a series of charts, models, or flash cards requires skillful integration of the aid into the lesson in progress. Such integration is seen at a highly professional level in such programs as that of Walt Disney and the Bell Telephone Company films on health and science in which audiovisual aids of a wide variety—ranging from animated cartoons to sound amplifiers (for example, for amplifying the heartbeat), scientific and medical instruments, mechanical and other demonstrations, films of microscopic life and bodily functions—are brought into play at precisely the time needed to advance the "lesson" in progress from one point to the next. Similarly, educational television being utilized by some departments of education is bringing audio-visual resources of unprecedented kind into many classrooms, although, as of the present writing, health teaching has by no means received the attention that its importance to human welfare would seem to justify. At any rate, health teaching can benefit greatly from the techniques observed even though comparable resources are not at present available to those who endeavor to teach health in schools.

A group of outstanding teachers was interviewed by one of the present authors in order to discuss some of the teaching techniques which seemed to make their teaching especially effective. Special attention to techniques of presentation seemed to loom as major factors in successful teaching in the thinking of these people. One of these teachers pointed out that although the pupils do not realize it, each lesson is a "production." In such planned "productions," attention of the class might be shifted from chalkboard work (vocabulary, names, key points, and diagrams), to models, specimens, charts or flannel boards, or demonstrations, to activities (for example, question-and-answer sequences, discussions, application of first aid, taking the pulse before and after exercise), to films or recordings, if pertinent and available.

It may reasonably be protested that the teacher simply does not have time for elaborate productions or presentation of the kind indicated above. In response, two points need be made, even though the present authors are fully aware of the innumerable demands made upon the time of elementary teachers and of the limited resources made available to some: (1) Few teaching areas are so richly endowed with varieties of teaching aids as health education. As may be seen from the Appendix, "Sources of Teaching Materials," almost limitless resources are available even though very little if any money may be on hand for purchasing health teaching aids. (2) It is obvious that an entire series of high-quality health teaching lessons or "productions" cannot be expected to appear in the first year of health teaching. Such a series can, however, be expected over a period of time—if the teacher develops what units or lessons he can one year and preserves them for use (with desired modifications) the next year. *Over a period of time,* such a plan makes possible the accumulation of an entire series of well-planned units and lessons. Of course, the key point is that good teaching plans and materials developed one year should be carefully preserved for use in the future.

Follow-Up

Follow-up in teaching, like follow-through in throwing a ball or swinging a golf club, has to do with the effective completion of a process. The valuable concepts conveyed by the teaching aid may now be "nailed down" by means of such things as reviews, discussions, and question-and-answer sequences designed to explore its

meaning to the pupils. Moreover, the basic question of how to proceed needs to be raised. In other words, now that the concept is
learned, how is it to be used? It is true that a great many children
are simply not in a position to translate newly acquired knowledge
immediately into altered modes of living. For example, the established dietary practices of a family may not be readily changed by a
pupil, nor may family practices that are not conducive to physical
fitness or mental health be easily changed, regardless of the value
or soundness of a pupil's newly acquired insights. Environmental
health factors such as air pollution, radiation, pesticides, and food
additives may be beyond the child's—or any individual's—control.
Still, newly learned concepts may be placed in life context in such
a way that they may be used when the opportunity arises. Thus,
even though a child cannot appreciably alter the diet available at
home, he can learn the basic elements in a well-balanced diet; participate in the planning of meals for a sports training program, a
make-believe (or real) camping trip, or day camp experience; demonstrate the ability to select well-balanced meals in a real or classroom
cafeteria; or analyze the food offering of the school cafeteria or of
paper pin-up plates on the bulletin board. In relation to mental
health, the elementary school child can participate in the analyzing
of human behavior portrayed in books, films, television, or tape recordings, not to mention such possibilities as classroom sociodramas and situations in games, in order to identify modes of speech
and action that are conducive to good or poor mental health and
social adjustment. In other words, even though more healthful behavior cannot always be the immediate outcome of health teaching,
understanding of the uses of knowledge and putting it to work even
on a minor scale can help to insure gradual movement in the direction of healthful living. Following-up in relation to health teaching
aids can improve the chances that behavior relative to health will
improve when the opportunity arises.

Another aspect of follow-up has to do with the teacher's evaluation of the teaching aid on the basis of its effectiveness. For future
reference, it is useful to know the inadequacies, special merits, problems, and teaching techniques that worked especially well in relation to the teaching aid. As has already been pointed out, it is
economical in terms of time and effort if teaching aids—such as
models, charts, displays, and so on—which have been pointed out, or

made or developed are stored for future use when the same or similar lessons are to be taught again.

READING MATERIAL, FILMS, TELEVISION, RADIO, AND RECORDINGS

As was pointed out, these teaching aids are discussed as a group because of their very considerable self-teaching capabilities, which the teacher may direct and utilize in the health education process.

Reading Material

Suitable textbooks are of great importance in health teaching. A number of publishers provide a series of health texts, one for each grade. The advisability of utilizing a health series is fairly obvious. To illustrate, not only does the health series provide a book for each grade of the elementary school, but also the series is designed presumably to "mesh in" with the total educative process of the elementary school. For example, the vocabulary and concepts are selected on the basis of suitability for the grade level.[4] Pictures are used supportively as aids to understanding; and scientific sophistication in terms of vocabulary, concepts, illustrations, demonstrations, class activities, and so on, keeps pace with the sophistication of other scientifically oriented subjects.

Of prime importance in a health series is the way that health teaching is presented as a subject-matter area in its own right; like other subjects it should move in logical steps from the simple to the increasingly complex and build up in terms of sequences of concepts. In other words, health education does not—or at least should not— stand still, monotonously barking the same sterile health rules, grade after grade, to the distress of pupils who have heard it all before.

Newspapers and popular magazines offer a rich source of health information, some of which can be particularly valuable in the upper elementary grades. These may frequently be used effectively to supplement available textbooks. For example, children can be encouraged to develop health scrapbooks from their readings in

4 See Joan W. Blos's critical discussion of children's books, "The Words in Picture Books," *Saturday Review*, November 7, 1959.

newspapers and magazines and thereby cultivate an interest in this expanding and exciting field. However, it must always be borne in mind that most newspaper reporters and magazine writers are neither trained scientists nor health educators, and care must be taken to evaluate information from these sources cautiously.

In a similar way, newspaper and magazine advertising that is associated in some way with health can be of considerable value in health teaching. That is, these sources contain numerous colorful pictures which can be used as cutouts for the constructing of displays, scrapbooks, and other teaching aids. A favorite utilization of such pictures is to prepare a well-balanced meal using various pictures of foods taken from advertisements. Ideas may also be developed in relation to physical fitness, recreational sports, grooming, and so on. Here again, however, great caution is needed to avoid having pupils take what they find in advertising at face value—even though the statements are very convincing and the pictures appealing. On the other hand, the thoughtful teacher can turn this situation to advantage by helping children develop the practice of viewing all advertising critically and understanding quite clearly the motives of the advertisers. For example, at present there is every indication that smoking is particularly dangerous for those who begin it at an early age. Teachers of the young can perform a great service by bringing them to understand the tobacco advertisements and their clever appeals.

There are numerous other types of reading material available to elementary school teachers, and much of this is free or inexpensive. The Appendix may be examined for a list of some of these aids.

Motion Pictures and Other Films

During the last few years, a large number of films have been developed which bear directly or indirectly on health subjects. These range from those dealing with nutrition to others dealing with sex education. At the present time, the majority of these films are perhaps more suitable for the secondary school level than for the elementary grades. A few, however, have been designed for the primary grades, and more still have been prepared for the intermediate level. One of the first things that the teacher who is preparing to teach health should do is to contact all available film sources. Frequently, the school itself will have designated a person to be in charge of audio-visual aids and the catalogues in which various organizations list their film offerings. City, county, and state education departments and health departments should be considered as likely sources for films, and usually they provide listings of their offerings. In some instances, the major film resource is a local university.

In any event, every effort should be made to preview films which seem suitable for the elementary level. A great many teachers find it useful to keep a card file of films that they have previewed and/or used. Notations on the cards should include information as to the coverage of each film, its suitability for a particular grade level, its new vocabulary, major points made, and technical quality (that is, whether the film gives evidence of high-quality production, good sound, and so on). Such a card file makes refreshing the mind a simple matter when considering whether or not to use a film, and how best to incorporate it into a health teaching unit.

Other types of film devices, such as film strips and slides, are usually available from the same sources as the motion pictures, and have certain advantages. Projection equipment is relatively light and inexpensive, and film strips, especially, are readily stored and inexpensive to mail. Moreover, although moving pictures have obvious advantages of their own, they have the disadvantage that the teacher and pupils cannot ordinarily comment on the picture while it is being shown. Still pictures, on the other hand, give the class an opportunity to deal with one picture as long as seems desirable.

It is common practice for teachers to obtain clearance from their principals before showing any particular film. The young teacher needs to be particularly careful on this point because, unwittingly, established city or county school health policies may be violated. An example should make this clear. In recent years, there has been a tendency for the schools to assume increased amounts of responsibility for providing basic sex education. This is out of recognition of the fact that large numbers of parents are not qualified to present the basic information concerning human reproduction to their children in the home setting. As a result, audio-visual aids have been developed to assist the teacher in providing appropriate sex education. At the elementary level, teaching concerned with menstruation has taken the lead in this connection because of the obvious need of

10-, 11-, and 12-year-old girls for facts and wholesome attitudes concerning the topic. The serious teacher is likely to make every effort to provide needed instruction to girls in the interests of healthy psychophysical development. Unfortunately, however, in numerous individual schools and entire communities, this kind of teaching is still absolutely forbidden under all circumstances; and the showing of even such an innocuous film as Disney's *Story of Menstruation* would not be tolerated. The young or new teacher should apprise herself of the local attitudes and existing policies before undertaking such teaching. However, if one may judge by developments in recent years, attitudes relative to sex education are changing rapidly, and in time basic instruction on this subject is likely to become routine for both boys and girls.

Television

Television,[5] with its extraordinary potentialities for constructively or destructively influencing human attitudes, deserves special attention in relation to its possible role in health education. What is said here should be interpreted in light of the fact that the law under which all rights are granted by the Federal Communications Commission states quite clearly that all television must operate *with due regard to the public interest or in the public interest*. This law has commonly been ignored, but the value of television in public education generally is dependent in large measure upon it.

To begin with, commercial television is already a major medium for the propagandizing of health products. It is the most common form of advertising appearing on television. Some of this advertising is responsible; however, many of the claims are exaggerated, and some are absurd. Research has shown, nevertheless, that, regardless of what claims are made, they tend to be effective. The pupils who have been studied were found to consistently parrot the advertising claims associated with the various products.[6] The danger in this

5 For a survey of developments in "educational television," see F. Dunham, R. Lowdermilk and G. Broderick, *Television in Education*, U.S. Office of Education, Washington, D.C., 1957. Further information on educational television may be found in *Teaching by Television*, Ford Foundation Publication, May, 1959, and other publications listed in the chapter references.

6 Bernard Lowell, *An Investigation into the Role of Television Health Advertising and Its Relationship to Health Attitudes as Measured by a Sentence Completion Test*, Doctoral Dissertation, College Park, University of Maryland, 1962.

situation is that the advertisers are not *primarily* concerned with child health or the public health at large. That is not their business. Their primary concern is, obviously, sales. Considering the extreme importance of sound health education for human welfare and progress, this state of affairs seems comparable to having schools maintained *primarily* to raise money by selling books and lunches. The public is not receiving health education on anything like the scale it is receiving "product education" designed to condition its buying responses.

An immediate objective of health education which is stressed repeatedly in this chapter, and which has special application to television, is that pupils (and the public generally) must be taught to examine all advertising and propaganda with an eye to the motives of the program producers, and with awareness of which claims might be reasonable and verifiable and which might not. A major contribution that teachers can make in relation to all the mass media of communication is to help pupils to learn to subject all reporting and advertising to objective scrutiny, and to be skeptical of it. As increasing numbers of people behave in this way, higher standards of reporting and advertising may be looked for.

Television has found its way into the schools in two ways. A considerable number of stations have attempted to cooperate with local schools in such ways as advising them of coming programs related to school subjects, including health education. However, despite the commendable effort, without sound and informed educational orientation the stations can be of limited value—even though individual programs may be exceptional in their health educational value. Of far greater significance has been the growing tendency of school systems to acquire blocks of existing television station daytime hours so as to televise their own programs; some even set up their own television stations. Under direct education-department control, programs may be designed to be adjusted to specific grade levels and to serve as true *teaching aids*—presumably integral parts of a learning sequence. Utilizing qualified health educators, classroom teachers, and television technicians, such programs can prove of enormous value to both school health education and ultimately to the general public health.

Clearly, educational television is still in the early experimental stage of its development. It faces numerous problems of a technical and financial nature. However, the central problem of educational television appears to be closely related to a point emphasized earlier. That is, even with plenty of money and know-how, how are televised programs to be adjusted to individual classrooms where teachers are dealing with unique personalities and not just a "class of fourth graders"? At least one large school system has recently abandoned its rather extensive educational television program because this fundamental question did not then appear answerable. Educational television will not achieve its potential as a teaching aid until the problem is solved.

To date, health subjects have been far from prominent in the programs of educational television. This deficiency is surprising when one considers both the extreme importance of health education for human welfare, the richness and appeal of health subject matter, and the availability of visual aids related to health. Of the various subject-matter areas, health would seem to be unusually susceptible to televised presentation. Most teachers welcome assistance in their health teaching because they tend to be aware of the crucial role of education for healthful living—and of their own lack of adequate preparation in providing such education on a par with reading, arithmetic, and other basic skills. Unfortunately, health education television of a systematic kind is undetectable at present. (Of course, we hope at some future date to report that the foregoing statement is no longer true.)

It should be noted that in certain cities and counties some health teaching is done by way of educational television. For one example, in the Baltimore city schools, the Division of Health and Physical Education of the Department of Education has a regularly scheduled program during the school year which includes teaching related to physical fitness, an aspect of health education. In that city, the schedule of all television programs is distributed to the teachers of the city so that they may (1) select programs which will fit into their units of instruction and/or (2) adjust their teaching plans in such a way as to make utilization of the televised programs appropriate. However, fitness programs necessarily involve physical activity and are therefore of limited use in the classroom. Moreover, although physical fitness is basic to health, it is only an aspect of health; and it should not, therefore, be considered more than a step in the right direction. For another example, the Dade County, Florida, public schools are providing telecasts on health education, safety education, and driver education as part of their regular telecast schedule.

Radio

Much that was said of educational television applies also to educational radio. Obviously radio's potentialities as a teaching aid are fewer because it is exclusively audio rather than audio-visual. On the other hand, radio does have the advantage that program production is far less expensive and more simple, and in certain types of health teaching it may indeed be desirable to deal in purely verbal terms. To illustrate, learning objectives may include improving ability to follow verbal instructions, improving ability to analyze verbal material for its emotional appeal (for example, "tired blood," "sex appeal," "personality"), and so on. Moreover, certain kinds of programs could be made virtually as effective by radio as by television, and good radio programs have the further advantage that they lose nothing when transformed into tape recordings. Quiz shows, panel discussions, narratives, reviews of recent developments in the health field, and so on, can be adapted for use in health teaching in some grades at the elementary level.

A major use to which radio may be put in health education is the creation of mock radio programs by pupils. Many of the objectives of health education—acquiring and evaluating health knowledge, discussing ways in which human behavior may be brought more nearly into harmony with what is now known about human health, becoming critical of health propaganda, for instance—may be pursued in developing, presenting, and evaluating interesting radio health programs. In one especially effective radio "show" of this kind, fourth-grade children discussed the question, "How Can Children Improve Health and Safety Practices in Their Homes?" The pupils discussed an extensive variety of ways, and took into account the various problems involved when children attempt to teach their parents how things should be done in the home. Programs which require preparatory study and organization of information tend to be especially valuable.

As with the other mass media of communication, the advertising via radio of products related in some way to health provides numerous opportunities for critical analysis of advertising claims. (Advertising may be tape-recorded for evaluation in class.) Pupils may be taught to notice how repetition and colorful, emotionally charged words are utilized to establish favorable attitudes toward the products being presented. Lacking as it is in visual appeal, radio advertising offers a special opportunity to examine critically the techniques of exclusively verbal propaganda. A public trained to evaluate critically what it hears will, in time, force advertisers to more factual presentation of their products.

As in the case of television, if radio is to be used on a systematic basis in the schools, it needs to be brought under educational control, so that it may function properly as a teaching aid. The same considerations that tend to disqualify commercial television from serving as a teaching aid on a regular basis apply to commercial radio as well.

Recordings

Some recordings dealing with various aspects of health are available commercially or through industrial concerns, and several have been prepared to accompany film strips on some subjects, such as sex education. However, in the present discussion emphasis is placed upon the making of recordings by pupils and teachers for their own use in class.

The cost of recording instruments has doubtless been a major factor in their relatively small use in elementary classrooms. Still, they are available to teachers often enough to be seriously considered as aids in health teaching. In the present authors' experience, tape recorders have been available in some schools, but have almost never been used because their potentialities were not fully appreciated.

Recording instruments tend to be of great interest to children, and their use can have excellent incentive value in some aspects of health teaching. Radio and television programs prepared and "staged" by pupils can be tape-recorded for replaying and evaluation. Actual radio and television reporting and advertising can also be recorded for classroom analysis and discussion. As one of many possible examples, one teacher tape-recorded a variety of different weather reports and then used these as the basis for a fourth-grade lesson concerned with dressing properly for the weather and the avoidance of colds.

Suitable speeches and other programs can be recorded for subsequent playing in classrooms. Extremely interesting tapes have been made and presented in class by pupils and teachers who have interviewed various people concerned in some way with the health field. Thus, a fifth-grade boy served as reporter for his class and tape recorded his conversation with a well-known local coach on the subject of muscle building and food. Other tapes have involved conversations with dentists, physicians, nurses, and mental hygienists. It occurred to one teacher to record her butcher's hints on buying and tenderizing of meats. Clearly, innumerable opportunities of these general kinds exist.

It is highly recommended that when arranging sessions with specialists for recording, the specific needs, interests, and maturation level of the pupil "consumers" of the tapes be taken into account. Moreover, the specialists being interviewed need definite information as to the kind of audience for whom the recording is being made, its objectives, its status as to knowledge, and so on. Without information of this kind, the person being interviewed may feel quite helpless or may fail to provide the desired information because of his misunderstanding of just what is expected of him. Clearly, planning is needed before recording is undertaken. To illustrate, a pupil might start an interview by saying: "My fifth-grade class has been studying dental health. We have learned that foods are important for good teeth. Will you please tell us what foods are especially good for our teeth and what foods are not so good?' In like manner, the dental specialist or health educator may be asked to comment on the benefits and hazards of fluoridation, the use of hypnosis in dentistry, and so on. The point is that the person being interviewed is guided in such a way that he knows what is expected of him, the level of knowledge and sophistication of his audience, and so forth. For his part, the properly prepared interviewer is armed with a list of *specific* questions.

COMMON CLASSROOM TEACHING AIDS

Early in this chapter a second type of teaching aid was distinguished—that which is used by the teacher while actively engaged in teaching but which in no real sense, or only in a very limited way, takes over, even temporarily, as the "teacher." Aids of this kind are commonly made by the individual teacher and/or class. Several of this second type of aid will be discussed quite briefly, and some examples will be presented which are intended to stimulate thought as to how they might be developed and utilized in specific situations. Only those aids are mentioned which seem to have special value in health teaching; it is taken for granted that common but highly valuable aids such as chalk boards will be used routinely in health teaching, as in the teaching of other subjects. Readers are referred to standard books on audio-visual education and to other audio-visual publications for more detailed discussions of these and other teaching aids.

Bulletin Boards

A great variety of valuable bulletin board displays may be developed as aids in health teaching. These displays may contain pictures of various kinds, charts, graphs, specimens, and so on. They may be composed of relatively independent elements—such as a variety of health publications, including booklets, leaflets, and the like, intended to suggest the range of such literature. On the other hand, they may be composed of many elements which fit together in an interdependent manner—such as a world map identifying major centers of World Health Organization activity with strings extending out from these centers beyond the map to pictures depicting the kinds of work being done in each. (Incidentally, the World Health Organization's *News Letter* and its other publications are excellent sources for such pictures.)

As in other subject-matter areas, the bulletin board provides an excellent place for displaying pupil work, and their planning and preparation of bulletin boards can be an important aspect of virtually any unit of study. Here again, the individual child's work may be independent of the other work on the bulletin board, as in the case of pin-ups of colored paper pictures of well-balanced meals on paper plates. In contrast, pupils may develop a complete bulletin board display to express a single concept or series of concepts. For example, "physical fitness" may be portrayed as dependent upon nutrition, physical activity and recreation, and rest and sleep. Attractive pictures and/or art work may be used to portray these aspects of fitness.

In one class, lessons were concerned with the relationships of mental health and community recreation, and the pupils analyzed a typical community for its recreational potentialities. When the teacher raised the question of how their findings and ideas might best be shown, the pupils decided upon their bulletin board. A map of the community was placed in the center; and portions of it showing recreational possibilities were depicted in larger form on the remainder of the board. For example, school playgrounds, gymnasiums, and shop and craft rooms were shown; a group of back yards revealed how several families could cooperate to make net games, a golf putting area, bars, rings and swings, a basketball backstop, and horseshoes available to all; and a small wooded area was shown as it could be developed for picnics, overnight camp-outs, nature study, and woodcraft. One corner of the bulletin board contained a listing of resources to which, the pupils learned, the community might turn for guidance and assistance in the development of a recreation program. (These included the recreation and education departments, the local university, and the Scouts.) In connection with this same bulletin board display, a small committee of pupils made a model of some houses in the neighborhood and a little park, showing how each yard and the park could be developed for recreational purposes.

Models

In addition to models of the type mentioned above, teachers and their pupils can make numerous models related to both personal and community health. For example, many models of various body parts can be made of clay or plaster, cutaway or cross-section models of muscles, skin, bones, teeth, blood vessels, and nerves are helpful. Pieces of wood, hinges, cord, and rubber bands may be used to show how muscles contract and bring about movements of the body.

In recent years some excellent commercial models of the human body and its parts have become available. These can be very useful as health teaching aids. However, care should be taken to avoid two possible misuses of such models: (1) Pupil planning and participation in the making of models are valuable learning experiences and should not be lost because ready-made or put-together ones are obtainable. (2) In some instances it has been noted that excellent models tempt some teachers to devote health teaching time to the memorizing of anatomical parts. Half a century ago many pupils knew health and hygiene instruction as human anatomy and physiology. Although it is possible that some modern health textbooks have gone too far the other way in avoiding the presentation of basic structures and functions associated with healthful living, the fact remains that health education is not the same as anatomy and physiology—any more than it is the same as bacteriology, medicine, or nutrition.

Specimens

Teachers who attempt to tap their local resources for specimens are usually surprised at the wealth of material that is available. When presented with the idea of how specimens can be obtained which have an important health message, pupils are usually able to produce interesting and useful items.

Following are a few of the specimens produced by pupils as a result of planning in a single classroom. A pupil obtained a frozen calf heart from a butcher for dissection and examination in class. A pupil made a collection of old shoes and (1) showed patterns of wear on heels and soles that are indicative of good and poor body and foot mechanics, and (2) cut away tops and sides of some shoes in order to show how excessive wear and attaching a new sole over an old one produces a low spot in the shoe which tends to be damaging to the transverse arch. Several pupils obtained pulled teeth from dentists and were able to show various kinds of decay and deformity and to describe the likely causes of and preventive measures for these conditions. A pupil obtained the skeleton of a rattlesnake's head so as to show how the snake bites and how deep the fangs may be expected to penetrate the flesh.

It should perhaps again be stressed that these specimens, like the other audio-visual aids described, were utilized as functional parts of health learning experiences and were not merely "thrown in," without regard to the subject under study.

An example of an unfortunate misuse of a specimen will illustrate the need to evaluate them carefully and present them in such a way as to avoid the inaccurate and overly dramatic. One pupil obtained a preserved human heart which had become quite blackened. The man who provided this specimen attributed the blackness of the organ to its possessor's having been a heavy smoker. The heart represented an effort on the part of the lender to frighten the pupils away from smoking, and he was obviously more concerned with attacking smoking than with presenting factual information.

Exhibits

An exhibit is developed to tell a particular story and is, to a considerable degree, self-teaching. It is especially useful for summarizing in simple terms what may be a prolonged and/or complex process or situation. To be effective, an exhibit must reduce its subject to basic terms in a concise and interesting way; thus it tends to demand thought and imagination as well as knowledge on the part of those who develop it. Audio-visual applications in exhibits are limited only by the resources and ingenuity of their creators. That is, verbalizations (written and/or spoken), pictures, mobiles, models, specimens, and demonstrations are some of the aids which may be utilized in exhibits.

An example will show how an interesting exhibit may be used to communicate some basic concepts, as well as to provide an excellent learning experience for its creator. A sixth-grade class was studying certain aspects of community health, including some contrasting historical and cultural considerations. One committee took as its activity the creation of an exhibit having to do with the health and health beliefs of some southwest Indians. A panel on the left had to do with their food and its nutritional values, and some modern problems associated with soil debilitation. Dried corn, a picture of Indians grinding corn, and carefully lettered information were the main items of this panel. The center panel had to do with the physical and religious aspects of Indian life. Rain and snake dances and other ceremonial aspects of life and death were portrayed, and the written message pointed up certain parallels between primitive and modern concepts of psychosomatic relationships. The third panel depicted primitive ideas of injury, disease, and death. The pupils who developed this panel had access to the Smithsonian Institution in Washington, D.C., and other exceptional resources for study. Moreover, they were able to tape-record a statement from an anthropologist which could be played in association with the exhibit. However, the point is that these pupils utilized the resources available to them. When thought and imagination are stimulated, resources seem to have a way of taking care of themselves.

Flash Cards

In some situations, fast identification of an object may be crucial for safety. During World War II, it was learned that combat fliers frequently did not have time to identify enemy planes by the details of their shape. Rather they had to be able to distinguish friend from foe at a glance—just as most people distinguish one popular car from another at a glance instead of a point-by-point analysis. Pilots were then trained in aircraft recognition by flashing silhouette pictures of planes on a screen for fractions of a second; they soon became able to identify the planes shown merely as flicks.

For similar reasons some teachers make a point of preparing classes for certain hazards by means of flash cards, a quick identification technique. Where snakes are common, cards showing the typical venomous and nonvenomous head and neck structures may be used. Poisonous and nonpoisonous leaves (for example, poison ivy versus ordinary ivy) may also be contrasted, especially in those areas where poisonous plants are a threat.

Flash cards may also be used when pupil alertness to key points is being tested. For example, "What is the matter with this picture?" cards can show properly and improperly proportioned meals; bicyclists behaving safely and dangerously; pedestrians crossing streets correctly and incorrectly; games being played in safe and dangerous places and ways; sports being played safely and unsafely (for example, tackle football being played without proper uniforms and on sand lots, or rough games being played on crowded playgrounds or on ice where recreational skating is taking place); clothing that is and is not suited to the weather; tools being correctly and incorrectly used (for instance, knives, axes, saws); and so on.

(In connection with the examples having to do with safety, it is urged that teachers avoid "overteaching." Teachers, like parents, can easily become so concerned with the safety of their charges that their prescriptions for safe behavior become unrealistic, especially perhaps for little boys. It is not possible to make life entirely safe, and certainly if all recreational sports and games which involve an element of danger were discarded, virtually all such activities would have to be eliminated. The point is that reasonable precautions should be taken so as to reduce hazards to a minimum without unduly restricting or intimidating children and youth.)

Adhering Boards

Adhering boards offer many excellent possibilities as teaching aids in health education.[7] Flannel and felt boards may be made easily by tacking or gluing flannel or felt over light plywood or other suitable material. These devices are well adapted to pupil as well as teacher use.

Paper cutouts backed with light sandpaper will adhere to the flannel boards. However, flannel or felt cutouts have certain advantages, both in terms of durability and the fact that one cutout can be built up on top of others, thus showing how structures fit together. For example, one teacher likes to begin his visual health unit by building up a representation of the human eye, a structure at a time. The parts are in different colors so as to stand out clearly. Of course, other parts of the body can also be presented in this way.

Adhering boards provide the special advantage that the cutouts are movable and can be quite large. The basic pattern of a body region, a playground, or an intersection can be set up and parts and objects can be added as desired. For example, in a physical fitness unit, a fifth- or sixth-grade teacher may add muscle groups to a skeleton or selected skeletal parts in the course of showing how one set of muscles moves an arm or leg one way and the other set the opposite way. In the course of learning how the muscles grow, pupils may be asked to select and add flannel cutouts to skeletal parts to show the effects of specific exercises upon muscular development. Charts and graphs on a wide range of subjects may be constructed of flannel and serve as interesting teaching aids. Primary grade children may select flannel representations of foods to portray the elements of a balanced diet.

Flannel or felt boards may serve as useful evaluation devices in a variety of ways. Of several cutouts, children may be asked to select the correct one to add to the board. For example, such questions

[7] Flannel or felt boards with folding stands may be purchased from several companies, including: Story-O-Graph, P.O. Box 145-M, Pasadena 16, Calif.; Oravisual Co., 321 15th Ave. S., St. Petersburg, Fla.; E. J. Blosser Co., 2239 Oros St., Los Angeles, Calif.

as the following may be raised to determine whether the correct cut-out(s) will be added:

What basic food is lacking from this meal?
What muscle will this movement improve?
Where should the bicyclist go in this traffic situation?
What would be a good place on our play area to set up a soccer field?
In what position should injured persons be placed for first aid?

A sheet of metal and objects with magnets glued to their backs or bases provide useful teaching aids for many situations. Boards of this type have been used especially to portray traffic and sport situations.

ADDITIONAL TEACHING AIDS AND PUPIL PROJECTS

In addition to the teaching aids discussed in some detail in this chapter, the following aids and projects should be considered for use in elementary school health teaching. Numerous variations and applications will be conceived by the thoughtful teacher and by pupils invited to help with their ideas.

Teaching Machines

In recent years "teaching machines"[8] have been developed which free the teacher from certain routine instructional tasks and permit pupils to work at their own speeds. To the best of the present authors' knowledge aids of this kind have not as yet been utilized extensively in health teaching; but many possibilities suggest themselves. Although some such machines are electrically operated and quite complex, relatively simple ones may be developed which would be useful in some health teaching. One such device, which would be usable in virtually any subject-matter field, presents a question in one "window" (a slit in a box). The pupil writes his answer beside the question and then pushes a lever. The lever

[8] Interested readers who may wish to experiment with teaching machines should consult A. A. Lumsdaine and R. Glaser, eds., *Teaching Machines and Programmed Learning: A Source Book,* Washington, D.C., National Education Association, 1960.

action moves his answer up to the next window and simultaneously moves the correct answer up into view beside his.

Field Trips

Words and imagination sometimes become divorced from reality to the extent that the child is confused as to which is which. Samuel Johnson once commented: "The use of travelling is to regulate imagination by reality, and, instead of thinking how things may be, to see them as they really are." A number of studies have been reported which tend to substantiate the subjective opinions of health educators regarding the value of field trips as an effective medium for learning (for example, see the chapter references by Curtis and Josephson). Of course, the improvements noted in these articles did not "just happen"; the teachers handled the situations with these kinds of objectives in mind.

Numerous opportunities exist for field trips—so as to see things "as they really are." Teachers should carefully evaluate their school areas for their health field-trip possibilities. Moreover, they should familiarize themselves with their school's policies and procedures relative to transporting large and small groups during school hours.

Special thought should be given to the general principles for using teaching aids that were suggested earlier in this chapter. That is, pupils should be prepared for the experience in advance, and should be helped to notice the significant elements in what they see; further, follow-up activities should help to "nail down" the meaning and uses of the experience.

Demonstrations

Here again, possibilities are limited only by the imaginations of teachers and pupils. Some demonstrations may be noted in the chapter of this book that is concerned with integrating health and science teaching; others are suggested in the references on health teaching found at the end of this chapter.

In connection with demonstrations, the teacher needs to give special thought to such considerations as: Will it work as planned? Can it be seen by the class? Does it make the point or points it is intended to make? Does it accurately portray a process or function? In the case of such items as (5) to (9) below, pupils may work in pairs to perform the experiments, following the teacher's demonstration.

A few examples of health and safety demonstrations or laboratory problems may stimulate thought:

1. Effect of a shoulder harness device on a driver model brought to a sudden stop.
2. Effect of running muddy water through a sand purifying system.
3. Effect of refrigeration and nonrefrigeration on various foods.
4. The functioning of various body parts, such as the lungs and eyes.
5. The correct utilization of techniques such as those in first aid and artificial respiration.
6. Basic procedures involved in medical and dental examinations.
7. Effects of different amounts of exercise upon pulse rate and respiration rate.
8. Correct body mechanics when sitting, walking, running, throwing, swimming, and so on.
9. The operation of body reflexes such as the knee jerk, when the knee is struck just below the patella (patellar reflex), and the reaction of the pupil of the eye to changes of light.

Small-Animal Experiments

Many individuals have considered their animal experiments to be of great value in health and science teaching,[9] and qualified individuals are certainly encouraged to conduct animal experiments in the interests of such teaching. For example, experiments of this kind can be very effective in nutrition and growth studies and in naturalistic observation of various phases of reproduction. However, it must be admitted that animal experiments are not a widespread practice because of technical problems related to research methodology and animal care. Such problems should be carefully considered before animal experiments are initiated.

Health Plays

Health plays may be presented through any one of the various forms of dramatics: dramatic play, pantomime, informal drama-

[9] See the chapter references by Mullen and Grant as to the values of animal experiments, and those entitled "Care of Rats, Mice, and Guinea Pigs," and "Care and Management of Laboratory Animals," for information concerning matters of animal care.

tization, puppetry, and formal dramatization.[10] Plays can be developed around such ideas as how to improve health and safety practices, how to deal with emergency situations, and what to do and what not to do when someone becomes ill or injured under various conditions.

Interesting sociodramas may be acted out in relation to numerous aspects of living, including those dealing with stressful situations. The key to this type of acting is a loose structuring of the particular situation under consideration and freedom of the individual to act spontaneously in accordance with the meaning that situation holds for him. Commonplace occurrences such as meals can furnish the basis for attitudes and health. "Playing" doctor, dentist, nurse, or scientist can be used as a valuable learning experience, and such play can also provide valuable insights as to just how children perceive such people and why.

Slogans

Catchy slogans which are useful in making a point may be created by pupils and teachers. For example, a teacher drew a cartoon of one child walking down steps, while another, obviously rushing, was shown in a ridiculous fall. Pupils added the slogan-caption, "People in the know—go slow!" In some schools contests have been held to select "best slogans," and these in turn have served as topics for poster-illustrating contests.

Notebooks and Scrapbooks

These may be developed regarding health generally or they may be specific to a particular area of interest. Articles and pictures from newspapers and magazines may be scrutinized for their reasonableness. Advertisements may be examined for the way in which words and pictures are used to make unknown products appear very attractive.

[10] A number of ideas in this listing were borrowed from a paper provided in the Elementary School Health Section of the American Association for Health, Physical Education and Recreation by Robert F. Adams, Donald Andersen, and Elaine Casteline (Miami Beach, Fla., 1960). These Dade County, Florida, teachers report a widespread use of pupil projects in health teaching throughout the elementary schools of that county. The reader is also referred to Chapter 16, "Integration of Health and Creative Expression."

Photographs

Some elementary school children take an interest in photography, and they may be encouraged to make pictures related to health subjects. Moreover, incentive is lent to the carrying out of many class projects (for example, bulletin boards, exhibits, demonstrations) if pupils know that their work will be preserved in pictures.

Cartoon Strips

The popularity of this medium can be capitalized upon by obtaining cartoon strips concerned with health from commercial concerns, or developing them in class. However, care should be taken that the cartoon strips make some worthwhile point and are not merely for entertainment purposes. Care should also be taken that the concepts presented are accurate and not lost in the humor of the strip.

Health Parades

Some teachers have found health parades to be an excellent summary activity for the presentation of certain individual and group projects to a class or before larger groups.

Health Clubs

Health clubs have been set up to study aspects of health and fitness that are of special interest to individuals. Notebooks and scrapbooks may be developed, and the status of various health areas may occasionally be summarized for other pupils. Some writers have reported that pupil health clubs have been very effective in helping to solve school health problems.[11]

Puppets

Children commonly take a great interest in puppets and other figures which can be manipulated manually. These may be used

[11] See two articles that have appeared in the *Health Education Journal of the Los Angeles City Schools*—those by Douglas and Proul in the chapter reference list.

creatively in the presenting of stories concerned with many phases of health, fitness, and safety.[12]

REFERENCES

Babcock, D. D., "The Teacher, TV and Teaching Machines," *National Education Association Journal,* May, 1960.

"Care and Management of Laboratory Animals," Department of the Army and Air Force, Washington 25, D.C., May, 1958.

Curtis, D. K., "The Contributions of the Excursion to Understanding," *Journal of Education Research,* November, 1944.

Dale, E., *Audio-Visual Methods in Teaching,* New York, Dryden, 1954.

Douglas, E. G., H. Strauss, and H. C. Putnam, "Health Club Tackles School Health Problems," *Health Education Journal of the Los Angeles City Schools,* March, 1960.

Dunham, F., R. Lowdermilk, and G. Broderick, "Television in Education," Washington, D.C., U.S. Office of Education, 1957.

Evry, Hall, "TV Murder Causes Bad Dreams," *Child Development Abstracts and Bibliography,* February, April, 1952.

Fulton, W. R., and A. W. White, "What Constitutes Teacher Competence in Audio-Visual Communication?" *Phi Delta Kappan,* January, 1959.

Gable, Marthe A., "The Viewer's Views on Classroom TV," *Child Development Abstracts and Bibliography,* February–April, 1952.

Goldsenson, Robert M., "How to Get the Best Out of Television," *Parent's Magazine,* November, 1956.

Grant, F., "The Use of Animals in Science Units for Fifth Grade Pupils," *School Science and Mathematics,* May, 1948.

Haas, K. B., and H. G. Packer, *Preparation and Use of Audio-Visual Aids,* 3rd ed., New York, Prentice-Hall, 1955.

Harnett, A. L., and J. H. Shaw, *Effective School Health Education,* New York, Appleton-Century-Crofts, 1959.

How to Conduct a Rat-Feeding Experiment, Wheat Flour Institute, 309 W. Jackson Blvd., Chicago 6, Ill.

Irwin, L. W., J. H. Humphrey, and W. R. Johnson, *Methods and Materials in School Health Education,* St. Louis, Mosby Co., 1956.

Josephson, R. A., *A Study of the Value of Field Trips for the Teaching of Natural History in the First Grade Curriculum of the Fox Point–Bayside School, Fox Point, Wisconsin,* Master's Essay, Ithaca, N.Y., Cornell University, 1952.

[12] Refer also to Chapter 16.

Mullen, R. F., "An Analysis of the Mental Reactions of Children at Different Grade Levels to Certain Living Animals," *Science Education*, December, 1939.

Naumann, C. E., *A Comparative Study of the Semantic Reactions of Selected Students to "Loaded" Words and Phrases Related to Health*, Master's Thesis, College Park, University of Maryland, 1961.

Proul, R., and M. Basil, "Rockdale School Health Club," *Health Education Journal of the Los Angeles City Schools*, November, 1955.

Sands, L. B., *Audio-Visual Procedures in Teaching*, New York, Ronald, 1956.

Schneider, R. E., *Methods and Materials of Health Education*, Philadelphia, Saunders, 1958.

Seldes, G., "The Bold Concept," *Saturday Review*, May 28, 1960.

Teaching by Television, Ford Foundation Publication, May, 1959, p. 1–15, 46–61, 70.

Wagner, Guy, "Instructional Materials," *Education*, January, 1957.

Ward, Pearl L., "Quality of Children's Books," *Saturday Review*, December 26, 1959.

Willey, R. D., and H. A. Young, *Radio in Elementary Education*, Boston, Heath, 1948.

Willgoose, C. E., *Health Education in the Elementary School*, Philadelphia, Saunders, 1959.

INTEGRATION OF HEALTH AND ARITHMETIC

1 *Which computational skills are encountered in the daily health experiences of the pupils?*

2 *What are some of the arithmetic concepts that are inherent in the daily health experiences of the pupils?*

3 *How can arithmetic be used to develop health concepts?*

4 *Which health activities provide experiences for the pupils to use arithmetic in a functional way?*

5 *What are some of the arithmetic concepts needed by the pupils in order to understand the health concepts in units for a particular grade?*

Elementary education is concerned with the achievement of the individual in all areas of his growth and development. The elementary school pupil needs to acquire proficiency in the skills of communicating through the language arts. He also needs skills in communicating through listening, speaking, reading, and writing in quantitative situations involving numbers. Arithmetic, as one of the traditional "three R's" continues to be an essential area of learning in the elementary school. The child encounters daily situations, both in school and out, that require quantitative thinking. In the teaching of arithmetic, the major objectives tend to center around developing the ability to think precisely, to reason logically, to judge soundly, and to solve problems accurately. In other words, it is hoped that the child will acquire computational skills in order to meet effectively, and with confidence, the quantitative aspects of daily living.

With the present emphasis on arithmetic as a mental process involving the ability to think quantitatively, the way a pupil learns arithmetic can affect his mathematical competency as well as his total well-being—mentally, socially, physically, and emotionally. Research in arithmetic has contributed much knowledge upon which to base teaching procedures and grade placement of content. There seems to be rather common agreement that if the objectives are to be realized, the teaching procedures should be such that the pupil can derive meanings and develop concepts for himself. To be meaningful, the teaching of arithmetic should bring into account the pupil's experiences, for when a child understands the applications of arithmetic he is more apt to think with numbers.

Health and arithmetic tend to be closely related in a number of significant respects. Planning for the teaching of health and arithmetic involves certain considerations. Some of these include the following:

1. Health activities provide practical experiences for pupils to have recurring and varied contacts with the fundamental ideas and processes of arithmetic through concrete application.
2. Arithmetic concepts are inherent in numerous health concepts.
3. Arithmetic serves as a suitable "tool" in developing health concepts.

Certain aspects of the pupil's total growth and development depend to some extent upon the joint understandings derived from health and arithmetic, which complement each other. The subsequent discussions in this chapter will be devoted to ways and means of integrating health and arithmetic.

HEALTH ACTIVITIES AID IN THE DEVELOPMENT OF ARITHMETIC CONCEPTS AND SKILLS

Arithmetic is largely a sequential program of learnings that develops through the growth of mathematical concepts based upon previous learnings. The importance and necessity of the pupil's acquiring meaningful mathematical education through the use of his experiences need to be underscored for emphasis. Thus, the classroom teacher, at each grade level, faces the daily necessity of promoting activities which are meaningful, applicable, and of genuine interest to the pupil. It is perhaps in this respect that health appears to be somewhat unique, because it includes many of the activities in which the child expresses himself as a dynamic human organism. For this reason, through the medium of health, innumerable activities which can serve to develop arithmetic concepts and to improve basic skills may be furnished.

When planning purposeful activities, the kinds of instructional materials and the sequence of their use should receive very careful attention in the arithmetic program. Consideration might well be given to materials relating to the various aspects of health which might serve to make the learning of arithmetic more meaningful to the pupils. The following example of a teaching procedure is intended to show how health activities and materials can be used to aid in the development of arithmetic concepts and skills.

AN EXAMPLE OF CONCEPT DEVELOPMENT OF THE NUMBER 2

(First grade lesson at the lower levels of concept development)

STEP 1. The pupils learn through *real* experiences that follow the natural sequence of language development; thus, the pupils begin the development of mathematical concepts at the "listening" and "speaking" levels of learning.

Teacher: Yesterday we made plans to take a walk. We talked about how we were going to observe the out-of-doors. Who can read these two sentences telling what we plan to do when we take our walk this afternoon?

Pupil: (reads from illustrated chart)
We will look with our two eyes.
We will listen with our two ears.

Teacher: You read well. Now, how many eyes will we use?
(*Note:* The pupils begin to develop the *concepts* of: (1) quantity or "how many," and (2) the cardinal *number 2*.)

Pupil: Two eyes.

Teacher: Let's point to our two eyes.
(Pupils point to their two eyes.)

Teacher: How many ears will we use?

Pupil: Two ears.

Teacher: Let's point to our two ears.
(Pupils point to their two ears.)

Teacher: For our arithmetic lesson today, we are going to learn about the number 2, and what it means. We have just pointed to our two eyes and two ears. Let's think about other parts of our body. As we do, I am going to ask you to do two things: first, find two other parts of the body that are alike; second, tell us what the two parts are.

(*Note:* The teacher introduces the *ordinal* numbers, *first* and *second,* as a part of the pupils' "listening" vocabulary.)

Pupil: I have *two* feet.

Teacher: Let's point to our two feet and count them—one, two.

(*Note:* Pupils point to their feet as they begin to develop the *concept of rational counting.*)

Teacher: Who can tell us about two other similar parts of the body?

Pupil: I have *two* hands.

Teacher: Let's point to our two hands and count them—one, two.

(*Note:* Under teacher guidance the pupils continue to develop the *concepts of quantity and rational counting,* as they identify two similar parts of the body.)

Pupil Responses:

I have *two* cheeks—one, *two.*
I have *two* lips—one, *two.*
I have *two* eyebrows—one, *two.*
I have *two* shoulders—one, *two.*
I have *two* arms—one, *two.*
I have *two* elbows—one, *two.*
I have *two* wrists—one, *two.*
I have *two* thumbs—one, *two.*
I have *two* hips—one, *two.*
I have *two* legs—one, *two.*
I have *two* knees—one, *two.*
I have *two* ankles—one, *two.*

STEP 2.   The pupils manipulate concrete objects involving the play aspects of health to develop and extend their concepts of the number 2. This activity is presented also at the "listening and speaking" levels.

Teacher: When we go outside to play this morning we can take turns playing with the different things I have for you on the table. As you come to the table I would like you to do two things: first, select *two* items that are alike to take outside, second, tell us how you can use them.

(*Note:* The teacher again presents the *ordinal* numbers, *first* and *second,* as a part of the pupil's listening vocabulary.)

Pupil: I have *two* bean bags. I will throw my *two* bean bags.

Teacher: To whom will you throw them?

Pupil: To Billy.

Teacher: If Billy and Jack play with the bean bags, how many children will be playing together?

Pupil: Two children.

Teacher: Billy and Jack, please stand so we can count you.

Pupils: One, two.

Teacher: Then for two things to play with we need two children. We are finding many ways to use the number 2, aren't we?
            (*Note:* Under teacher guidance, the pupils use the number 2 in their "speaking" vocabulary, as they manipulate the concrete objects. The building of a number vocabulary—little, big, short, long—proceeds concurrently with the development of the number concept.

Pupil responses:
            I have *two* jump ropes.
            Two of us can jump rope.
            I have *two* long jump ropes.
            Two of us can hold each rope.
            Two children can jump the *two* ropes.
            I have *two* wooden blocks.
            Two of us can make up a game to play with them.

Teacher: You may put the things that you will play with under your chairs until it is time for outdoor play.

STEP 3.   The pupils use semiconcrete objects (pictures) to extend their concepts of the number.

Teacher: On the chalkboard ledge there are colored pictures of things to eat. You may keep the pictures you select to paste in your own arithmetic scrapbook. As you come up I would like you to do two things: first, select two items of food that are alike, and second, tell us in a sentence what you have selected as you count the items.
            (*Note:* Again the teacher presents the *ordinal* numbers, *first* and *second,* as a part of the "listening" vocabulary.)

Pupil: I have *two* eggs—one, *two*.
          (*Note:* Under teacher guidance at this level of concept develop-
          ment the pupils use the number 2 to identify semiconcrete
          objects.)

Pupil responses:
          I have *two* oranges—one, *two*.
          I have *two* pears—one, *two*.
          I have *two* carrots—one, *two*.
          I have *two* potatoes—one, *two*.
          I have *two* slices of toast—one, *two*.
          I have *two* heads of lettuce—one, *two*.
          I have *two* bunches of celery—one, *two*.

Teacher: We have used the number 2 to talk about many things this
          morning.
          What are some of the ways we used the number 2?
          (*Note:* Teacher helps the pupils to arrive at generalizations,
          such as, "The number 2 can be used to mean two people, two
          parts of the body, two play things, two foods, and other things,
          too. The number 2 can be used to count.)

Teacher: Did you realize that so many things come in two's?
          Tomorrow we are going to learn even more about the number 2.

Teacher: It is now snack time. Today as usual you will be served milk,
          and how many cookies?

Pupil: Two cookies.

Teacher: Let's stand and go to wash our two hands before eating.

Pupil: I'm going to say, "Thank you two times when I take my two
          cookies."

STEP 4.   This usually involves the use of the abstract symbol in the
"reading and writing" stage of development (2—two). The use of the
arithmetic textbook can be introduced at this point for additional information and practice.

While reinforcing these concepts, other ideas will be introduced to
extend the meanings in the growth of mathematical concepts associated
with the number symbol 2, at the primary level, as well as at all higher
levels. As illustrated in the preceding lesson the resourceful teacher can
then turn to health for many meaningful activities to develop and
extend such concepts as:

1. *Cardinal* aspects of quantity and grouping, including the ability to
   associate a quantity with the corresponding number symbol.
   Example: two dots (. .) can be associated with the number symbol 2.

2. *Ordinal* or "place in a series" aspect of number.
   Example: Jack is *first;* Mary is *second.*

3. *Rote counting* in sequence involving learning to speak, read, and write the symbol and corresponding number name.
   Example: Counting in sequence by saying "1, 2, 3," and so on.
   Knowing which number *comes before 2* (sequence).
   Knowing which number *comes after 2* (sequence).
   Writing the number symbol and corresponding number name—2, two.

4. *Rational counting* involving a one-tone relationship.
   Example: Pointing to an object such as an apple and saying "one," pointing to the next apple and saying "two," and so on.

5. Development of a meaningful *arithmetical vocabulary* involving the number 2, such as:

   Number words: two, twice, pair, half, second, and so on.
   Example: Two is twice as big as 1, or 2:1 (ratio)
   Two is one-*half* of 4, or $2/4 = 1/2$ or $4 \div 2 = 2$
   "I have a *pair* of gloves."
   "I sit in the *second* seat."

   Placement: "two" can have many positions left and right of the decimal.
   Example: 2 tenths of 1 is 0.2
   2 *hundredths* of 1 is .02
   2 *ones* or 2
   2 *tens* or 20
   2 *hundreds* or 200
   2 *thousands* or 2000

   Inequality of numbers: more than, less than, the same as, and so on.
   Example: 2 is *more than* 1
   2 is *less than* 3
   1 and 1 are usually *the same as* 2 and 0

   Measurements: area, time, temperature, and the like, using the number 2
   Example: temperature (72°)—room
   weight (2 ounces, 2 pounds, and so on)—foods
   liquid measures (2 cups, 2 pints, and so on)—milk, water
   linear dimensions (2 inches, 2 feet, and so on)—clothing
   area (2 sq. inches, 2 sq. feet)—play and safety areas
   time (2 seconds, 2 minutes, 2 hours, and so on)—sleep, rest
   money (2 coins, 2 cents, 2 nickels, and so on)—cost of foods

6. *Mathematical concepts* that spiral to higher levels:
   Commutative Law: The order in which numbers are added does not affect the sum.

Example: 2 and 1 are 1 and 2

$$1 + 2 = 2 + 1$$
$$1 + 0 + 2 = 2 + 1 + 0$$

Commutative Law: The order in which numbers are multiplied does not affect the product.

Example: $2 \times 1 = 1 \times 2$

$$\begin{array}{cc} 2 & 1 \\ \times 1 & \times 2 \\ \hline 2 & 2 \end{array}$$

Associative Law: The order in which numbers are grouped does not affect the sum.

Example: $1 + (1 + 0) = (0 + 1) + 1$

Associative Law: The order in which numbers are grouped does not affect the product.

Example: $(1 \times 0) \times 2 = 1 \times (0 \times 2)$

Distributive Law: To multiply an indicated sum by a number, each addend must be multiplied by that number.

Example: $2 (1 + 0) = (2 \times 1) + (2 \times 0)$

Identity Law of Addition: Adding zero to a number does not change the number.

Example: $2 + 0 = 2$

Two and zero are two.

Identity Law of Multiplication: Multiplying a number by 1 does not change the number.

Example: $1 \times 2 = 2$

7. *Two dimensions of a plane.* Illustrations are limited for the most part to *two* dimensions.

8. *Square root.* In finding a square root, 2 is the index of the radical.

9. *Equations.* An equation is an algebraic expression in which *two* quantities under certain conditions are equal.

10. *Base of the binary system.* The binary system uses 2 as a base. The binary system is used extensively in present-day high-speed computational machines.

The sequence of materials used in the preceding example follows a rather structured pattern: step 1, use of real experiences; step 2, use of concrete objects; step 3, use of semiconcrete objects; step 4, use of the abstract symbol. Steps 1 and 2 are at a low concept level and the experiences are at the "listening and speaking" stage of development. Step 4, using abstractions, is at the "reading and writing" stage of development. Arithmetic concepts started at the lowest level, as in the above example of the number 2, can continuously be expanded into more complex and difficult mathematical ideas.

It is hoped that the preceding discussion has served to identify a few of the numerous aspects of health, such as body parts, play activities, and foods, which could be used to give practice in basic number skills, as well as to develop and extend arithmetic concepts.

DEVELOPMENT OF ARITHMETIC CONCEPTS AND HEALTH CONCEPTS

As indicated, health activities can provide meaningful experiences to aid in the development of health concepts. On the other hand, health teaching, to accomplish its total objectives, must rely to a certain extent upon the effective use of arithmetic concepts and skills. From this point of view, the obvious necessity for the integration of health and arithmetic takes on added significance.

In many cases numerous arithmetic concepts are inherent in health concepts. When the teacher is aware of this it is more likely that a better development of *both* types of concepts will accrue. In planning for this integration the teacher should consider the suggested grade level of both the arithmetic and the health concepts. For purposes of selecting appropriate health content, the concepts used in this discussion are taken from those delineated in Chapter 9, "Health Teaching Content for the Various Grade Levels."

In arithmetic teaching, as in health, it is essential that basic mathematical concepts be developed and extended continuously through the entire mathematics curriculum from kindergarten through college. Thus, no one concept can be said to begin or end at any particular level in one's education. In this connection, research studies have been conducted over a period of years in an attempt to discover when most children can best be taught the various parts of arithmetic.

An examination of the concepts listed below should serve to illustrate some of the arithmetic concepts that are inherent in health teaching at the primary and upper elementary levels.

Health Concepts	Inherent Arithmetic Concepts

PRIMARY LEVEL

We drink water every day.	Liquid measurements.
Regular hours for going to bed and for getting up help us get the sleep we need.	Time involving minutes, hours, days of the week.
We should know our name, address, and telephone number.	Number sequence, ordinal numbers, cardinal numbers.
We care for our teeth by brushing them or rinsing our mouth after meals.	Rational counting, time involving minutes, hours, days.
We grow during the night as well as during the day. When weighed and measured regularly, we can check on how much we are growing.	Measurements of time, weight, length.
Milk helps us grow strong and healthy.	Vocabulary including "how much"; liquid measurements.
Some foods that help us grow strong and healthy are meats, fruits, and vegetables, milk and milk products, bread and cereals.	Grouping, counting, addition, measurements.
Our shoes should fit properly.	Whole numbers and fractions; dimensions and size relationships.
We should take good care of our baby teeth, so our permanent teeth will be strong and healthy.	Counting, addition, subtraction.
When we walk, stand, and sit correctly we help ourselves grow. Height and weight are measures of growth. Each boy and girl grows in his own way.	Measurements of height, length, time.
Our ears can be tested by a machine called an audiometer.	Reading numbers; vocabulary including "more than" and "less than."

HEALTH CONCEPTS	INHERENT ARITHMETIC CONCEPTS
The doctor uses a stethoscope to listen to the sounds our heart and lungs make. The sounds he hears help him to find out about our health.	Rational counting, combining into tens, addition with carrying.
A regular amount of sleep each night can make us lively and happy.	Time, involving minutes, hours, days of the week.
We have five senses that help us know about and enjoy life.	Rational counting, grouping.
When we take our pulse we feel the pressure of the blood as the heart sends it through the tubes of the body.	Rational counting; time, involving seconds and minutes; comparison of the number of heart beats per minute with the number of seconds per minute.

UPPER ELEMENTARY LEVEL

There are four groups of foods important to good health.	Grouping, circle graphs.
Sufficient sleep aids growth.	Measurements of time in whole numbers and fractions.
We should know how to call the fire department in case of an emergency.	Number sequence, comparison of ways to read numbers in a telephone book, on houses, in a story book.
Clothes help us maintain normal temperature.	Reading and writing numbers used on thermometers; decimals.
Changes in size are an important aspect of physical growth; we grow at different rates, in different ways, at different times.	Measurements, averages, fractions.
We have four kinds of teeth, each useful in a different way.	Addition, grouping, division involving partition.

Health Concepts	Inherent Arithmetic Concepts
We can help to care for our eyes by sitting a proper distance from a television or movie screen.	Measurements of length.
We can help to keep our schoolroom healthful by maintaining a room temperature of about 70°F.	Reading and writing numbers used on a thermometer; decimals; addition and subtraction.
First aid is different for different types of accidents.	Percentage of various types of accidents.
Vibrations of the vocal cords in the larynx make us able to speak.	Comparison of frequencies of different sound waves; comparison of speed of light to speed of sound.
When we are well, oral temperature remains at approximately 98.6° and rectal temperature at approximately 99.6°.	Use of decimal fractions.
Our framework consists of the head, neck, trunk, arms, and legs; the trunk consists of the chest and abdomen, which contain vital organs.	Counting, grouping, addition with carrying.
We are made up of millions of living cells which require food to grow, to repair themselves, and to produce energy and heat.	Multiples of millions, relationship of millions of cells to thousands, hundreds, and tens of cells.
The smallest part of us is a cell; we grow because cells divide to make new cells.	Comparison of sizes; fractions; multiplication.
The pituitary gland, located at the base of the brain, regulates our growth in height.	Measurement of growth.
Individual differences in height, weight, and build among children of the same age are to be expected.	Comparisons of size; relationships of length of arm spread to height.

HEALTH CONCEPTS	INHERENT ARITHMETIC CONCEPTS
The age which a person begins to grow tall, the way he grows, and the time he stops growing are individual matters.	Comparison of size of chest to hips and other parts; relationships of size of feet to height.
Our brain is made up of millions of nerve cells.	Multiples of millions; relationship of millions of cells to billions and trillions of cells.
Since no single food contains all essentials, our cells require a supply of the four basic elements daily.	Comparison of caloric count in foods; addition of caloric count of foods in daily diet; averaging of calories.
Physical activity increases the respiration rate and the rate of the heart.	Averaging rates; comparison of respiration rate and rate of heartbeat.
Physical activity conditions us and adds to our strength, endurance, and agility.	Recording measurements of strength.
A change in air pressure causes a new sensation in the ear due to changes in pressure on the eardrum.	Recording of air pressure; measurements of volume.

ARITHMETIC AS A "TOOL" IN DEVELOPING HEALTH CONCEPTS

The previous discussions give some indication of the extent to which arithmetic concepts are inherent in those of health. The development of these health concepts and others involving quantitative thinking are dependent to a large extent upon the pupils' ability to apply appropriate arithmetic concepts and to use the necessary basic number skills. A relatively large number of arithmetic activities for the primary and upper elementary levels are included in the following pages. It should be understood that the activities presented here by no means exhaust the possibilities. Teachers should use their own resourcefulness and ingenuity when planning arithmetic activities to develop and extend health concepts.

CONCEPTS	ACTIVITIES

PRIMARY LEVEL

Foods and Nutrition

Measurements—value (money); counting—rational.	Count the change needed for milk or the entire school lunch.
Measurements—value (money); multiplication.	Compute the cost of milk per pupil for a week, a month, 180 school days.
Counting—rational.	Count the number of times one chews a bite of bread before swallowing.
Measurements—linear.	Measure the length of the rows in the school vegetable garden; measure and mark the places in the rows to plant the vegetables.
Measurements—time (calendar).	Mark a calendar and compute the number of days needed for the germination of each of the various vegetable seeds to be used in the school or home garden.
Division—measurements (value of money).	Compute the cost per pupil for a class trip by bus to a bakery or dairy.
Measurements—time (seconds, minutes).	Have each pupil keep a record of the time it takes him to eat a full lunch from the cafeteria. Find the average amount of time.
Addition.	Prepare a point system which pupils might use to score themselves during lunch period.

How Many Points Can You Make at Lunch Time?

Food Selection	75
Milk	15
Fruit	15
Vegetables	15
Meat	15
Bread	15

CONCEPTS	ACTIVITIES
	Practices 25
	Hands washed 5
	Use of napkin 5
	Use of knife and
	fork 5
	Quiet, pleasant
	conversation 5
	Neat clean-up 5
	Total 100 points
Relationship.	Plan refreshments to serve parents after a health play, figure the amount of food needed (cookies per person and total number of cookies needed, also cup of orangeade per person and total number of cups needed); compute the total cost of food and paper napkins and cups; find the cost per pupil.
Measurements—volume (gill, pint, quart, gallon).	Compare the volume of the different types of containers in which milk is sold.
Counting—rational—quantity.	List a number of different kinds of fresh fruit available in the community food stores.
Measurement—time (hours).	Have pupils record on a clock the time of each meal; figure the lapse of time between meals.
Measurement—liquid.	Measure the average amount of drinking water required for good daily health; compute the amount of water consumed at mealtime, and the amount needed between meals.

Exercise and Physical Activity

Counting—rote and rational.	Jump rope and count the number of jumps that can be made without missing.

CONCEPTS	ACTIVITIES
Addition—carrying.	Give each pupil three chances to jump; add to find the total number of jumps.
Subtraction—borrowing.	Subtract the smaller number of times a pupil hops on one foot from the number of times he hops on the other.
Addition—carrying.	Give each pupil three turns at bouncing a ball; add to find the total number of times the ball was bounced.

	Anne	*Bill*
	12	15
	19	16
	14	17
	45	48

CONCEPTS	ACTIVITIES
Measurements—time (hours, minutes); subtraction.	Record the time of sunrise and sunset on various days of the year, such as June 22 and December 22 or March 22 and September 22; compare the number of hours of daylight; relate the number of hours of daylight to the number of hours available for out-of-door play in the sunlight.
Counting—rational; multiplication.	Count the number of breaths taken in one minute; find the number of breaths taken in one hour.

Sleep, Rest, Relaxation

CONCEPTS	ACTIVITIES
Counting—rational; addition and division.	While relaxing count the number of heartbeats in one minute, in two minutes, in three minutes; add; find the average per minute.

Safety

CONCEPTS	ACTIVITIES
Counting—rote and rational.	Count the number of street crossings on the way to school.

Concepts	Activities
Counting—rote and rational.	Count the number of street crossings on the way to school that have safety patrols, policemen, or crossing guards.
Counting—addition with carrying.	Count the number of pupils in the room who walk, ride on buses or in cars, or ride bicycles to school; add to get the total number of pupils in the room.
The number system.	Have each pupil copy his telephone number and bring it to school; make a class telephone directory; add the telephone number of the school and fire department to the directory; learn how to read and write telephone numbers.
The number system.	Have each pupil bring his home address to school; make a class address book; add the address of the school and fire department; learn how to read and write addresses.

Clothing

Concepts	Activities
Measurements—temperature.	Read an outdoor thermometer and record the temperature at regular intervals during the school day.
Measurements—temperature and time (noon, calendar); subtraction; counting—rational; fractions (½ month).	Keep a record of the noon temperature on a calendar for the month; arrange the temperature readings from highest to lowest to note degree differences, and median temperature.
Measurements—time (calendar); counting—rational; addition with carrying.	Use symbols such as a drawing of a cloud or the sun to record the weather on a monthly calendar; count to find number of days it

CONCEPTS	ACTIVITIES
	was cloudy, rainy, or sunny; add to find the total number of days for which the weather was recorded.
The number system.	Have pupils learn to read their shoe sizes for correct footwear.
The number system.	Have pupils learn to read their coat, shirt, or dress sizes for proper fitting.
Measurements—temperature.	Have pupils read outdoor thermometer to help in deciding appropriate wraps to wear.

The Human Organism, Its Structure, Function, and Care

Measurements—weight (lb.); subtraction; vocabulary development —pounds, lb.	Teach the pupils how to weigh themselves; have them keep an individual record of their weight by months. Subtract to find the gain in weight from month to month, and gain for the nine school months; learn the abbreviation for pounds.

Weight Record—Fred

May _____lb.	Dec. _____lb.
April _____lb.	Nov. _____lb.
Mar. _____lb.	Oct. _____lb.
Feb. _____lb.	Sept. _____lb.
Jan. _____lb.	

Measurement—linear (ft. in.); subtraction with number line; vocabulary development feet (ft.) inch (in.).	Teach the pupils to read a measuring tape; have them keep an individual record of their height by months; use a number line to find the increase in height during the nine school months; learn the abbreviations for feet and inches.

CONCEPTS   ACTIVITIES

Height Record—Mary

May   _____ft._____in.
Apr. _____ft._____in.
Mar. _____ft._____in.
Feb. _____ft._____in.
Jan. _____ft._____in.
Dec. _____ft._____in.
Nov. _____ft._____in.
Oct. _____ft._____in.
Sept. _____ft._____in.

Measurement—temperature.   Check the classroom thermometer at regular intervals during the day in order to maintain healthful classroom temperature.

Counting—rational.   Count the number of various parts of the body, such as joints, fingers, teeth, arms, legs, toes, and so on.

Quantity.   List by number the ways germs get from one person to another.

Comparisons.   Record and compare the number of times per day one cares for the body by brushing teeth, washing hands, combing hair, cleaning fingernails, and so on.

Health Services

Measurement—reading   time   on   Put a time schedule on the board
clock.   for the pupils to use for their school dental appointments.

Morning		*Afternoon*	
Paul	9:15	Sally	1:00
Nell	9:45	Ann	1:30
Frances	10:15	Leigh	2:00
Jane	10:45	Mary	2:30
Ralph	11:15		

Quantity.   List and number the health services available at school.

CONCEPTS	ACTIVITIES

Foods and Nutrition

CONCEPTS	ACTIVITIES
Comparison of prices.	Study the price lists of foods to determine the best buys.
Fractions.	Compute the cost of 1½ lb. grapes, 2¾ lb. oranges, and the like, needed for making a fresh fruit salad for the class.
Relationships.	Compute the savings on foods purchased in large cans as compared with small cans.
Measurements—liquids.	Find the number of liquid ounces of milk in a baby's bottle which holds one-half pint or one cup.
Measurements—temperature.	Learn to read a cooking thermometer and to note its uses.
Measurements—weight, liquid, number.	List fruits and vegetables sold by the pound; note other measures used to sell fruits and vegetables, such as pint, quart, peck, bushel, and dozen; compare the amount of lima beans in a pint with the amount that weighs one pound.
Measurements—liquids.	Find the number of gallons of milk one drinks in a month by drinking a quart a day; compute as denominate numbers.
Measurements—dry, liquid; fractions; multiplication.	Measure the ingredients needed to make bread; find the fractional and multiple parts of the recipe.
Addition; subtraction.	List the most common foods and the total calories for each; with the pupils, arrive at the approximate number of calories each pupil needs for the day; have the

CONCEPTS	ACTIVITIES
	pupils keep a daily record of their caloric intake from food at each meal and in-between snacks.
Comparisons; percentage.	Compare the percentages of butter-fat in the different types of milk.
Addition; multiplication; division; measurements—value (money).	Have each pupil prepare a week's marketing list for his family and include costs; find the average cost per person for the week's food.

Exercise and Physical Activity

Measurements—area of square (sq. ft.).	Mark off a softball diamond; find the area of the diamond; arrive at the formula $a = l \times w$ (area equals length times width).
Measurements—linear.	Measure the distance a pupil can throw a softball; record the distance in yards, feet, and inches.
Measurements—linear.	Measure the chest expansion before and after a deep breath.
Comparison.	Compare the number of heartbeats and pulse rate before and after vigorous exercise.
Measurements—linear.	Use a pedometer to learn the distance covered during a physical education period.

Sleep, Rest, Relaxation

Addition; division; comparison.	Find the average heartbeat per minute when relaxing; compare with number of heartbeats after vigorous exercise.
Fractions.	Compute the fraction of a total day spent in sleep, rest, and relaxation.
Percentage.	Compute the percentage of a day set aside for sleeping.

CONCEPTS	ACTIVITIES

Safety

Graphs—bar.	Construct a bar graph to show how pupils get to school; indicate the number of pupils who walk, ride buses, or ride bicycles.
Graphs—circle; fractions.	Construct a circle graph to show fraction of pupils who walk, ride buses, or ride bicycles to school.
Graphs—line; fractions.	Make a line graph to show distances pupils live from school; the graph might be sectioned into fractions of a mile and miles.
Graphs—picture.	Make a picture diagram of the school to show the number and place of the entrances and exits to the building.
Graphs—bar.	Have pupils prepare a graph to show where school accidents occurred last year; these areas might include on the playground, inside the school building, en route to and from school, and so on.

First Aid

Quantity.	List and number the items in the first-aid kit.
Measurements—liquid; linear; number.	Study instructions on items in the first-aid kit; record directions which include numbers to note importance of understanding arithmetic concepts in relation to the use of any external or internal medication.

Clothing

Measurements—temperature.	Learn to read centigrade and Fahrenheit thermometer; compute the temperature on a centigrade ther-

CONCEPTS	ACTIVITIES
	mometer to correspond with the same temperature on a Fahrenheit thermometer.
Percentage.	Compare the readings on wet and dry bulb thermometers; compute the relative humidity.
Measurements—value (money).	Have pupils prepare a plan for buying clothes; list items needed and their cost; compare the cost with quality and durability.

The Human Organism, Its Structure, Function and Care

CONCEPTS	ACTIVITIES
Measurements—area (sq. ft.); division.	Find the area of the classroom and determine the amount of floor space available per pupil.
Measurements—volume (cu. ft.).	Find the number of cubic feet in the classroom and determine amount of air space; inductively arrive at the formula, $v = l \times w \times h$ (volume equals length times width times height); find the average amount of air space per pupil.
Graphs—line; percentage; average.	Have each pupil make a line graph to show his weight as recorded on the first Monday of each month; figure the percentage of weight increase from October to May; find the average amount of weight gained each month.
Measurements—linear; percentage.	Have each pupil make a line graph to show his height in feet and inches as recorded on the first Monday of each month; figure the percentage of increase between October and May.

CONCEPTS	ACTIVITIES
Graphs—line.	Make a line graph to show height in feet and inches of the entire class when standing with backs against the wall; find the median height.
Graphs—line.	Make a line graph to show the height in feet and inches of the entire class when seated with backs against the wall; find the median height.
Graphs—line.	Make a line graph to show the length in feet and inches from wall to end of each pupil's heel when the class is seated with backs against the wall; find the median length.
Measurements—linear; comparisons; reading and interpreting graphs.	Compare the line graphs of the pupils when standing and seated to note the tallest pupil, the shortest pupil, the pupil with the longest legs, and so on.
Percentage; division; averages.	Keep a class attendance record for a month on a large chart; record the number of pupils absent daily and the causes; find the fractional part of the class present and absent each day; find the average daily attendance, and the percentage of class present and absent for the month; find the percentage of pupils absent because of common colds.
Graphs—circle.	Have the pupils make a circle graph to show the results of their recent vision tests.
Measurements—temperature.	Learn how to read a clinical thermometer to note the range of body temperature.

CONCEPTS	ACTIVITIES
Counting; grouping; quantity; addition; subtraction.	Make a chart to show the number of teeth you have:

	Baby Teeth	Permanent Teeth
Bicuspids for Crushing		
Cuspids for Tearing		
Incisors for Cutting		
Molars for Grinding		
Total		

Health Services

Graphs—line.	Make a time line showing the dates of such events in medical history as the: discovery of radium; discovery of X-ray; first use of diphtheria serum; discovery of Salk vaccine; first use of smallpox vaccination; first school of nursing; first use of microscope; first use of antiseptics; and so on.
Relationships.	By using the number of dentists and physicians in the community, and the most recent population census, have pupils determine how many people each dentist and physician must serve on an average, if everyone were to visit the dentist and physician twice

CONCEPTS	ACTIVITIES
	a year; determine the approximate number of patients a dentist or physician can see per day in order to arrive at the relationship between the medical and dental needs and services available.
Percentage.	Have pupils find the minimum percentage of butterfat required by law for milk and ice cream sold in the state.

REFERENCES

Grossnickle, Foster E., and Leo J. Brueckner, *Discovering Meanings in Arithmetic,* Philadelphia, Winston, 1959.

Hollister, George E., and Agnes G. Gunderson, *Teaching Arithmetic in Grades I and II,* Boston, Heath, 1954.

Hunnicutt, C. W., and William J. Iverson, ed., *Research in the Three R's,* Part III, "The Third R," New York, Harper, 1958, pp. 351–429.

Morton, Robert L., *Helping Children Learn Arithmetic,* Morristown, N.J., Silver Burdett, 1960.

Mueller, Francis J., *Arithmetic: Its Structure and Concepts,* New York, Prentice-Hall, 1956.

National Council of Teachers of Mathematics, *The Growth of Mathematical Ideas,* Twenty-fourth Yearbook, Washington, D.C., The Council, 1959.

National Elementary School Principal, "Arithmetic in the Elementary Schools," Washington, D.C., National Education Association, October, 1959.

Spitzer, Herbert F., *Practical Classroom Procedures for Enriching Arithmetic,* St. Louis, Webster, 1956.

United States Department of Health, Education and Welfare, Office of Education, *How Children Use Arithmetic,* Washington, D.C., Government Printing Office, 1951.

Wheat, Harry G., *How to Teach Arithmetic,* Evanston, Ill., Row, Peterson, 1951.

INTEGRATION OF HEALTH AND LANGUAGE ARTS 12

1 *Why are skills involving the use of spoken and written language of vital importance to the health and well-being of the elementary school child?*

2 *How can effective listening be taught to aid the child in a better understanding of the multiplicity of present-day information pertaining to health?*

3 *Why is bibliotherapy considered an important part of the curriculum offerings for all children?*

4 *How can practice in the skills needed for effective speaking aid the child in acquiring valid health information?*

5 *What opportunities for creative writing can purposeful health activities offer?*

In our present civilization, the use of spoken and written language constitutes the most effective means of communication known to man. Upon the effective use of language rests heavily the acquisition and maintenance of world peace, the aspirations of people in a democratic society, and indeed the destiny of mankind.

Not only can language affect the institutions of our present society, it can affect the total health of the individual within that society. Through the use of language, thoughts and feelings are transmitted, and ideas exchanged. This continuing process of transmission and exchange interacts upon the physical, mental, social, and emotional health of the individual. As a result of these daily experiences the individual emerges with feelings, attitudes, and values which influence his personal health and the health of others.

Classroom teachers realize fully the impact and significance of language in the lives of their pupils. In many cases they attempt to capitalize upon the many opportunities to integrate the teaching of language skills with the various subject-matter areas of the curriculum. In so doing, it is hoped that this integration will serve the purposes of (1) effective learning of the subject matter, and (2) greater proficiency in the functional use of language skills.

FACETS OF LANGUAGE

The language arts program in the elementary school involves the use of language as an instrument for learning. The child uses language in four ways—he *listens,* he *speaks,* he *reads,* and he *writes.*

Current educational terminology refers to *listening* and *reading* in such descriptive terms as the "receptive" phase, the "impressive" phase, or the "intake" aspect of communication. Concurrently, *speaking* and *writing* are described as the "expressive" phase, the "productive" phase, or the "outgoing" aspect. Thus, language has a dual nature. The child has two means—listening and reading—of receiving the thoughts and feelings of others, and two means—speaking and writing—of expressing his own thoughts and feelings to others.

Oral language consists of listening and speaking, while written language consists of reading and writing. Listening, speaking, reading, and writing are closely related each to the other, and represent a single pattern of interrelated, interdependent skills. This is probably best illustrated by the sequence in which the child usually acquires the language arts.

SEQUENCE OF LANGUAGE DEVELOPMENT

Language development tends to correspond to the child's individual growth pattern and to the quality and quantity of his language experiences. For the very young infant listening experiences come first. Later, he speaks the words he hears. Ordinarily, during the first year of school, he reads the words in sentences which he has previously heard and spoken. A short time later he writes the words. As an example, an infant listens to the word, *milk.* Later in his growth and development, he speaks the word; when he goes to school, he reads the word; and soon he writes it.

The order and sequence of language development influence teaching in the elementary school. Teaching in one facet of language arts tends to facilitate and reinforce the development of skills in the three other facets. For instance, while the infant is listening and speaking, he is really taking his first steps toward reading and writing. It is conceivable that a child can neither write nor read a sentence composed of words he does not speak, or to which he has not listened.

This functional relationship between the facets of listening, speaking, reading, and writing can be further emphasized through a discussion of each facet and its implications for teaching health.

Health and Listening

It was indicated in the previous discussion that:

1. Listening is an instrument of communication and learning.
2. Listening is one of the two facets of language for receiving the thoughts and feelings of others.
3. Listening precedes speaking, reading, and writing in the developmental language pattern for most children.
4. Listening skills are interrelated with the other language arts skills.

For purposes of placing *listening* in its proper perspective as an instrument for health teaching, a treatment of each of the above points is given.

1. *Listening is an instrument for communication and learning.* Based upon one's personal observations, it appears rather obvious that listening is the most widely used facet of language. Listening is used by people from infancy to old age. It is used during most waking moments of the day either by direct contact with people or by mass audio-communications, such as television, radio, stage, screen, and recordings. People of all races and creeds engage in listening during any hour of the day, any day of the year, and in most situations of life where man finds himself.

Through the ages man has apparently considered listening as an instrument for learning. The history of education records the lecture method as one of the earliest techniques for learning. Listening is used at every level of education in our culture from nursery school through the university.

It appears that listening, on its own merit, would be considered of such importance, that the teaching of listening skills would be concentrated upon at all levels of learning. It is interesting to note, however, that various research studies indicate quite the contrary to be true. For example, Duker[1] found in an examination of 124 curriculum bulletins in the language arts that listening was given an important place in only 51 of them, and was not mentioned at all in 36 of the bulletins.

2. *Listening is one of the two facets of language for receiving the thoughts and feelings of others.* The other facet is reading. In other words, the skills of listening and reading are similar in that both of these procedures are used by man (1) for securing information, (2) for enjoyment and appreciation, (3) for critical evaluation, and (4) for specific purposes as an individual or member of a group. Consequently, strengthening skills in listening involves strengthening those of reading, because one tends to complement the other.

Perhaps the most significant difference between listening and reading is one of stimuli. In listening, the stimulus is the spoken word, while in reading it is the written word. Wiksell elaborates on this by stating that:

Effective listening differs from effective reading because of certain factors in speaking which complicate the situation: loaded words, intensity, color, and inflections which influence the listener, as well as the effect of group experience. These factors demand keener perception or greater alertness at the moment than in the reading situation. And while there may be potentially many more possibilities for enjoyment of learning through listening than through reading, yet there are many more possibilities for misunderstanding or misinterpretation, more possibilities of being influenced adversely, and many more possibilities of being misled in listening than in reading.[2]

Listening requires comprehension at the rate set by the speaker. For instance, words are usually spoken once, giving the listener little time for reflection. Whenever attention wanders, portions of

[1] Sam Duker, "In an Age of Communication, Are We Listening?" *Educational Forum*, May, 1954, p. 405.
[2] Wesley Wiksell, "The Problem of Listening," *Quarterly Journal of Speech*, December, 1946.

what is being presented can be lost. These are tangible factors in effective listening which need to be recognized *by the pupil* and to be taken into account when thinking through what he has heard.

3. *Listening precedes speaking, reading, and writing in the developmental language pattern for most children.* Listening constitutes an essential medium for learning until the child can read. In this regard it should be understood that for effective listening, "telling" is not enough. The listener needs meanings for the language he hears. Language grows out of concepts which come from personal experiences. For example, the infant learns through firsthand experiences. He acquires these experiences through seeing, hearing, tasting, smelling, and feeling. By using his senses, he involves the nervous system and arrives at a concept which he associates with a particular object. Language begins with the word or label which he attaches to that object. Therefore, whenever the word which he attaches to the object is spoken, that word has meaning to him. By way of illustration, the infant sees, smells, hears, tastes, and feels the milk from his bottle. From these firsthand *experiences,* he builds a *concept* for which he has the meaningful word *milk* in his vocabulary.

Curriculum offerings in the primary grades should be purposely planned to give pupils numerous firsthand experiences from which to develop concepts, and thus to build a meaningful language vocabulary. As a concrete example, in a health unit on foods, second-grade pupils may examine and classify foods into groups of fruits, vegetables, meats, and breads and cereals. This experience helps the pupils to develop concepts concerning the distinguishing of gross characteristics of each food group. In so doing, the words *fruits, vegetables, meats, breads,* and *cereals* take on meanings for the individual pupil. Meaning is *not* found in the word; meaning comes through experiences, for concepts rarely go beyond the child's experience.

Building a meaningful vocabulary does not cease with one firsthand experience. Carrying the above example further, let us say that the next day the pupil handles many kinds of fruit. From this experience, he learns about kinds of fruit and differences between citrus fruits and fruits that grow on vines, bushes, and so on. Now his concept of foods has been broadened and extended, and the term *citrus fruit* is more likely to have meaning for him.

As has been mentioned previously, merely "telling" does not insure effective listening comprehension. Without firsthand experiences similar to those cited, the words *citrus fruits* could mean little or nothing to a child listening to a teacher read a story about citrus fruits grown in Florida.

At times teachers, in all good faith, think the pupils comprehend what she is saying, when actually the children may have only a vague idea, and can only "parrot" answers. Many times, the teacher who becomes discouraged because pupils have not remembered what she labored so hard to teach, might well look to the concepts or meanings which pupils have for the words she is using. The startling fact is that at times the most commonly used words may lack meaning for children.

A procedure for diagnosing the depth of concepts might include a series of questions which attempt to get at the meaning or lack of meaning a word might have for the pupil. The following conversation is an example of this procedure. (The conversation took place during a health lesson with fifth-grade pupils. The pupil in question was a boy with approximately 130 IQ on a group intelligence test. He was receiving reading instruction from a sixth-gade basal reader.)

Teacher: What is meant by the word *grain?* (Word was selected from a fifth-grade health lesson planned by the teacher on the food elements in bread.)

Pupil: Seeds are grain.
   (A meager concept.)

Teacher: What do you mean by seeds?
   (Teacher asks the pupil the meaning of the most important word used in his definition or description.)

Pupil: Seeds are little—uh, things—grains used to make bread.
   (This answer is merely a repetition of statement, "Seeds are grain," with little added to indicate the word *grain* has much meaning to him.)

Teacher: How is grain used to make bread?
   (Again teacher asks the meaning of the explanation given by the pupil.)

Pupil: Seeds are crushed and mixed with other ingredients to make bread.
   (This is another answer that indicates little meaning.)

Teacher: What part of the seed is crushed?
           (For the question, the teacher again rephrases the answer the
           pupil gives to "push" for meaning.)
Pupil: (Hesitantly) Inside, I think.
           (This answer indicates that the pupil has probably told much
           of what he knows about grain. His vocabulary also lacks the
           word used for the "inside of grain.")
Teacher: Is any other part of the grain used in bread?
           (Again, teacher uses the pupil's answer in phrasing her ques-
           tion.)
Pupil: (Guessing) Yes. No. I guess so.

By relying only on the above background information and without diagnosing the depth of meaning that the word *grain* had for
this pupil, the teacher might have readily assumed that his concepts were adequate. Further diagnosis revealed that this commonly
used word had little meaning for the other pupils. Because of this,
during the study of the food elements in bread, the teacher brought
in grains of wheat for the pupils to examine. These fifth-grade
pupils, in addition to listening, used the other facets of language
(speaking, reading, writing) to learn more about grains. Indeed,
pupils will comprehend and remember those words that are "full
of meaning" for them.

4. *Listening skills are interrelated with the other skills of communication.* Consequently, the effective teaching of listening skills
could mean better speaking, better reading, and better writing.
Just the opportunity to listen perhaps has little to offer from a
standpoint of teaching a child to listen effectively. Direct teaching
for planned systematic instruction in listening seems imperative if
pupils are to improve in speech, broaden vocabulary, and improve
in reading and writing. Rather than involving separate lessons, the
teaching of listening tends to be most effective when integrated with
the content areas of the curriculum, including health teaching.

Listening Experiences Involving Health.   When selecting content from the various subject-matter areas for integration with
listening, it is recommended that (1) the material have a high interest appeal to children; (2) the information be of such importance
to the pupils that they seek it; (3) the use of listening skills appears
to be the most effective instrument by which the children can acquire the information.

It should be expected that pupils would tend to listen most attentively to material that has a high interest appeal. Health content by its very nature centers around the child as a living, growing organism; that is, it contains subject matter which should be of basic interest and prime importance to most children. Because of this unique characteristic, it might be said that the subject matter of health has "built-in" motivation—a prerequisite to effective learning through listening. For example, first-grade pupils want to "grow big." Therefore, it should be expected that they would want to listen with intent to information about their bodies growing, not only during the day, but during the night as well. As another example, sixth-grade pupils seem curious, and at times concerned, about their physical growth and development. They may be aware of the uneven growth of their bodies and want to know what is happening to them and why. Their reasons for attentive listening are real and genuine. In such a case, listening serves as a functional instrument for securing information.

As has been previously pointed out, listening is the most universally used form of language communication. Therefore, when planning for the teaching of listening skills the teacher might want to take into consideration such questions as:

1. What are the experiences relating to health in which direct teaching of listening could be involved?
2. What are the listening skills the pupils will need to function as intelligent listeners in matters relating to health?
3. How are these skills taught?

Numerous classroom situations lend themselves to the direct teaching of health subject matter and the corresponding listening skills. These experiences involve listening to (1) announcements and directions, (2) choral reading, (3) conversation, (4) discussions, (5) music—songs, dances, instrumental, (6) poetry, (7) programs and assemblies, (8) reports, (9) stories which are read or told. Outside of school, elementary school pupils are involved in many of the above experiences through personal contacts or through the media of movies, radio, recordings, telephone, and television.

Listening is more than hearing. Intelligent listening involves thinking or a critical examination of what was actually heard. In planning for the teaching of listening skills, teachers should carefully (1) identify each skill the pupils will need to use to comprehend the subject matter intelligently, and (2) plan questions to give practice in these skills. However, in the actual teaching of the lesson, the teacher tends to omit bringing the pupils in on what she is trying to do and why—that is, *identifying with the pupils the skills they use and need to comprehend what they hear.* In other words, a fifth-grade teacher when working with pupils on listening skills might say: "Boys and girls, our health question for today is, 'Why do some people have naturally curly hair?' I have some information on this question which I will read to you. After we listen, it will be interesting to find out what we have actually heard. So listen carefully."

The teacher reads the selection. Then she begins the discussion with her planned questions to emphasize the development of listening skills:

FACTS

Teacher: What *facts* did you hear?
(The teacher records the pupils' answers on the board without comment. If some pupils question whether or not the answers are facts, the teacher assists with the discussion and rereads so the pupils may check. If no challenges arise through the indirect approach, further questions which she will ask later should bring the pupils to question some of the statements listed as facts. At that time the statements that are not facts are deleted.)

Teacher: Yes, we listened for facts. So we can say we used listening skills involving facts. I'll make a list of these skills on the board.

MAIN IDEAS

Teacher: What were the main ideas concerning why some people have naturally curly hair?
(She writes the pupils' answers on the board.)

Teacher: For what did we listen to get this information?

Pupil: We listened for main ideas.

Teacher: Yes. I'll add the words *main ideas,* to our list of *listening skills.*

SUPPORTING IDEAS

Teacher: What were the *other ideas* that helped us understand the main ideas?
(Writes the pupils' answers on the board.)

Teacher: We can call these statements, *other ideas* or *supporting ideas*. (Writes words *supporting ideas* over the pupils' statements.)

Teacher: Then for what did we listen to get this information?

Pupil: Supporting ideas.
(Teacher writes the words *supporting ideas,* under *listening skills.*)

SEQUENCE

Teacher: As we look at the sentences on the board, let's number them in the order or *sequence* which the writer used.
(Numbers the statements in the sequence which the pupils indicate.)

Teacher: Which listening skill can we say we used?

Pupil: Sequence.

OPINION

Teacher: What *opinion* did the writer express?
(Writes the pupils' answers on the board.)

Teacher: How can we distinguish the facts from the opinions?
(It may be that some of the statements listed under facts will now be erased and put under statements of opinion.)

Teacher: Which listening skill did we use?

Pupil: Opinion, and that was a difficult one.
(Teacher writes word *opinion* under *listening skills.*)

DRAW CONCLUSIONS

Teacher: What *conclusions* can you *draw* from what you have heard?
(Pupils draw conclusions.)

Teacher: Did we have to listen well to be able to draw valid conclusions?

Pupil: Yes. It is fun to think like this.

Teacher: Then, I'll write the words *draw conclusions* under our list of *listening skills.*
(Writes words.)

Teacher: Are there other questions we need to discuss to understand
            better what we heard about why some people have naturally
            curly hair?
            (Pupils assume responsibility for listening.)

Teacher: The next time we work on listening skills, let's use the list
            we made today. It could be that we'll have other skills to add.
            I'm pleased with how well you listened. You are good thinkers.

The preceding discussion should be considered *one* way to teach
listening skills. Resourceful teachers find various ways to help
pupils become aware of what is involved in intelligent listening.
For the first lesson, it is suggested that a few skills, possibly three or
four, be identified. Certain material lends itself better to concentra-
tion on specific skills rather than to the teaching of a variety of
skills. For instance, a period on listening could be devoted to facts
versus opinions, or to generalizations drawn from insufficient evidence. In health teaching it seems extremely important to assist the
pupil to listen critically, to discern health facts, to discriminate between what he actually heard and what he thought he heard. These
skills are among those needed in situations concerning health outside of the classroom. Such a procedure might be employed in discriminating the scientific health information from the emotional
appeal sometimes used in advertising products through a medium
such as television.

It should be understood that not all lessons involving listening
would be devoted to identifying skills, any more than having the
pupil give a book report on every book he reads. Language arts
skills are related, so further practice comes from work on the skills
in the other areas. That is, the listening skills, involving facts, inference, main ideas, supporting ideas, sequence, opinions, and conclusions, are among those taught in reading, as well as in speaking
and writing. The pupils need to become aware of this interrelatedness of skills. Better listeners could mean better speakers, better
readers, and better writers.

Teachers sometimes ask whether or not pupils in the primary
grades need to identify listening skills. Inasmuch as language is a
developmental process, it seems important at any grade level that
pupils understand *why* they are doing what they are doing. The
concepts at the upper elementary levels may be more difficult and

subtle, but the skill remains the same. For instance, first-grade pupils listen to the teacher read, "Jack and Jane looked out the window. It was snowing. They hurried to put on their snowsuits." To get at the implied meaning, the teacher asks, "What season of the year do you think it is?" (an inference question based on first-grade material).

When selecting material to teach listening skills at any grade level, it proves helpful to use material of extremely high interest appeal that does not require the pupils to listen for too long a time. In this way, success in identifying listening skills is more likely to be assured, and learning is more apt to take place.

Listening requires hearing. People who cannot hear well may encounter difficulty in listening well. As suggested by Burton, "Hearing is a multiple function, and a person with auditory acuity can: (1) hear sounds covering a considerable range of sound wave frequencies; (2) distinguish between sounds of different frequencies and pitch; (3) blend or fuse sounds effectively through the use of both ears."[3]

Listening involves the use of a sense organ for receiving aural stimuli. Thus, an understanding of and appreciation for the ears as a sense organ might well be an outcome of the subject matter taught to broaden and extend the pupil's concepts of listening. The teaching plan which follows is illustrative of this procedure.

A Sixth-Grade Plan—The Ears and the Sense of Hearing[4]

I. Overview

"Hearing is priceless! Protect it!" This is an excellent slogan for everyone, particularly for elementary boys and girls. It has been said that next to the eye, the ear is the most important of all our sense organs. It not only helps us to hear but it also helps us to keep our balance. Without being able to hear, we could not exchange our ideas and opinions with other people through the medium of speech.

In order for boys and girls to realize the importance of their ears and ear health, we will try to find out, in our classroom, some

3 William H. Burton et al., Reading in Child Development, Indianapolis, Bobbs-Merrill, 1956, p. 430.
4 Mrs. Louise Bowen, sixth-grade teacher at Severna Park Elementary School, Anne Arundel County, Maryland, developed this plan.

things which they can do to understand more fully the foregoing slogan. This unit will provide learning experiences to help boys and girls know more about their ears and how to take care of them.

II. Objectives—Health Concepts to Be Developed
  A. Sound waves are channeled from the outer ear to the canal leading to the eardrum.
  B. The vibrations of the eardrum set in motion the three small bones in the inner ear.
  C. The inner ear is filled with liquid and lined with tiny threads of nerve cells.
  D. When the liquid of the inner ear is disturbed by the vibrations of the bones, the nerve ends transmit messages to the brain, and hearing takes place.
  E. A change in air pressure causes a new sensation in the ear due to changes in pressure on the eardrums.
  F. Conservation of hearing is our personal responsibility.

III. Introduction to the Unit
  Since we give the audiometer test early each fall to every child in the school, a bulletin board depicting pictures and diagrams of the ear, suggestions for ear care, photographs of children taking the audiometer test, and a homemade telephone were displayed in the hall. Even the younger children, who are sometimes apprehensive about this audiometer testing, seemed to have their fears dispelled.

  The following questions were posted on the classroom bulletin board for several days before the test:
  1. What do you know about your ears?
  2. How do they help you?
  3. What are sound waves?
  4. What are vibrations?
  5. Do questions 3 and 4 have anything to do with *your* sense of hearing?

The bulletin board helped to stimulate interest in the unit, "Our Ears and Their Care," and the questions helped the pupils to determine their present knowledge about ears—what they would like to know and what they needed to find out.

IV. Introductory Lesson
  Teacher: I noticed that many of us have enjoyed looking at the bulletin board display, "Your Ears and Your Sense of Hearing."

(Allows pupils to make any comments.)

Teacher: What do you know about your ears?

Pupils: They help us hear sounds of all kinds.
They help us with our school work.
We have *two* ears.
We sometimes get earaches.
We should give them proper care.
We sometimes have wax in our ears.

Teacher: What would you like to know about your ears?
(Lists questions on board.)

Pupils: What are the important parts of the ear?
How should we take care of our ears?
How do our ears work?
Why do we have *two* ears?
What causes earaches?
Does the wax in the ear help or hinder our ears?
How can people with poor hearing or deafness be helped?
What do we mean when we say we have a sense of hearing?

Teacher: What are some things we may need to know about our ears?

Pupils: We must know how our ears are built if we are going to give them the best of care. We must be sure to know when our ears ache so that we can see a doctor at once.

Teacher: Let's look at the questions we have listed. Which one would you like to choose to discuss first?
(Allows children to choose.)
Example: "What are the important parts of the ear?"

Teacher: How shall we go about getting this information?
(Possible suggestions.)

Pupils: We might discuss the problem at home.
We might look through our health books.
We can use the encyclopedia.
We can study the charts on the bulletin board.
My mother is a nurse, perhaps she can help me.

Teacher: Let's think about this problem tonight and be ready to start our discussion tomorrow.

V. Learning Activities Involving Integration with Other Curriculum Areas

A. Oral Languages.
  1. Discuss what we know about the ears.
  2. Discuss and list questions.
  3. Organize questions for study in outline form:

  The Ear and the Sense of Hearing
  a. Parts of the ear:
    (1) What are the parts of the ear?
    (2) What are the small bones inside the middle ear?
  b. Functions of the ears:
    (1) How is sound received?
    (2) Why do we have two ears?
  c. Care of the ears:
    (1) How should the sound canal be cared for?
    (2) How should ears be cared for in general?
    (3) What causes earaches?
    (4) Does wax help or hinder our ears?
  d. The sense of hearing:
    (1) What is meant by the sense of hearing?
    (2) How can people with poor hearing or deafness be helped?

B. Reading.
  1. Read textbooks, reference books, pamphlets for information.
  2. Check and confirm information.

C. Creative Writing.
  1. Write original poems and stories about how we hear.
  2. Write an essay on Helen Keller, Thomas Edison, Beethoven, or Bell.
  3. Write a quiz program as a summarizing activity.

D. Speaking.
  1. Teach good diction, pleasant tone.
  2. Teach the science of good listening.

E. Social Studies.
  1. Learn about the development of the telephone.
  2. Learn about the development of the telegraph.
  3. Recall Indian ways of sending messages.

F. Arithmetic.
  1. Measure distance for hearing experiments.
  2. Find out how many feet sound travels per second.

G. Music.
  1. Learn about how musical instruments make sounds.
  2. Discuss vibrations (piano and violin).
  3. Learn about tone deafness.

H. Physical Education.
   1. Listen to instructions and directions.
   2. Work and play together in a group.
   3. Observe playground safety.
   4. Dance to rhythmic activities.

I. Art.
   1. Draw inner and outer ear.
   2. Make posters on hearing.
   3. Construct clay models.
   4. Make charts—"Do's and Don'ts for Good Hearing."

J. Science Experiments.
   1. Identify sounds.
   2. Test ability to tell from which direction a sound is coming.
   3. Make telephones through use of tin cans and string.

K. Written Language.
   1. Learn to spell words associated with study of the ear.
   2. Record the learnings as the unit evolved (individual notebooks used).
      Example of written work recorded in the pupil's individual health notebook:

The Ear and the Sense of Hearing

a. Parts of the ear
   (1) The ear is divided into three parts, the outer ear, the middle ear, and the inner ear.
   (2) The outer ear acts as a funnel and catches and directs sounds through a small canal to the middle ear. It also protects the more delicate parts of the ear and improves our appearance.
   (3) The eardrum is a thin piece of skin stretched across the end of the sound canal. It separates the canal from the middle ear.
   (4) The Eustachian tube leads to the throat.
   (5) Fine hairs and yellow wax protect the drum and middle ear.
   (6) The hammer, anvil, and stirrup are small bones inside the middle ear.
   (7) The hearing nerve is called the auditory nerve. This picks up the sound messages carried from the middle ear to the inner ear. It carries the sound messages to the brain.

(8) The inner ear is buried deep in a large bone in the head at the base of the brain. It consists of a canal in the bone, wound around in the shape of a snail shell. The canal is filled with liquid and lined with nerve endings which receive sound.

b. Function of the ears

(1) Sound is produced by vibrations in the air. A sound is caught by the outer or external ear. It enters the sound canal and then strikes the eardrum which vibrates, thus causing the three small bones to move exactly as the eardrum is moved. This sound carries the vibrations of air in the eardrum and across the middle ear to the inner ear and on to the auditory nerve to the brain.

(2) We have two ears to help us to locate kinds and directions of sounds correctly and quickly. (Safety uses.)

c. Care of the ears

(1) Care of the ears includes regular daily washing with soap and water.

(2) Hearing actually takes place in the brain, but your ears are sound catchers.

(3) The ear is the organ of the sense of hearing.

VI. Review lesson on "Parts of Ear"

Teacher: For the past several days we have been talking and reading about the main parts of the ear. What do you remember about them?

Activities: Have pupils tell what they remember. Show flash cards of the following words.

> Inner Ear
> Nerves
> Outer ear canal
> Eustachian tube
> Middle ear
> Bones (hammer, anvil, stirrup)

Have pupils flash card in proper place on large drawing of the ear on front chalkboard.

Seatwork: Give each pupil a copy of a puzzle showing parts of the ear. The pupils cut the parts and put them together correctly. These are pasted on construction paper and put in the individual's health notebook.

VII. Evaluation

A. Children plan a quiz program about "Ear Health."

B. Pupils evaluate knowledge gained about ear health by writing own reports.

C. Teacher observations of the general behavior of pupils in relation to care of ears.

D. Written knowledge test (prepared by teacher).

  1. Completion

    a. The parts of the ear are _____.

    b. The small bones of the middle ear are _____.

    c. The eardrum is a _____.

    d. The eardrum separates _____.

    e. The sound canal _____.

    f. The auditory nerve _____.

  2. List four suggestions for the care of the ear.

  3. Give the meaning of: auditory, sensitive, external, vibration, canal.

  4. Discuss how you should blow your nose, and why.

VIII. Resources

REFERENCE BOOKS FOR TEACHERS

Arey, Charles K., *Science Experiences for Elementary Schools,* New York, Bureau of Publications, Teachers College, Columbia University, 1952.

Baker, Arthur O., *Your Science World,* Chicago, Rand McNally, 1955.

Blough, Glenn O., *Elementary School Science and How To Teach It,* 2nd ed., New York, Dryden, 1951.

Carlson, A. J., and V. Johnson, *The Machinery of the Body,* Chicago, University of Chicago Press, 1953.

Craig, Gerald S., *Science for the Elementary School Teacher,* Boston, Ginn, 1940.

Kranz, F. W., *Mechanical Principles of the Human Ear,* Elmsford, N.Y., Sonotone Corporation, 1952.

REFERENCE BOOKS FOR CHILDREN

(Multiple texts are listed for various grade levels in an attempt to care for individual differences in achievement and to give a wider coverage of content on the particular topic being studied.)

Batchelor, Julie F., *Communication from Cave Writing to Television,* New York, Harcourt, Brace, 1953.

Bauer, W. W., *et al.*, *The Basic Health and Safety Program*, Fair Lawn, N.J., Scott, Foresman, 1957–1960.
Grade 4, *Going on Ten*, pp. 91–93, 98, 144.
Grade 5, *About Yourself*, pp. 20, 23, 24, 27, 37–43, 61.

Brownell, C. L., *et al.*, *ABC Health Series*, New York, American, 1959.
Grade 4, *Among Friends*, pp. 44, 110, 112, 113, 249.
Grade 5, *Broad Streets*, pp. 95–102, 120, 185, 269, 271.
Grade 6, *Crossroads*, pp. 60, 63, 64, 70–77, 88, 95.

Byrd, Oliver E., *et al.*, *The New Road to Health Series*, Summit, N.J., Laidlaw, 1960.
Grade 4, *Building For Health*, pp. 70–80.

Hallock, G. T., *et al.*, *Health for Better Living Series*, Boston, Ginn, 1958.
Grade 4, *Growing Your Way*, pp. 189–191.
Grade 5, *Keeping Healthy and Strong*, pp. 71–78.
Grade 6, *Teamwork for Health*, pp. 24, 26, 65, 66, 81–84.

Irwin, L. W., *et al.*, *Health, Happiness, and Success Series*, Wilkes-Barre, Pa., Lyons and Carnahan, 1958.
Grade 4, *All Aboard for Health*, pp. 144, 145.
Grade 5, *Better Health for You*, pp. 197, 199, 201, 202.
Grade 6, *Safeguard Your Health*, pp. 200–202.

O'Keefe, P. R., *et al.*, *Winston Health Series*, Philadelphia, Winston, 1960.
Grade 4, *Bigger and Better*, pp. 65, 67, 74, 129, 159, 288.
Grade 5, *Getting Acquainted*, pp. 10, 14–17, 19, 34, 214, 215, 263, 264.

Parker, Bertha M., *Sound*, White Plains, N.Y., Row, Peterson, 1957.

Podendorf, Illa, *The True Book of Sounds We Hear*, Chicago, Children's Press, 1955.

World Book Encyclopedia, Chicago, Field Enterprises, 1957, Volume V.

AUDIO-VISUAL MATERIALS

Films

Hear Better: Healthy Ears; Nature of Sound, Coronet Building, Chicago 1, Illinois.

Nose, Throat and Ears, McGraw-Hill Book Company, Inc., Text-Film Division, 330 West 42nd Street, New York 18, New York.

Filmstrips

Care of Eyes and Ears; How the Ears Function, Curriculum Materials
Corporation, 1319 Vine Street, Philadelphia, Pennsylvania.

Protecting Our Eyes and Ears, McGraw-Hill Book Company, Text-
Film Division, 330 West 42nd Street, New York 18, New York.

How We Hear (A578-2); *Your Ears and Hearing* (69-G), Society for
Visual Education, Inc., Chicago, Illinois.

Pamphlets

The Ear Drum and Canal (No. 193, 1956); *The Internal Ear* (No.
199, 1957), Abbott Laboratories, Chicago, Illinois.

Hearing ABC's for Boys and Girls, Chicago Hearing Society, 30 West
Washington Street, Chicago 2, Illinois.

Eyes That See and Ears That Hear, John Hancock Mutual Life Insurance Company, Boston, Massachusetts.

Your Hearing and Health (1954), Sonotone Corporation, Elmsford,
New York.

Posters

Better Hearing for Life; Good Hearing Must Be Protected; Hearing
Is Priceless (boys); Hearing Is Priceless (girls); Hearing Is Priceless,
Protect It; Help Conserve Hearing: American Hearing Society,
1800 H Street, N.W., Washington 6, D.C.

Health and Speaking

Speaking is the oldest art in terms of language communication.
Of necessity, the spoken word no doubt came into being long before
the written word. Through the ages speech has remained the social
or "outgoing" aspect of language. It is a means for integrating the
individual and the society in which he lives and learns. "Speaking
represents the pervasive element in daily living. Man speaks in an
attempt to persuade or influence his hearers, to entertain them, to
give aid or give help in making decisions, to report on past activities, to spread the news, to work out his social relations, or to trans-
act his business. In all such talking there is a purpose."[5] Thus, for an
effective speaker, there is a listener. Concurrently, when the speaker
and listener exchange ideas the listener becomes the speaker, and
the speaker becomes the listener. During discussions, and while engaging in conversation, a person assumes a dual role. He uses both
listening and speaking to learn.

[5] Mildred A. Dawson and Marian Zollinger, *Guiding Children's Learning,*
Yonkers, N.Y., World, 1957, p. 11.

This interrelatedness of speaking and listening has implications for teaching at all levels. The elementary school child, by and large, *speaks* the language he hears. In language development, speaking holds an undisputed position. As has been pointed out, speaking is a salient factor of learning in its own right. In addition, speaking is basic to reading and writing. When a child speaks in sentences, he is better prepared to read in sentences and to write the language he speaks. In this context, speaking takes on significant portions as an area of learning in which pupils need direct teaching and guidance.

Speaking is the second most commonly used facet of language. "Throughout his school days and throughout his life, the child will probably use oral communication much more than any other of the language arts except listening. For every word he reads or writes, he will speak and listen to a thousand."[6] Some studies indicate that prior to entering first grade the child has learned to speak somewhere around 2500 words. Throughout the elementary school years the teacher uses various ways to enrich and enlarge the meaningful *speaking* vocabulary of pupils. Among the most common practices involving language are (1) listening and speaking activities commonly associated with firsthand experiences, (2) reading instruction, and (3) extensive reading by the pupil independently and "on his own."

Through the study of health, many areas of interest, such as food, exercise, sleep, care, structure, and function of the body, are available in which the child may express his thoughts and feelings.

Speaking represents one facet of language for expression. The other facet is writing. As previously stated, the skills of speaking and writing are interrelated. Both of these aspects of expression involve the following:

1. Organization of ideas
2. Choice of words to express meaning precisely, convincingly, and clearly
3. Correct grammatical usage
4. Correct sentence and paragraph structure

There are certain elements of speaking and writing that are different. The elements of speech which differ from those of writing

---

[6] National Council of Teachers of English, *Language Arts for Today's Children,* New York, Appleton-Century-Crofts, 1954, p. 106.

include articulation, change in stress, enunciation, gesture, pitch, posture, pronunciation, and voice. The elements of writing not contained in speech are those which involve capitalization, format, handwriting, punctuation, and spelling.

Successful teachers report that elementary school pupils profit from "thinking through" and listing their objectives or standards for speaking for the year. For instance, under teacher guidance pupils might examine the tables of contents and indexes of various English textbooks, skim for information, discuss the previous year's objectives, and organize their own thinking. Sometimes their goals can be stated in question form as follows:

1. Is my voice audible and pleasing?
2. Do I speak clearly and distinctly?
3. Do I stand correctly?
4. Do I use correct English?

This procedure can lead into a discussion of what is involved in giving an oral report. Again, the teacher guides the pupils in the use of multiple English texts to find out what the authorities say. Since the organization of information for an oral report usually involves writing, time should be spent in finding out how oral and written reports are similar. The common elements of speaking and writing should be listed. Pupils should then arrive at the conclusion that one way to improve an oral report is to improve the notes or outline, or way that they record the information. Thus, their generalization involves the functional relationship between speaking and writing. In other words, one way to improve speaking is to improve writing.

The material which follows is intended to serve as an example of evaluative criteria for speaking.[7]

EVALUATION FOR ORAL REPORTS

Did the speaker hold our interest? How?
Did he know his topic?
Did he speak so that all could hear?
Did he stand straight and still?
Did he give us a question for which to listen?

[7] These procedures were developed by fifth-grade pupils under the guidance of Mrs. Irene Dullea, Brooklyn Park Elementary School, Anne Arundel County, Maryland.

HOW TO BE A GOOD CHAIRMAN

Tell the topic to be discussed.

Introduce the members of the committee.

See that the discussion goes ahead in an interesting manner.

Ask for questions and comments from the audience.

Close the discussion by:

    1. Making some summary statements

    2. Thanking the participants

    3. Thanking the audience

While it is important that pupils work toward attainable standards for speaking and for preparing oral reports, this is not necessarily the ultimate goal. In other words, the question arises as to whether the focus should be on the mechanics rather than the developmental aspects of oral language? Or, should the emphasis be on freedom of expression, creativity, ingenuity, spontaneity, and the development of personality? It should be kept in mind that pupils learn to talk by talking freely and naturally.

Health Activities Involving Speaking.   Many situations pertaining to health teaching provide satisfactory opportunities for various types of expressional activities. Some of these "speaking" experiences include the following:

1. Discussing, planning, summarizing and/or evaluating

    Discuss and demonstrate good posture when standing, walking, running, sitting, dancing.

    Discuss conditions which cause and spread communicable diseases.

    Discuss new and/or unfamiliar foods.

    Discuss why we should never accept rides without our parents' permission.

    Plan a trip to the health clinic.

    Summarize what was learned about going in bathing immediately after eating.

    Evaluate the effectiveness of a health unit upon practices.

2. Making announcements and/or explanations

    The school lunch menus for the week

    The meeting of the Health Club

    The decisions made by the Safety Patrol Council

3. Giving directions

    Compose chart on care of teeth.

    Compose necessary rules for safe use of playground equipment.

    Explain directions for making butter.

4. Interviewing

Talk with the school doctor, health nurse, dentist about important health practices.

Talk with the safety patrol boy or girl about his or her problems.

Talk with a policeman about the kinds of accidents in the neighborhood.

Talk with the school cook about important foods.

5. Telephoning

Call an absent class member on the phone who cannot be visited because he has a communicable disease.

Call class mothers inviting them to assist with the class luncheon.

6. Presenting an illustrated talk or report

Things We Can Do to Be Healthy

Health Heroes I Admire

What I Look for in a Friend

An Example of Being a Good Sport

When I'm Afraid

7. Participating in a panel discussion

The Meaning of Good Grooming

The Need for Health Inspection of Public Beaches

The Importance of Health Inspection of Public Eating Places

8. Conducting a meeting of the Health Club

How to preside

How to read minutes

How to make a motion

How to conduct a discussion

9. Presenting original poems, stories, plays, riddles, limericks on health topics

10. Participating in choral speaking of health poems

11. Participating in creative dramatics[8]

Playing role of school nurse.

Playing role of mother at mealtime.

Playing role of daughter wanting to wear a particular dress to school.

The foregoing health activities involving speaking are merely indications of the many possibilities inherent in health teaching. The teacher's manuals to the many fine health textbooks also offer many worthwhile suggestions. The resourceful teacher needs only to rely upon her own initiative in order to provide purposeful activities.

[8] The reader should consult Chapter 16 for a detailed account of creative dramatics.

Speaking represents an area of learning which can contribute to the wholesome development of elementary school pupils. When planning for learning activities involving speaking, the teacher once again should take into consideration the needs of the pupils as individuals. For instance, the pupils who omit endings of words ("runnin'," "playin' ") or have difficulty with initial consonants ("wabbit" for "rabbit") might possibly profit through choral speaking. The pupil who has the tendency to ramble on and on might benefit by talking from an outline. The timid pupils might lose themselves in creative dramatics. The value of such experiences lies in the desirable behavioral changes in the individual pupil. Creative dramatics might well be considered as an example, as indicated by the following suggestion by Dawson and Zollinger:

> Dramatic play and dramatization are creative in nature; together they constitute creative dramatics, an important phase of a child's language development. The child observes and listens—the intake aspect of language growth; as a result, he experiences feelings and gains concepts that he reflects through dramatic action—the *outgo* or expression. Consequently, he builds up his vocabulary, his sentence structure, his organization of ideas, his social understandings, his emotional reactions and control.[9]

Health and Reading

Reading is generally recognized as a most important medium of learning and, as such, it is a part of all subjects, as well as a part of living. Some of the more subtle types of learning which could involve reading include discriminating, reasoning, judging, evaluating, and problem-solving.

There are significant aspects to language development which involves the process of reading. From the previous discussion at least four generalizations concerning reading can be drawn:

1. Reading is one of the four interrelated aspects of language communication.
2. Through the process of reading, one is able to receive the thought and feelings of others.
3. Listening and reading are considered the receptive aspects of language communication.
4. For most elementary school pupils, the development of reading ability is dependent upon and related to the ability to listen and to speak.

[9] Dawson and Zollinger, *op. cit.,* p. 444.

Reading involves thinking stimulated by written symbols. The little black marks on a white page mean nothing to a child until he is taught to get from them the meaning the writer had in mind. A part of this involves a basic sight vocabulary and the ability to sound out words by syllables and individual sounds. These are known as *word-attack skills* and include phonetic analysis (phonics) and structural analysis. Phonics deals with the sounds attached to the letter symbols. The teaching of phonics is most important, but it should be kept in mind that the English language is only partially phonetic. For instance:

1. There are twenty-six letters in the alphabet, each with a letter name—*a, b, c*, and so on.
2. In speech, the same sound is seldom applied as in reciting the alphabet.
3. It is further complicated by the fact that many letters have several sounds. All the vowels have varying sounds (*a* as in map, mate, ant, care, hearth). Consonant sounds also vary (*c* as in cigar, cabinet).
4. Many sounds are represented by as many as a dozen different symbols (*sh* as in she, nation, ascension, sure, leisure).

The word-recognition program includes (1) phonetic analysis: consonant sounds, vowel sounds, and rules; (2) structural analysis: root words, prefixes, suffixes, and principles of syllabication and inflected forms; and (3) semantic analysis: meanings and dictionary skills. These represent aids to word recognition and word-calling which the pupils use to read.

However, it should be clearly understood that reading is more than merely sounding out words. Reading involves a thinking process which includes many complex skills of comprehension. The story is told of a child who read fluently to his mother from a page in his reader. When he finished his mother asked, "Johnny tell me about what you have read." Johnny replied, "I don't know. I wasn't listening." Could he have meant he wasn't thinking? A pupil must be able to do more than call words. He must be able to understand the explicit meaning of words, sentences, paragraphs, and passages. Consider the following examples:

1. "A *young* prince stood at the foot of a hill overlooking a *nearby* town."
   The skillful teacher does not consider a pupil a good reader when he can read fluently all the words in the above sentence, or answers such a factual question as "Who stood at the *foot* of the hill?"

The teacher's line of questioning might be "How *young* is the prince? Describe the *foot* of a hill. What other meanings do you know for the word *foot*? How far away is *nearby*?"

2. "A soldier *without arms* stood by the door."

The teacher does not ask a question which requires only the parroting of facts, such as, "How did the soldier stand?" Her questions get at the meaning which the author intended to convey: "What do the words *without arms* mean?" "What other meanings do you know for the word, *arms*?"

These examples should serve to illustrate that sometimes the easiest words to pronounce can cause difficulty in reading comprehension because of their various meanings. A pupil with word-recognition (word-calling) trouble ordinarily is noticed immediately by both parents and teachers. A pupil with reading comprehension trouble is seldom or ever noticed except by a skillful teacher.

Building a meaningful vocabulary and developing word recognition skills are but two of the many, many comprehension skills needed by pupils for intelligent reading. The many basal reading series, from the reading readiness books through the sixth-grade readers, tend to focus attention upon the identification of these numerous comprehension skills and suggest procedures for teaching each in a developmental program.

In numerous elementary schools the basal reading series constitutes one phase of the total reading program. Among other things, these reading series aim (1) to aid pupils in acquiring functional skills of comprehension, (2) to help pupils solve their problems, (3) to give practice in reading for many purposes, and (4) to stimulate interests that lead to other reading materials. Thus, successful teachers at all grade levels are expected to assume responsibilities for providing additional reading experience in many areas and for many purposes. However, it appears that in some cases this phase of the total reading program might have been interpreted to mean that pupils first *learn to read* and then *read to learn*. This generalization tends to imply a transfer of learning and a one-to-one relationship between reading from a basal reader and a textbook of less, or of comparable, difficulty. For the most part, observations of teachers tend to suggest that this statement is true only in part. For instance, no basal reading series could be expected to develop meaningful vocabulary in all of the various subject-matter areas.

Each subject has certain concepts peculiar to itself, for instance, nutrition, communicable disease, aorta, and calories in health; climate, weather, hemisphere, zones, and natural vegetation in social studies; and so on. Without adequate concepts and word meanings related to the vocabulary that is characteristic of the subject, many of the various comprehension skills could likely lose some of their functional value.

As the teachers re-examine their thinking concerning the most effective ways to teach pupils to read intelligently in the subject-matter areas, they should perhaps give consideration to some of the following questions:

1. Is it necessary daily to have a reading lesson from a basal reader, and a reading lesson from textbooks in the various subject-matter areas?
2. Can the pupils learn the reading comprehension skills needed to understand the subject at the same time that they are studying that subject? For instance, is it not economical in terms of time to teach the reading comprehension skills needed to understand the health textbook during the health period?
3. Is it not efficient and effective to teach the reading comprehension skills in a functional situation, that is, a situation such as health, where the pupils see the need for specific skills in order to get the information they need to solve their problem in the day's lesson?

In other words, the point of emphasis involves *reading to learn,* rather than just learning to read. In the final analysis, reading should be considered an instrument for learning and a facet of language communication, rather than a body of subject matter. In such a context, the basal reading book might well serve to sharpen, and to give additional practice in, the comprehension skills which pupils need. Experience has shown that pupils readily understand why they are reading from a basal reader when the teacher makes such comments as, "Boys and girls when you read from the health books you had some difficulty distinguishing facts from opinions. This is a skill which you will need more and more as you get older. For our reading lesson today, I have selected a story to give more practice in this skill. I think you will enjoy the story." Or, the teacher might say: "In our health lesson yesterday, we read about and discussed safety in the water. I have found a story in our reading book which I think you will enjoy. It is about the rescue of a young child from a lake. Furthermore, this is a good story to give us practice in noting the sequence in which the events happened. Turn to the table of contents in the reader."

From this point of view it should be readily discerned that basal reading books can serve to re-enforce and strengthen skills needed by the pupils. It should be borne clearly in mind that this should not be construed to mean that all comprehension skills are not needed, but rather that the teacher through careful diagnosis comes to know the comprehension reading skills in which the pupils are the least proficient, and as a consequence will concentrate on teaching these skills. The importance of this approach becomes all the more meaningful when it is understood that pupils tend to become bored when faced with drill or busy work involving skills which they maintain through daily use.

In the previous discussion, listening and reading were developed as the receptive phase of language communication. The interrelatedness of comprehension skills was noted and procedures were suggested for helping pupils identify certain listening skills needed to comprehend intelligently what was heard.

It should be pointed out that pupils also profit from identifying the reading comprehension skills needed to read intelligently. For example, the teacher might refer to previous lessons involving listening skills in the following manner:

Teacher: Boys and girls, you recall that when we listened to information about why some people have naturally curly hair, we listed those skills that we used in order to understand what we heard. On your desks you have various reading materials to use in solving today's problem: "What happens when we sleep?" After you finish reading silently, we will do two things. First, we will discuss what we have read, and second, we will list the reading skills we used.
(After the silent reading the teacher begins the discussion with planned questions.)

RECALL

Teacher: What did you find out that would help us answer our own questions or the class question?
(The teacher does not repeat the questions. By phrasing her question in the above manner, she gives practice in the skill of "recall"—a necessary skill of remembering. The teacher listens and guides the discussion.)

FACTS

Teacher: Let us list some of the things you have been saying. What *facts* did you find concerning what happens when we sleep? (Lists the facts on the board.)

Teacher: What did you need to do to get this information?

Pupil: We needed to get the facts.

Teacher: Yes, we read to get the facts. It takes skill to select the facts. I will make a list of these reading skills on the board.

MAIN IDEAS

Teacher: What were the *main ideas*? (Lists the main ideas on the board.)

Teacher: What did you need to do to get this information?

Pupil: We needed to recognize the main ideas. (Teacher writes the words, *main ideas* on board under *reading skills*.)

As the lesson continues the pupils often become aware that these skills are the same as those previously listed on a chart entitled "Listening Skills." It is not unusual for a pupil to make statements such as: "These skills are the same." "Does listening help us read better?" "I never knew that reading could help us listen, too."

For follow-up work, successful teachers report that further practice can be given in reading skills by asking the pupils to read a given selection silently and write answers to such questions as:

1. What are the facts?
2. What are the main ideas?
3. What are the supporting ideas?
4. What might be a good title for the third paragraph?
5. What are the opinions stated by the writer?
6. What outcomes would you predict?

If the pupils are to become intelligent readers, this might serve as one technique to use when assisting the individual pupil to diagnose the skills needing more practice, if he is to get the precise meanings the writer intended to convey.

The point should be made here that the quality of an individual's reading is not to be measured in terms of the degree of mechanical skill he has attained, but by the quality of personal satisfaction and enrichment that he finds in the experience of reading.

Throughout the elementary school year, pupils read for information to use in answering questions and solving their problems. Effective teaching in health should operate on the premise that pupils learn *by* solving problems that are real and meaningful to them. Although the elementary school is designed to help pupils grow in their ability to think critically and to solve problems, problem-solving apparently begins long before the child starts to school. There is probably no "age of reasoning" which a child must obtain before he can do problem-solving.

Reasoning ability seems to begin at an early age and to develop gradually with experience and language. It is a continuous process, rather than one occurring at fixed stages. Even before the child can put into words what he is thinking he attempts to solve problems. It is possible that because of the fact that young children do not ordinarily solve problems in words that many people discredit their reasoning or problem-solving ability. For example, the 1-year-old child, pulling the table cloth toward him to get something, is making an attempt at solving a problem.

Recently one of the authors observed a mother and father with their 2-year-old daughter seated between them on stools at a soda fountain. The parents were having a soft drink, and the 2-year-old had been given a taste of the drink in a paper cup. She hurriedly drank it, and then holding the cup toward the clerk, said, "More-e." The clerk looked at the mother who was saying, "No, thank you, not any more now." The father shook his head no, too. The youngster tilted her cup to her mouth, but it was evident that she had not solved the problem with the first attempt. Then she proceeded to climb into her father's arms. She kissed and begged her father whispering, "Pease." As she took a sip from her father's cup, it was evident that the youngster had solved *her* problem. (Although this example violates a health practice, it should serve as a suitable illustration of an attempt at problem-solving by a 2-year-old.)

The use of language as an effective tool in reasoning and problem-solving is one of the great responsibilities of the elementary school. Language includes the printed letter symbols (reading) as well as the printed number symbols (arithmetic). The use of reading for solving health problems needs to be taught.

Reading and the Health Series for the Elementary School. An effective health program offers many types of reading for the elementary school pupil. The current series of health books provide one important aspect of health teaching. These textbooks are prepared by multiple authors, including authorities in health and child growth and development, as well as specialists in the language arts. From the primer through the sixth-grade books, there is a gradual increase in vocabulary load, as well as an increase in the length and complexity of sentences, and length of story and maturity of health concepts used. The teacher's manual accompanying each text gives suggestions for developing the health concepts, and identifies the reading skills needed to read the material intelligently. The effective use of health textbooks can foster wholesome child development while exercising reading skills.

Bibliotherapy and Health.   During the 1950s some attention was focused upon another aspect of health reading known as *bibliotherapy*. The term *bibliotherapy* is composed of the words *biblio,* meaning *books,* and *therapy,* meaning *treatment.* Thus, bibliotherapy deals with "treatment through books." Bibliotherapy is concerned essentially with the kinds of reading materials which can help the individual pupil to develop a better understanding of himself and his personal problems. Bibliotherapy in this context refers to preventive treatment; that is, the book purportedly helps the child with his developmental tasks.

Reading exerts a certain amount of influence on personality through identification and insight. As a consequence, it should be an encouraging factor in wholesome development. In light of existing indications and predictions concerning the mental health of children, it becomes imperative that all elementary teachers continuously evaluate the effectiveness of their teaching in terms of observable behavioral changes in the total health of pupils. Whether bibliotherapy is used in a reading clinic, psychological clinic, or classroom, it should have some sort of potential contribution to make to wholesome child development. As such, it constitutes a significant type of reading in the total health program. The implementation of bibliotherapy involves getting the *right child* and the *right book* together at the *right time.*

In this general frame of reference it has been suggested by Burton that "reading is concerned with the creation of meanings for better understanding of self and environment. Reading may be defined as a vital part of a rich and varied program of learning experiences through which an individual learns to know and to manage himself, to know and to mingle with other people, and to know and to utilize his environment."[10]

As in other learning situations, the teacher is the crux of the program. It is the teacher who can provide innumerable daily opportunities through reading which contribute to the emotional stability, social adjustment, physical fitness, and mental alertness of pupils. There are many aids available to the teacher for planning a health reading program which has therapeutic value for pupils.

The present era might be appropriately termed "The Golden Age of Children's Books." Hundreds of outstanding children's books are published each year. Some of these are classics; others are new books destined to become classics. Many large book companies employ an editor of juvenile books, with the idea of assuring quality in the quantity of books published.

With the present existing knowledge of child growth and development, the characteristics, needs, and interests of elementary school pupils are well defined. A teacher needs only to consult reputable book lists which categorize books children can read under such headings as age, grade level, interest, sex, and subject. Some basic guides to children's books can be secured from such sources as:

American Library Association
50 East Huron Street
Chicago 11, Illinois
> *A Basic Book Collection for Elementary Grades,* "Suggestions of a group of books which in itself would make a workable library."

Library Journal
62 West 45th Street
New York 36, New York
> *Growing Up With Books,* 250 of the best books in print.
> *Library Journal,* bimonthly publication giving frequent reviews of current books.
> *Recommended Children's Books,* 750 of the year's best children's books.
> *Starred Books from the Library Journal,* 750 of the best children's books in print.

McCall's Modern Homemaker
P.O. Box 1390
Grand Central Station
New York 17, New York
> *100 Best Books for Children,* McCall List, 1956.

[10] Burton, *et al., op. cit.,* vii.

The H. W. Wilson Company
950 University Avenue
New York 52, New York

> Children's Catalogue, A classified catalogue of children's books recommended for public and school libraries with author, title, and subject index.

Individualized Reading. Individualized reading represents another procedure for integrating the teaching of reading skills and health—especially from the standpoint of bibliotherapy.

Various terminology is used in the literature to describe and define this particular procedure. It may be referred to by such terms as "personalized reading," "extensive reading," and "recreational reading." In keeping with the terminology used by the International Reading Association, the procedure will be referred to as "individualized reading." As the term implies, individualized reading is a developmental approach to reading based upon the specific capacity and needs of the individual child and how he learns. The major features include opportunities for the pupils to (1) read independently rather than in groups, (2) read books of their own selection rather than of the teacher's selection, and (3) read at their own rate rather than the rate of the group.

The merits of individualized instruction need no explanation or justification. For the most part, some aspects of individualized reading instruction are present in classrooms during the library and literature periods. However, many of the proponents of such reading view it as a primary aspect of the basic reading program, not as subordinate, or an adjunct. In this particular regard Larrick comments as follows:

> Because the individualized reading program is based on children's free choice of reading materials, it has occasionally been confused with what is sometimes called "free reading or recreational reading." A child may use the same library books for both kinds of reading and may put the same enthusiastic drive in both. But to the teacher there is a great distinction—individualized reading to her means a time for instruction and development of skills, while recreational reading means reading for fun and relaxation with little or no instruction from the teacher.[11]

[11] Nancy Larrick, "You Need Good Libraries to Teach Reading Today," *Junior Libraries*, September 15, 1954, p. 4–6.

The same general idea is conveyed by Garrettson:

When a child is allowed to use material of his own choosing, move at his own pace, in an atmosphere where how he moves is no longer public classroom concern, he relaxes his defenses and begins to feel the security of accomplishment.[12]

And finally Evans suggests that:

Basic to the success of an individualized reading program is the philosophy that children should learn to assume considerable self-direction and self-control as they mature.[13]

The extent to which the individualized reading program is carried on is a matter for the individual teacher. However, the authors tend to believe that such a reading program has much to offer which can contribute to the total health of the individual elementary school pupil, and they strongly recommend that teachers attempt to keep abreast with the current research in this area.[14]

It has been pointed out that in the wholesome development of children, reading and health are closely integrated. The reading materials which can contribute to the desirable objectives include the basic series of health textbooks and the hundreds of suitable library books. The appropriateness and effectiveness of procedures rests upon the "know-how" of teachers, for the way they teach reflects what they believe and accept as their responsibility for the mental, social, physical, and emotional health of children.

Reading and Vision. Reading involves the use of the eyes for receiving visual stimuli. Thus, an understanding of and appreciation for the eyes as sense organs for vision might be an outcome of

---

12 Grace Garrettson, "How One School Read the Needs of the Slow Reader," *Nineteenth Yearbook of Claremont College Reading Conference.* Claremont, Calif., Claremont College Curriculum Laboratory, 1954.

13 N. Dean Evans, "An Individualized Reading Program for the Elementary School," *Elementary School Journal,* November 1953, pp. 157–162.

14 For further information concerning individualized reading, the following periodicals are suggested: William S. Gray, "Role of Group and Individualized Teaching in a Sound Reading Program," Marian Jenkins, "Self-Selection in Reading," Robert Karlin, "Some Reactions to Individualized Reading," May Lazar, "Individualized Reading," "A Dynamic Approach," *The Reading Teacher,* December 1957; Phyllis Parkin, "An Individual Program of Reading," *Educational Leadership,* October, 1956, pp. 34–38; Ruth Rowe and Esther Dornkoefer, "Individualized Reading," *Childhood Education,* November, 1957, pp. 118–122.

the subject matter taught to broaden and extend the pupil's concepts of reading. An examination of the various health textbooks shows a study of the eye at each grade level.[15] An example of a teaching plan for the sixth grade is given.

A Teaching Plan—The Eyes and the Sense of Sight
(Grade 6)

I. Suggested Approaches

   A. Show pictures of people with bright sparkling eyes and discuss effects on appearance.

   B. Demonstrate an eye screening test in class.

   C. Show in graphic form the results of an eye screening test which has been given recently to the class.

   D. Demonstrate in class the use of a lightmeter.

   E. List advantages of good eyesight.

II. Objectives—Health Concepts to Be Developed

   A. Light rays enter the pupil of the eye, and form a picture on the retina at the back of the eye.

   B. A special nerve from the retina carries the picture to the brain, where it is recognized and interpreted.

   C. The eye is protected by bones around it, by the eyelids and the eyelashes, by tears, and by its ability to adjust itself to light.

   D. Periodic eye examination by an eye specialist is one important means of maintaining good eyesight.

   E. Visual defects can be corrected by glasses.

   F. The eyeball, iris, pupil, lens, retina, cornea, optic nerve and tear gland each serve a unique function in helping us to see.

III. Problems for Study

   A. What parts of the eye can we see?

   B. What are the parts of the eye we cannot see?

   C. What two things are found in the eyeball?

   D. How do tear glands help the eyes?

   E. What is the function of the retina?

   F. What is the function of the pupil?

   G. What is the function of the lens?

   H. What is the function of the optic nerve?

   I. What is the function of the iris?

[15] For health concepts relating to the eye to be developed at each grade level, the reader is referred to Chapter 9.

  J. What is the function of the cornea?

  K. How do the eyes adjust to light?

  L. How is the eye like a camera?

  M. How should we protect our eyes?

  N. Why is good vision essential?

  O. How can we tell whether or not our vision is normal?

  P. When does a person need to wear glasses?

  Q. Why should we have our eyes tested?

  R. What are the main defects of the eyes and how are they corrected?

  S. What arrangement of the lighting in the home and in the classroom is considered best for conserving the eyesight?

IV. Learning Activities Involving Integration

 A. Oral Language

  1. Discuss what we know about the eyes.

  2. Discuss and list questions.

  3. Organize questions for study in outline form.
   An example of such an outline follows:

The Eyes and the Sense of Sight

  a. Parts of the eye

   (1) What parts of the eye can we see?

   (2) What two things are found in the eyeball?

   (3) What are the parts of the eye we cannot see?

  b. Function of the eyes

   (1) Why do we need two eyes?

   (2) How is the eye like a camera?

   (3) How do eyes adjust to light?

   (4) What is the function of the retina?

   (5) What is the function of the pupil?

   (6) What is the function of the lens?

   (7) What is the function of the optic nerve?

   (8) What is the function of the iris?

   (9) What is the function of the cornea?

  c. Vision

   (1) What happens to make us see?

   (2) Why is good vision essential?

   (3) How can we tell whether or not our vision is normal?

   (4) What is color blindness?

   (5) What is night blindness?

   (6) What are the main defects of the eyes, and how are they corrected?

    d. Care and protection of the eyes
      (1) How are our eyes protected?
      (2) How can we prevent eyestrain?
      (3) Why should we have our eyes tested?
      (4) What arrangement of lighting in the home and in the classroom is considered best for conserving the eyesight?
      (5) When does a person need to wear glasses?

B. Reading
  1. Read about occupations which require intensive use of the eyes.
  2. Read about how to help prevent night blindness.
  3. Read to find out the relationship of factors such as sleep, rest, and nutrition to good vision.
  4. Read to find out how television affects a person's eyes.

C. Spelling
  1. Add words to vocabulary in notebook while studying unit.
  2. Use new words, such as *ophthalmologist, optometrist, granulated lids,* in written work.

D. Speaking
  1. Give oral reports on seeing-eye dogs and the Braille system of reading.
  2. Interview "eye" professional personnel for information about their professions.
  3. Give an illustrated talk on the cleaning and care of glasses.

E. Arithmetic
  1. Secure a lightmeter. Test the lighting in various parts of a room. Compare findings with recommended standards.
  2. Invite an engineer to talk to the class regarding the number of foot-candles considered adequate for various types of work.
  3. Demonstrate the meaning of 20/20 vision.

F. Physical Education
  1. Discuss the importance of good vision for success in athletics.
  2. Discuss how to protect the eyes at play.
  3. Discuss games requiring eye protectors.

G. Art
  1. Prepare posters illustrating proper care of the eyes, stressing such points as the following:
    a. Prepare position for reading in relation to light
    b. Wear glasses when necessary
    c. Use paper towels in public places
    d. Exert care with scissors and other pointed objects
  2. Draw a diagram of the structure of the eye.

H. Science
   1. Demonstrate the various methods used for testing eyes.
   2. Give the Snellen eye test to class and discuss the reasons for variations in results.
   3. Compare the mechanism and functioning of the eye with that of a camera.
   4. Secure a pair of field glasses, microscope, or some other magnifying device. Demonstrate their uses. Discuss the ways they help in seeing.
   5. Demonstrate how depth perception is possible with two eyes and not with one (a stereoscope will help in showing this).
   6. Experiment with light and colors.
   7. Investigate lighting conditions in the classroom.
   8. Study a periscope and camera to note how each works.
I. Written language
   1. List symptoms and causes of eyestrain.
   2. Write a report on ways of protecting the eyes against rubbing, soiled objects, poor light, very bright lights, dust and dirt.
   3. Record the learnings in summary paragraphs as the unit evolves.

V. Evaluation in Terms of Observed Behavior of Pupils
   A. Protecting the eyes
      1. By using dark glasses (the correct type) when needed
      2. By caring for sore eye (pink eyes)
      3. By guarding against colds (which may infect the eyes)
      4. By protecting eyes by occasional rest
   B. Desiring to have eyes examined at school
   C. Appreciating the sense of sight
   D. Appreciating the importance of glasses to health and efficiency
   E. Seeking the best light for the classroom on cloudy and extremely bright days
   F. Bringing in articles from newspapers and magazines concerning the eyes and eyesight.

VI. Resources
   REFERENCE BOOKS FOR TEACHERS

   Arey, Charles K., *Science Experiences for Elementary Schools,* New York, Bureau of Publications, Teachers College, Columbia University, 1952.
   Baker, Arthur O., *Your Science World,* Chicago, Rand McNally, 1955.
   Blough, Glenn O., *Elementary School Science and How To Teach It,* 2nd ed., New York, Dryden, 1958.

Carlson, A. J., and V. Johnson, *The Machinery of the Body*, Chicago, University of Chicago Press, 1953.
Craig, Gerald S., *Science for the Elementary School Teacher*, Boston, Ginn, 1958.

REFERENCE BOOKS FOR CHILDREN

(Multiple texts are listed for various grade levels in an attempt to care for individual differences in achievement, and to give wider coverage of content on the particular topic being studied.)

Batchelor, Julie G., *Communication from Cave Writing to Television*, New York, Harcourt, Brace, 1953.
Bauer, W. W., *et al.*, *The Basic Health and Safety Program*, Fair Lawn, N.J., Scott, Foresman, 1957–1960.
  Grade 4, *Going on Ten*, pp. 91, 94, 95, 98, 102, 103, 144, 156, 190, 191.
  Grade 5, *About Yourself*, pp. 20, 23, 24, 26, 28–36, 44, 53, 55, 56, 58, 60, 62, 63, 84.
  Grade 6, *About All of Us*, pp. 45, 110, 115–117, 157, 160, 161, 186, 187, 198, 260.
Brownell, C. L., *et al.*, *ABC Health Series*, New York, American, 1959.
  Grade 4, *Among Friends*, pp. 44, 159–162, 164–166, 177, 249.
  Grade 5, *Broad Streets*, pp. 89–94, 101, 120, 169, 187, 190, 233, 254.
  Grade 6, *Crossroads*, pp. 64, 80, 90–96.
Byrd, Oliver E, *et al.*, *The New Road to Health Series*, Summit, N.J., Laidlow, 1960.
  Grade 5, *Your Health*, pp. 90–99, 164.
Hallock, G. T., *et al.*, *Health for Better Living Series*, Boston, Ginn, 1958.
  Grade 4, *Growing Your Way*, pp. 179–196.
  Grade 5, *Keeping Healthy and Strong*, pp. 58, 62–69, 85, 86.
  Grade 6, *Teamwork for Health*, pp. 18, 19, 28, 29, 79–81, 175, 176.
Irwin, L. W., *et al.*, *Health, Happiness and Success Series*, Wilkes-Barre, Pa., Lyons and Carnahan, 1958.
  Grade 4, *All Aboard for Health*, pp. 135, 136, 138–142.
  Grade 5, *Better Health for You*, pp. 186, 189–192, 194, 196.
  Grade 6, *Safeguard Your Health*, pp. 37, 191–199.
O'Keefe, P. R., *et al.*, *Winston Health Series*, Philadelphia, Pr., Winston, 1960.
  Grade 4, *Bigger and Better*, pp. 11, 60, 62, 63, 68–71, 73, 74, 79, 84, 85, 137, 158.
  Grade 5, *Getting Acquainted*, pp. 6, 10–14, 24, 34, 69.
  Grade 6, *Knowing Yourself*, p. 202.

World Book Encyclopedia, Chicago, Field Enterprises, 1957, vol. V.

AUDIO-VISUAL MATERIALS

Charts

Snellen Eye Chart

Massachusetts Vision Testing Chart

Films

Eyes: Structure and Care, Coronet Films, Coronet Building, Chicago 1, Illinois.

Filmstrips

Care of the Eyes and Ears, Curriculum Materials Corporation, 1319 Vine Street, Philadelphia, Pennsylvania.

Protecting Our Eyes and Ears, McGraw-Hill Book Company, Inc., 330 West 42nd Street, New York 18, New York.

How We See (A578-1), *Health and the Eyes* (29B), *Your Eyes* (69B), Society for Visual Education, Inc., Chicago, Illinois.

Pamphlets

Eyes That See and Ears That Hear, John Hancock Mutual Life Insurance Company, Boston, Massachusetts.

Health and Writing

It has been mentioned previously that writing is an expressive phase of language. Almost all children want to write. Prior to starting to school many children make an attempt. Usually between the ages of 3 and 4 years, the young child makes marks for his name on birthday and Christmas cards to relatives and friends. From 4 to 6 years of age, he may try to write his name, or to copy "thank-you" notes which he has dictated to his mother. At an early age children have been known, much to the chagrin of their parents, to write on the walls in order to express themselves. For the most part children enter the first grade with a desire to write. It is not unusual for a first-grade pupil to say: "How do you spell the word *like?*" Then later in the day, the teacher receives this note:

Dear Miss Brown,
I like you.
Love,
Ann

As the pupil develops and grows in his ability to express his thoughts and feelings well, he moves from writing one sentence "on his own" to writing many sentences involving length and structure and the organization of ideas into paragraphs. He uses writing for many purposes. Some of these are:

1. Recording summaries of activities such as news events, trips, and important learnings.
2. Keeping records, diaries, and notes.
3. Recording directions for experiments.
4. Writing letters, such as invitations, requests, "thank-you" and "get-well" notes.
5. Making labels, captions, signs, and posters.
6. Recording his creative expressions in the form of stories, poems, riddles, plays, and songs.
7. Writing his autobiography.

Some of the objectives of writing are well expressed in the following statement by the Commission on the English Curriculum of the National Council of Teachers of English: "The basic goals in written as well as oral language are four rather obvious ones. The first is *ease* in writing. If a child can approach his task with confidence and a sense of adequacy, he can put his energy into making his writing serve his purpose and often find pleasure in doing it. *Clarity* is intimately associated with ease. *Suitability* in writing is highly important for all social purposes, and originality adds flavor and interest for both writer and reader."[16]

Writing in the elementary school is a developmental process which requires planned, systematic, and sequential guidance. A rather acceptable practice of teaching is one which involves group or cooperative writing followed by the individual pupil writing "on his own." According to this procedure, in the first grade, and continuing at each grade level, the pupils as a group compose and dictate cooperative stories or class summaries about common experiences. Frequently the teacher records the stories on charts for the pupils to read and enjoy. An example of a second-grade cooperative health report for the school newspaper is submitted here as an illustration of this procedure.

[16] National Council of Teachers of English, *op. cit.*

OUR BREAKFAST PARTY

Mrs. Shaver's second grade had a breakfast party at Overlook School. We had cereal, cocoa, juice, and toast for breakfast. Each child had a job to do. It was fun doing our jobs. Our room mothers helped us. Mrs. Moore, our supervisor, and Mrs. Heptinstall, our principal, ate breakfast with us. We had good manners. We enjoyed our breakfast party.[17]

Merely providing opportunities to write will not necessarily mean that pupils will improve their writing. Direct guidance is needed from the teacher. For example, while recording the cooperative story for the class, the teacher should work with the pupils on the skills needed to improve the quality of expression, as well as the mechanics of their work. In such a context, the pupils are more apt to see the need for punctuation, capitalization, correct spelling, and format, as regards indentation and margins. In this process of group evaluation it is possible for pupils to use the skills practiced in the other facets of language arts, reflected in questions such as:

1. What is the main idea we expressed in this paragraph?
2. Did we include enough supporting ideas to clarify the main idea we were trying to express?
3. What should be the order (sequence) in which we should list our information?
4. What are the best words we can use to express our ideas precisely and clearly?
5. Have we used correct grammar? (And so on with the other skills to be taught.)

It appears that such cooperative efforts in writing serve at least two purposes:

1. To motivate the individual pupil to express his own thoughts and feelings through writing.
2. To foster feelings of adequacy in writing.

Again as has been emphasized in the other facets of language arts, skills should be considered as means to ends and not necessarily ends in themselves. The important factors to consider are that (1) most all of the children want to write; and (2) they will perhaps write with originality, creativity, and spontaneity.

[17] This procedure was employed by Mrs. Dorothy Shaver, second-grade teacher, Overlook School, Anne Arundel County, Maryland.

From the standpoint of health, writing has therapeutic value for some children. The following comment by the Commission on the English Curriculum of the National Council of Teachers of English is appropriate: "Through reproducing and reflecting upon experiences which trouble them, [children] are better able to accept and to live them, relieving fears and tensions as they write. Free writing can help teachers understand children. It can also help children to work through some of their problems, thus gaining in confidence and appreciation of their own potentialities and the worth of their own ideas."[18]

There is a high correlation between spelling and reading. To learn to spell a word the pupil uses the same word-recognition skills, involving phonetic, structural, and semantic analysis, that he uses in reading. As the pupil writes, he spells the words that he has heard (listening), has spoken (speaking), and has read (reading). This interrelatedness greatly facilitates the pupil's proficiency in spelling. With this in mind, health words for spelling should perhaps be selected on the basis of frequency and commonness of usage, and as regards cruciality, quality, permanency, and difficulty.

Handwriting involves physical coordination and manipulation. Thus, among other things, handwriting entails the use of muscles and bones of the hand and wrist. For reasons of physical development, *manuscript* writing seems best suited for pupils at the primary level. In this type of writing all the letters of the alphabet are formed with straight lines and circles or parts of circles. The size of the writing tends to decrease in direct relation to the child's development. Although the research in this area is inconclusive, the trend appears to be "much in favor of manuscript for the beginners." Children who begin their writing experiences with manuscript seem to write more freely; that is, they use a larger number of different words than do children who begin with the cursive form. (The latter type requires the joining of letters and involves varying degrees of slanting.) It is also interesting to note that children who begin their school experiences with manuscript seem to spell a larger number of words correctly than do children who begin with cursive writing. As the children develop, cursive writing is introduced.

[18] National Council of Teachers of English, *op. cit.*, p. 236.

Learning to write is a highly individualized skill. To serve its purpose as a form of communication, legible handwriting should be produced with ease and adequate speed. An important aspect is the development of what might be termed a "handwriting consciousness," or the desire to write well so that others may read it easily.

The curriculum area of health offers much material of importance to the individual about which he will perhaps want to write. The following examples illustrate integration of health and writing.

COOPERATIVE GROUP WRITING UNDER TEACHER GUIDANCE

GRADE 4 UNIT—MILK

The Cow Barn and Parlor

A cow barn and parlor were built near Federalsburg by John Smith in May, 1958. It is operated by a tenant farmer with one helper. Over $100,000 has already been spent on it. There are 164 head of Ayrshires in all, and 62 of them are being milked at the present time.

Six cows are brought up a passageway into the parlor at the time to be milked. They are washed with warm water first, and then milked with electric milkers. The milk is drawn up into an overhead glass tube from which it passes into a metal vat in the tiled cooling room next door. The vat has coils under the metal and cold air keeps the milk refrigerated to 36 degrees constantly. The vat holds 1065 gallons of milk at a time, and this one piece of machinery cost $5000.

A refrigerated truck from Washington collects 3000 pounds of milk from there every other day. The butterfat content averages 4.2 percent. The cows are fed corn silage, alfalfa, and dairy feed, plus pasture.

Mr. Smith owns four bulls. One of them has already killed two men. This bull is very fierce and weighs a ton. He cost $5000. In time, Mr. Smith hopes to have 150 cows giving milk each day.[19]

GRADE 2 UNIT—FOODS

Good Table Manners

We sit properly at the table.
We place the napkin on our lap.
We keep our free hand in our lap.
We keep our feet flat on the floor.

[19] This material is adapted from a procedure employed by Miss Ruth Brown, fourth-grade teacher at the Federalsburg School, Caroline County, Maryland.

We talk pleasantly and quietly.
We talk when there is no food in our mouth.
We use our napkin.

GRADE 2 UNIT—FOODS

Good Eating Habits

We wash our hands with soap and water before we eat.
We put a small amount of food in our mouth at a time.
We chew our food well.
We relax before and after we eat.[20]

GRADE 1 UNIT—FOODS

Manners at the Grocery Store

We look at and listen to Mr. Mann, the manager.
We keep our hands at our sides.
If we are in front we look at what is being shown. Then we move aside so others can see.
If Mr. Mann asks any questions we will raise our hand and wait to be called on by him.
If we have a question we want to ask, we wait our turn and ask it in a sentence.
We say "Thank you" quietly before leaving.[21]

WRITING BY INDIVIDUAL PUPILS

GRADE 4 UNIT—MILK

A Visit to Johnson's Dairy

On Monday, the fourth grade in Mrs. Gray's room went to Johnson's Dairy in Newtown, Delaware. When we got there, Mr. Johnson showed us around. The first thing we saw was samples of milk being tested for butter-fat. Next we saw the milk being pasteurized. They put the heat up to 144 degrees and keep it there for 30 minutes to kill the bacteria. Across from the pasteurizing machine was the homogenizing machine. That breaks down the fat so that it is mixed with the milk. No cream rises on homogenized milk. After this the milk is put into the cooler to be cooled to 36 degrees. The bottles to be filled are washed very carefully. Then they are put into a steamer to be sterilized. They go from there on a conveyor to be filled with the milk and then capped. Next, all the bottles are put in a big 32-degree refrigerated room to keep the milk cool until they are ready to

[20] These procedures were employed by Mrs. Dorothy Shaver, second-grade teacher at Overlook School, Anne Arundel County, Maryland.
[21] This procedure was employed by Miss Clarabelle Blaney, first-grade teacher at the Brooklyn Park Primary School, Anne Arundel County, Maryland.

deliver it. While we were there Mr. Johnson gave us each a half-pint of homogenized milk as a treat. We all enjoyed our visit to the Johnson Dairy.[22]

GRADE 2 UNIT—FOODS

Letter of Invitation

Dear Mrs. Heptinstall,

Please come to our breakfast party at 9:00 A.M. on Monday, February 2, 1959.

Love,
Beth Hamer

"Thank-You" Letter

Dear Mother,

Thank you for helping us with our breakfast party at school.

Love,
Chuckie Jackson[23]

GRADE 1 UNIT—A GOOD BREAKFAST

Couplets

"Milk comes from a cow
The farmer showed me h – –

Bread is good for Lee
A big piece I can s – –"

GRADE 5 UNIT—SAFETY

Couplets

Bobby Russell had a fall,
He was running down the h – – –.

"Don't stand near the batter," said Richard to Rose,
"He's liable to hit you and splatter your n – – –."

GRADE 4 UNIT—MILK

Quatrains (Posters made illustrating each)

We keep ourselves healthy and gay,
By doing the thing that is wise
At lunch we eat platters with free milk,
(Which vitamin D supplies.)

---

[22] This material is adapted from a report written by a fourth-grade pupil for the school newspaper.

[23] These procedures were employed by Mrs. Dorothy Shaver, second-grade teacher at Overlook School, Anne Arundel County, Maryland.

I'm Little Boy Blue with my golden horn,
My posture will please, sure as you're born.
I stand so tall and straight each day
(Milk makes strong bones that grow that way.)

We're Jack and Jill who climbed the hill,
Our pails with milk, we did fill.
Milk is good for us we know
(It gives us calcium to make us grow.)[24]

SPELLING LIST OF HEALTH WORDS
GRADE 4 UNIT—FOODS

bath	drink	nose
bathe	ears	posture
bread	eyes	sleep
breakfast	fruit	soap
brush	growth	strong
butter	hair	teeth
cereal	handkerchief	tooth
clean	health	vegetables
clothes	juice	wash
comb	milk	water

GRADE 5 UNIT—CARE AND IMPORTANCE OF TEETH

brush	dentist	root
cavity	enamel	structures
clean	molars	teeth
crown	neck	temporary
decay	permanent	tooth
dentine	pulp	

GRADE 6 UNIT—NUTRITION

alcohol	digestion	perspiration
anger	energy	phosphorus
beverage	enriched bread	protein
body-building	fats and oils	refrigerator
calcium	fuel	skim milk
cereal	growth	starch
cheerfulness	manners	sugar
citrus fruit	milk	vitamin
cocoa	minerals	whole-grain
coffee	napkin	worry
creamery	pasteurize	

24 This procedure was employed by Miss Ruth Brown, fourth-grade teacher, at the Federalsburg School, Caroline County, Maryland.

REFERENCES

Anderson, Paul S., *Resource Materials for Teachers of Spelling*, Minneapolis, Burgess, 1959.

Betts, Emmett, *Foundations of Reading Instruction*, New York, American, 1946.

Burton, William H. et al., *Reading in Child Development*, Indianapolis, Bobbs-Merrill, 1956.

Commission of the English Curriculum of the National Council of the Teachers of English, *Language Arts for Today's Children*, New York, Appleton-Century-Crofts, 1954.

Dawson, Mildred A., and Marian Zollinger, *Guiding Language Learning*, New York, World, 1957.

Freeman, Frank N., *The Teaching of Handwriting*, Washington, D.C., Department of Classroom Teachers, National Education Association, 1954.

Greene, Harry, and Walter Petty, *Developing Language Skills in the Elementary School*, Boston, Allyn and Bacon, 1959.

Hatchett, E., and D. H. Hughes, *Teaching Language Arts in the Elementary Schools*, New York, Ronald, 1959.

Herrick, Virgil, and Leland Jacobs, *Children and the Language Arts*, Englewood Cliffs, N.J., Prentice-Hall, 1955.

Hildreth, Gertrude, *Teaching Spelling*, New York, Holt, 1955.

Horn, Ernest, *The Teaching of Spelling*, Washington, D.C., Department of Classroom Teachers, National Education Association, 1954.

Humphrey, James H., and Virginia D. Moore, "Improved Reading Through Physical Education," *Education*, May, 1960.

Hunnicutt, C. W., and William J. Iverson, eds., *Research in the Three R's*, New York, Harper, 1958, Part I, "The First 'R' "; Part II, "The Second 'R.' "

International Reading Association, "New Frontiers in Reading Research," *Reading Teacher*, December, 1958.

International Reading Association, "Promoting Growth in the Interpretation of What Is Read," *Reading Teacher*, February, 1959.

International Reading Association, "The Perceptive Process in Reading," *Reading Teacher*, October, 1959.

International Reading Association, "Research in Reading," *Reading Teacher*, December, 1959.

Russell, David R., *Children's Thinking*, Boston, Ginn, 1956.

Spache, George D., *Good Reading for Poor Readers*, Champaign, Ill., Garrard, 1958.

Strickland, Ruth, *The Language Arts in the Elementary School,* Boston, Heath, 1957.

Tidyman, Willard F., and Marguerite Butterfield, *Teaching the Language Arts,* 2nd ed., New York, McGraw-Hill, 1959.

Tooze, Ruth, *Storytelling,* Englewood Cliffs, N.J., Prentice-Hall, 1959.

United States Department of Health, Education and Welfare, Office of Education, *How Children Learn to Write,* Washington, D.C., Government Printing Office, 1953.

Van Riper, Charles and Katherine G. Butler, *Speech in the Elementary Classroom,* New York, Harper, 1955.

Veatch, Jeannette, *Individualizing Your Reading Program,* New York, Putnam's, 1959.

INTEGRATION
OF HEALTH
AND SOCIAL STUDIES

13

1 *What specific objectives of education can be furthered through the teaching of health and social studies?*
2 *How can the social health climate of the classroom influence the quality of learning that takes place in both health and social studies?*
3 *How can the procedures involved in unit teaching be used as an effective procedure for carrying on democratic processes?*
4 *How can the methods used to teach health and social studies strengthen the democratic principles of identifying, nurturing, and wisely using the talents of people in a free society?*
5 *What are some of the social studies learning activities involved in the teaching of health?*

Throughout life, man, as a dynamic human being, is involved in the processes of social relationships. In our democratic society, human relationships, rights, and responsibilities constitute basic human values set forth as basic tenets. Hence, it follows that the philosophy of education includes an expression of the belief that each individual be afforded opportunities for optimum growth socially, as well as intellectually, physically, and emotionally. To this end, the school as an agency in a democracy is charged with the responsibility of offering experiences through which the individual grows and develops in his ability to function effectively as a participating member of society, at whatever his maturity level.

Social education is a broad term which refers in general to all of the experiences which contribute to the child's social learning. However, for purposes of this discussion, social education in the elementary school will be limited to the social learning situations inherent in the subjects of health and social studies.

A description of the area of social studies by Beck, Cook, and Kearney suggests that "Social studies include all man's group skills and attitudes, all the knowledge of man's interdependence with other men and with nature, all his social customs and mores, and all his moral and spiritual values as they affect his living with his fellows."[1]

In current educational literature there can be found some differences of opinion concerning the number of different subjects to be taught in the block of time that is assigned daily to the teaching of social studies. On the other hand, there seems to be rather common agreement among educators that geography, history, and civics constitute the major subjects in the social studies program for the elementary school. Among other things, this postulation is predicated upon certain generalizations, as follows:

1. From a study of the subject matter taught in the areas of geography, history, and civics, it is hoped that the pupils will arrive at basic concepts needed in becoming a *well-informed member* of a democratic society.
2. Through the teaching of social sciences involving individuals interacting with others in their environment, it is hoped that the pupils will gain competencies in the *processes of socialization.*
3. Through the use of appropriate methods in the teaching of social sciences it is hoped that the pupils will have opportunities to grow and develop in their abilities to use procedures needed to function effectively as *a participating member* in a democratic society.

In this context, health and social studies have a high degree of compatibility in at least two important respects. That is, both are concerned with (1) the kind of environment in which learning takes place, and (2) the quality of the learning experiences. Succinctly stated, the integration of health and social studies involves relating the so-called "whole" child to the environment in which he finds himself, to the end that both he and his environment may profit from the interaction.

[1] Robert H. Beck, Walter W. Cook, and Nolan C. Kearney, *Curriculum in the Modern Elementary School,* New York, Prentice-Hall, 1953, p. 288.

SOCIAL HEALTH CLIMATE OF THE CLASSROOM

The role of the pupil in the classroom might well serve as an identifying characteristic of any system of education. Based on the values placed upon the dignity and worth of the individual, the classroom in the modern elementary school should serve as a laboratory for human relations and be representative of a miniature democratic society. Learning thus becomes a matter of personal meaning to the individual.

Education, as we have known it, has done pretty well in two of its phases. It has been quite successful in gathering information and making information available to people. These problems we have pretty well solved. Our greatest failures are those connected with the problem of helping people to behave differently as a result of the information we have provided them. . . . Modern perceptual psychology is helping us to see the problem of learning in a somewhat different way. Learning, we are coming to understand, is not simply a matter of motivation, repetition, presentation, stimulation, conditioning, and the like, although, of course, all of these are part of the problem. Learning, we are coming to understand, is a problem of total personality. It is a problem of an individual's personal discovery of meaning.[2]

In a further analysis of the factors upon which an individual's perception is based, Combs lists the following:

1. The nature of the physical organism he possesses.
2. The length of time he has lived.
3. The opportunities he has had in the past to perceive.
4. The operation of his current needs. People perceive what they need to perceive.
5. The goals and values the individual holds. People perceive what they value.
6. The self concept. People perceive what seems to them appropriate to perceive. Men perceive like men; women perceive like women.
7. The experience of threat. Threat hinders perception.[3]

In the past, intelligence to some extent has been thought of as a somewhat static quality, remaining throughout life within a rather

[2] Arthur W. Combs, "Personality Theory and Its Implications for Curriculum Development," *Learning More About Learning,* Washington, D.C., Association for Supervision and Curriculum Development, National Education Association, 1959, p. 9.

[3] *Ibid,* pp. 13, 14.

narrowly measured range. However, if the quality and frequency of experiences through time tend to increase the individual's personal discovery of meaning, one might expect the individual to operate at increasingly higher intellectual levels. With the increased importance which perceptual psychology attaches to the significance of increasing the depth, richness, and extent of experience, the classroom teacher as never before faces the task of improving the quality of the educational experiences offered the pupils in the classroom.

UNIT TEACHING IN HEALTH AND SOCIAL STUDIES

Thus far it has been pointed out that the social health climate of the classroom used in the teaching of health and social studies contributes to the total growth and development of children in a democratic society.

With this thought in mind, it is more readily understood why the unit method[4] evolved as an effective procedure for teaching health and social studies. Among its many advantages, unit teaching lends itself to:

1. Democratic practices and procedures in the classroom
2. Individualization of instruction
3. Many kinds of achievement at many levels
4. Development of the uniqueness of the individual
5. Identification and development of talents and special abilities among pupils
6. Development of feelings of security, adequacy, and belongingness among the pupils
7. Learning experiences appropriate to each stage of pupil development with its accompanying developmental tasks
8. Integration of the physical, social, intellectual, and emotional aspects of the individual

HEALTH CONCEPTS INHERENT IN THE SOCIAL STUDIES CONTENT

The teaching of health and social studies deals with the child in his educative process. The discussion, thus far, espouses the demo-

[4] For a discussion of how to plan and teach a unit of work, see Chapter 6, "Planning for Health Teaching."

cratic processes employed in the teaching of health and social studies. In addition to the procedures used for teaching there is yet another relevant facet of integration. An analysis of the concepts in the social studies curriculum indicates the importance placed upon the teaching of health by including health content as an integral part of the social studies curriculum. Such integration enhances the effectiveness of social learnings for the pupil by strengthening, extending, and giving depth, meaning, and pertinence to the knowl edges he needs as an intelligent, informed person. Since health involves the functioning of man in his total environment, it seems logical to assume that not only the knowledge and wisdom derived from a study of geography, history, and civics, but that from arithmetic, science, art, music and physical education needs to be integrated with health.

With the present knowledge of child growth and development, and how learning is internalized, the *approach* to what children learn takes on new and added significance if the objectives of social studies are to be realized.

The objectives of social studies as stated by Tiegs and Adams represent an "extension of the prime purposes of the social studies which appeared in the Fourteenth Yearbook of the Department of Superintendence entitled *Social Studies Curriculum."* These four major objectives are:

1. Acquiring and using the abilities and skills essential in intelligent, cooperative participation in group activities; carrying individual as well as group (civic) responsibilities. (Stress is placed on learning through *group* processes as well as through individual effort.)
2. Building and using concepts, insights, and understandings which are important in carrying on daily activities at increasing levels of maturity. (The accent is on the *use* rather than on the *accumulation* of realistic knowledge, insights, etc.)
3. Developing and using the desirable ideals, attitudes, and skills which are essential in good human relations. (The emphasis here is on habitual desirable behavior in everyday relationships rather than achievement of an *appreciation* of the good or a desire to do what is right.)
4. Acquiring and using critical-thinking and problem-solving skills. (The *use* of these skills in the solution of personal as well as social problems is the important goal.)[5]

[5] Ernest W. Tiegs and Fay Adams, *Teaching the Social Studies—A Guide to Better Citizenship*, Boston, Ginn, 1959, p. 38.

An analysis of these objectives indicates the emphasis of the social studies program in the elementary school to be upon the life experiences of the child. In this context, certain aspects of health become an integral part of the social studies program.

Social studies involve more than the teaching of separate subjects such as geography, history, civics, and the like. The discipline involves the integration of various subjects, each contributing to the objectives as stated. To illustrate this point, parts of a resource unit on clothing are given. This particular topic was selected because:

1. Clothing is rather generally accepted as a social studies topic, with subject matter appearing in the most widely used social studies textbook series for the elementary school.
2. Clothing represents a need of people everywhere.
3. Clothing is also among the ten categories used in this text for organizing the health content at the various grade levels.

RESOURCE UNIT—CLOTHING (GRADE 3)

SUBJECT MATTER AREA	CONCEPTS	CONTENT
Health	Clothing is one of man's basic needs.	A. Why do we wear clothing?
Health	Clothes protect the body.	1. How does clothing meet bodily needs?
Health	Clothes satisfy certain social needs.	2. How does clothing satisfy social needs?
Social studies	The sources of clothing are numerous and varied.	B. What are the sources of our clothing?
Social studies	The knowledge and skills of many people are necessary for the production of materials for clothing.	
Arithmetic	Much time is required to produce the materials for clothing.	

PART I—ANIMALS
Animals That Give Us Wool

Science		1. What animals give us wool?

RESOURCE UNIT—CLOTHING (GRADE 3) (*Cont.*)

SUBJECT MATTER AREA	CONCEPTS	CONTENT
Geography-Science	Climatic conditions are a determining factor in the producing of wool.	2. Where are the wool-producing areas?
Science	The raising of sheep for wool requires special knowledge and skills.	3. How are sheep raised to produce wool for clothing?
Science	The fleece is spun into yarn which is used to make woolen cloth.	4. How is raw wool made ready for the mills? 5. What happens to the fleece at the mills?
History	Methods of making woolen cloth improve from time to time.	6. How is woolen yarn made into cloth?
Health	We wear many articles of clothing made from wool.	7. What articles of clothing are made of wool?

Animals That Give Us Silk

Science	Silk comes from silkworms.	1. How are silkworms raised to produce silk for clothing?
Geography-History	The first silk was produced in China long ago.	2. Where was silk first produced?
Science	Numerous processes, such as heating, soaking, reeling, and winding are used.	3. What processes are used to get raw silk for the mills?
Science	Much knowledge and care are required to produce silk cloth.	4. How is silk made into cloth?
Social studies	Pure silk garments are often expensive.	5. What articles of clothing are made of silk?

Animals That Give Us Fur

Science	Numerous animals produce fur used for clothing.	1. What animals give us fur for clothing?

RESOURCE UNIT—CLOTHING (GRADE 3) (*Cont.*)

SUBJECT MATTER AREA	CONCEPTS	CONTENT
Geography	Climatic conditions can affect the quality of fur.	2. Where are most fur-producing animals found?
Science-Geography	Animals are raised on ranches, or are hunted and trapped in their natural habitat.	3. How are animals obtained for fur?
Science	Special knowledge and skill are required to process fur.	4. What are the steps in processing fur for use?
Social studies	Fur serves in numerous ways for clothing.	5. How is fur used for clothes?

Animals That Give Us Leather

Science	Birds, fishes, mammals, and reptiles produce leather for clothing.	1. What animals give us leather for clothing?
Science	Numerous processes are used in making leather.	2. What processes are used in making leather?
Social studies	Articles of clothing made from leather serve many purposes.	3. What articles of clothing are made of leather?

PART II—PLANTS

COTTON

Science	Cotton is a plant.	1. How is cotton raised?
Geography-Science	Cotton grows in a warm climate.	2. Where is cotton raised?
Geography-Science	Much of the south has a mild climate, abundant rainfall, and a long growing season.	
Geography	Cotton is among the most important crops raised in the south.	

RESOURCE UNIT—CLOTHING (GRADE 3) (*Cont.*)

SUBJECT MATTER AREA	CONCEPTS	CONTENT
Science-History	The invention of the cotton gin greatly increased cotton-raising in the south.	3. How is cotton prepared for the mill?
Science-History	Modern machines make cotton into cloth.	4. How is cotton made into cloth?
Science-History Arithmetic	Articles of cotton are not as expensive today as in the past, because new machines have greatly lowered its cost.	5. What articles of clothing are made of cotton?

Flax

Science-Geography	Flax is a plant. Climatic conditions are a determining factor in the production of flax.	1. How is flax raised? 2. Where is flax raised? Why?
Science	Many operations are performed between the time the stalks are retted and the fibers are made into threads for weaving.	3. How is flax made into cloth?
Social studies	Pure linen garments can be expensive.	4. What articles of clothing are made from linen?

Rubber

Science-Geography	Rubber is a plant. Rubber comes from trees that grow in warm, rainy climates.	1. How is rubber raised? 2. Where is rubber raised?
Science	Numerous processes are involved from the time rubber sap leaves the tree until it is made into an article of clothing.	3. How is rubber made into articles of clothing?

RESOURCE UNIT—CLOTHING (GRADE 3) (*Cont.*)

SUBJECT MATTER AREA	CONCEPTS	CONTENT
Science	Some clothing accessories are made of pure rubber. Synthetic rubber is used also.	4. What articles of clothing are made of rubber?

PART III—SYNTHETICS

Science	Rayon, nylon, dacron and other synthetics are used for making clothing.	1. What synthetics are used for making clothing?
Science- Geography	Many materials used today are made from wood pulp, milk, soybeans, and coal.	2. Of what are synthetics made?
Science	Synthetics are man-made by "putting together" materials.	3. What does the word *synthetic* mean?
Science	Many articles of clothing are made from synthetics.	4. What articles of clothing are made of synthetics?
Science- social studies	Synthetics have special characteristics which make them attractive to the buyer.	5. Why are synthetics an increasing source of clothing?
Science	Synthetics are becoming increasingly important as a source of our clothing.	
Social studies- Science	Cloth from clothing goes from the mills to the factories.	C. How are clothes made? 1. Where are clothes made?
	Many processes are used in the making of clothes.	2. What processes are used in making clothes?
Social studies- Science	Many people and many different machines are necessary for the manufacturing of materials for clothing.	3. What machinery and other implements are used in making clothes? 4. What people make our clothing?

RESOURCE UNIT—CLOTHING (GRADE 3) (*Cont.*)

SUBJECT MATTER AREA	CONCEPTS	CONTENT
Social studies	Clothing can be made in clothing factories, at a tailor shop, or at home.	
Social studies	Clothing factories supply clothing to the wholesale house.	D. How are clothes bought and sold? 1. How do articles of clothing get from factories to retail stores?
Social studies	Wholesale houses buy and sell in large quantities.	
Social studies	Retail stores buy clothing to sell from the wholesale house.	
Social studies	We are dependent upon the employees of distributing houses and stores to make clothing available to us.	2. What services are provided by retail stores in selling clothes to us?
Social studies	Displays, advertisements, and sales persons help people know which clothing is for sale.	
Health-Arithmetic-Science	People select clothing on the basis of style, color, wearing qualities, cost, and the season of the year or the place where the clothing is to be worn.	3. What factors are considered in purchasing clothes?
Arithmetic	Many factors determine the price of clothing.	
Health	We have the responsibility to prevent undue wear and soiling of our clothes.	E. How are clothes cared for? 1. How can we maintain the appearance and durability of our clothes.
Health	The care of our clothes to make them feel better, look better, and last longer is the joint re-	2. How do others help us care for our clothes?

RESOURCE UNIT—CLOTHING (GRADE 3) (*Cont.*)

SUBJECT MATTER AREA	CONCEPTS	CONTENT
	sponsibility of ourselves, our parents, and other people.	
Social studies	Boys and girls of many countries wear clothes like ours.	F. What kinds of clothes are worn by people around the world?
Geography	Latitude, nearness to bodies of water, direction of winds, and altitudes influence climate.	1. What kinds of clothes are worn in hot, wet climates?
Geography	Climate influences the clothes people wear.	2. What kinds of clothes are worn in hot, dry climates? 3. What kinds of clothes are worn in and near the frigid zone?
History-Health	Festive occasions mean "dress up" time.	4. What kinds of clothes are worn by children in different countries for festive occasions?[6]

Social Studies Activities Involving Health

Through integration, certain health concepts tend to take on new and added meanings for the individual. Frequently health resource units and teaching units include activities involving the social studies. To illustrate this integration, examples of geography, history, and civic activities are listed. These activities appear under the categories used in this text to include the health teaching content for the elementary school.

FOODS AND NUTRITION

Make a pictorial map to show foods that are characteristic of particular countries throughout the world (geography).

[6] This unit was adapted from Board of Education of Anne Arundel County, *Social Studies Bulletin—Grade Three,* Annapolis, Md., Board of Education, 1957, pp. 140–180.

Make a study of the food habits of people in other countries of the world to note the influence of geographical conditions on kinds of food available (geography).

Select a dinner menu and find the possible geographical location where each food might have been grown (geography).

On a political-physical map of the United States, locate the regions where vitamin C foods are prevalent (geography).

Make a food-products map for each geographical region of the United States (geography).

Study the geographical distribution of foods (geography).

Make a table model relief map of the United States. Use appropriate symbols to indicate the grain-, fruit-, dairy-, vegetable-, and wheat-producing areas (geography).

Study the geographical conditions necessary to raise sugar cane and sugar beets (geography).

Compare a breakfast menu of the 1760s with a breakfast of today (history).

Trace the origin of some of the foods we eat today; such as corn bread and succotash (history).

Exercise and Physical Activity

Learn games, dances, and relays from different countries of the world. Locate countries in which these activities originated (geography).

Learn dances and games from colonial days (history).

Trace the history of the Olympic games and discuss their value (history).

Sleep, Rest, Relaxation

Mark time belts on a map of the world. Indicate what time it is in your locality when children in each of the other time belts might be going to bed (geography).

Make a study of the kinds of beds and bed coverings used in other countries (geography).

Discuss the siesta. Relate this practice to climatic conditions (geography).

Safety

Make a series of safety maps including school grounds and neighborhood (geography).

Have map legends include symbols for:

School map:

Halls

Corners

Stairways
Exits from buildings
Direction of traffic
Fire alarm boxes
School ground map:
Blacktop area
Grass area
Parking area
Playground equipment
Areas designated for different activities
Directions for flow of traffic to and from physical education and
recess periods
Neighborhood map:
Roads
Streets
Sidewalks
Traffic signals
Road signs
Marks on road
Safety patrol or police protected intersections

Make a spot map of your neighborhood showing types and places of accidents (geography). Indicate which accidents might have been avoided if traffic regulations had been obeyed or pedestrians had not been careless (civics).

Organize a bicycle club. Write a code of behavior for bicycle riders (civics).

Practice reporting fires and participate in fire drills (civics).

Make a survey of school and home for possible fire hazards (civics).

Visit a fire station to learn ways to prevent fires and to cooperate with firemen (civics).

Write notes to policemen, firemen, and safety patrol members to express appreciation for their protection (civics).

STIMULANTS

On a map of the world, locate the coffee- and tea-producing areas. Discuss the geographical conditions that contribute to the growth of these plants (geography).

CLOTHING

Study rainfall and temperature maps to note conditions favorable to the growing of flax (geography).

Locate the zones and hemispheres on a globe. Discuss the clothing which might be worn by children in each hemisphere and zone when it is New Year's Day in your community (geography).

Using an outline map of the world, make a pictorial map to show the areas where wool, silk, cotton, and flax are produced (geography).

Study the dress of peoples in various parts of the world to note geographical influence on clothing (geography).

Make a frieze to show how fur-bearing animals live in their natural habitat (geography).

Give oral reports on Eli Whitney, James Hargreaves, and other inventors who have contributed to the growth of the textile industry (history).

Compare clothes worn by children in colonial days with clothes worn by children today (history).

Examine a spinning wheel. Make and use a hand loom. Make natural dyes and dye cloth. Visit a cloth mill to observe modern machines for spinning, weaving, and dyeing (history).

Examine hand clippers and electric clippers used to shear sheep (history),

The Human Organism—Its Structure, Function, and Care

Trace the history of bathing, including such items as the introduction of soap, bathtubs, showers, Turkish baths (history).

Make soap. Compare soap-making today with soap-making by the pioneers (history).

Health Services

Play the role of nurse and doctor who are administering immunization "shots" to pupils (civics).

Discuss the significance of pure food and drug laws and other health legislation (civics).

Discuss the significance and implications of the World Health Organization and the "health for peace" movement (civics).

Participate in city-wide health campaigns (civics).

Survey the health problems existing in your community (civics).

Discuss health problems related to specific geographical areas (geography).

Study the history of the following (history):

>   Use of antiseptics (Lister)
>   Discovery of microscope (Leeuwenhoek)
>   Discovery of X ray (Roentgen)
>   Discovery of vaccination (Jenner)

Discuss the evolution of hospitals and the medical and nursing profession (history).

REFERENCES

Ambrose, Edna, and Alice Miel, *Children's Social Learning,* Washington, D.C., Association for Supervision and Curriculum Development, 1958.

Association for Supervision and Curriculum Development, *A Look at Continuity in the School Program,* Yearbook, Washington, D.C., the Association, 1958.

Association for Supervision and Curriculum Development, *Learning and the Teacher,* Yearbook, Washington, D.C., the Association, 1959.

Association for Supervision and Curriculum Development, *Learning More About Learning,* Washington, D.C., 1959.

Association for Supervision and Curriculum Development, *Fostering Mental Health in Our Schools,* 1950 Yearbook, Washington, D.C., 1950.

Carpenter, Helen M., ed., *Skills in the Social Studies,* Twenty-fourth Yearbook, Washington, D.C., National Council for the Social Studies, 1953.

Hanna, Lavone A., Gladys L. Potter, and Neva Hogaman, *Unit Teaching in the Elementary Schools,* New York, Rinehart, 1956.

Lane, Howard, and Mary Beauchamp, *Understanding Human Development,* Englewood Cliffs, N.J., Prentice-Hall, 1959.

Michaelis, John U., *Social Studies for Children in a Democracy,* New York, Prentice-Hall, 1950.

Miel, Alice, *et al., Cooperative Procedures in Learning,* New York, Columbia University, 1952.

Miel, Alice, and Peggy Brogan, *More than Social Studies,* Englewood Cliffs, N.J., Prentice-Hall, 1957.

Preston, Ralph C., *Teaching Social Studies in the Elementary School,* New York, Rinehart, 1955.

Tiegs, Ernest and Fay Adams, *Teaching the Social Studies,* Boston, Ginn, 1959.

INTEGRATION
OF HEALTH
AND SCIENCE

1 *What are some of the present trends in the teaching of elementary school science and health?*

2 *How can the scientific approach to learning be used effectively to develop health concepts?*

3 *Which skills needed in everyday life situations can be used to develop health concepts?*

4 *What desirable changes in the child's behavior might be evident as a result of experiences with the scientific approach to health?*

5 *Which health concepts are inherent in the science content for the elementary school child?*

The health program and the science program in the elementary schools are characterized by divergent yet somewhat similar practices. These practices are evident from the available textbooks, recent courses of study, and the teaching units used in the classrooms. For instance, some publishers offer separate series of health and science textbooks. Other publishers have science-health series for the elementary schools. Further examination reveals separate courses of study in health and in science, while other courses of study include health and science as a part of the total social studies program. Teaching units follow the same practices; that is, there are separate units for health and for science, or ones integrating health and science. One generalization seems rather apparent; that is, there is a common agreement that health and science are essential, and that

1 The authors are grateful to Alan L. Dodd, Visiting Lecturer in Elementary School Science, University of Maryland for his critical reading of this chapter.

both should be included in the curriculum offerings for elementary school children. It is the purpose of this discussion to examine the teaching of health and science, with special attention given to integration.

TRENDS IN THE TEACHING OF ELEMENTARY SCIENCE AND HEALTH

Until recently elementary school science tended to emphasize biology, that is, the nature study approach, rather than physical science. In more recent years there appears to be more emphasis upon the *physical* aspects of matter, such as motion, force, friction, sound, light, gravity, air pressure, and the like. Whereas, in past years, health in the elementary school, tended to deal with the biological aspects of animal life, with emphasis on the structure and function of the human organism.

In more recent years many influences have come to bear upon elementary education. Teaching as a profession has become more scientific as a result of advances in many fields affecting learning. As an example, the present knowledge of human growth and development provides scientific information in such areas as (1) the characteristics of elementary school children; (2) their developmental tasks; (3) their needs and interests; and (4) the psychology of their learning. In turn, this and other scientific advances influence not only what is taught but how it is taught, in terms of evolving objectives of elementary education.

While in the past, the lines of demarcation seemed somewhat sharply drawn between science and health, a more careful study of current trends seems to indicate that the two aspects of elementary school science—physical and biological—are more compatible and more integrated in the actual teaching-learning situation than might appear at a casual glance. With this in mind the following discussion might serve to identify current thinking and practices concerning the integration of health and science.

During the 1950s, some science-health textbooks became available for the elementary schools. Recently, leading publishers of textbooks have offered complete series of science-health textbooks for Grades 1 through 6. These books were probably designed to take the place of two separate series—one in health and one in science. When a science-health text approach is used, it is expected that the teaching of health and science will follow a planned, developmental, and sequential program. Among other things, attention is given to planning the sequence to make sure that the concepts increase in difficulty in relation to the pupils' maturity, and that the foundation for particular concepts is laid in an earlier grade. In such a program, concepts grow gradually and mature as they grow.

Through the use of a definite course of study materials the practice of integrating science and health tends to eliminate the chances of incidental teaching of these subjects. They are not incidental in the everyday experiences of elementary school children. The growing child spurred by his curiosity explores, investigates, and attempts to learn about his environment, regardless of whether or not he is taught about it. When there is a planned science-health program centered around his needs and interests, the pupil is provided with the learnings and "know-how" that he needs to understand himself and his environment, and to relate himself to that environment as a participating member. An example of the feeling of some science educators in this regard is brought out rather forcefully in the following statements by Blough, Schwartz, and Huggett: "The health education program and the science experiences go hand in hand in today's elementary school program. A well-designed science program helps pupils to see the "why" of some of the health education experiences. . . . It is highly desirable that the two areas of study be taught together or at least be considered together in the planning. Such planning would eliminate needless overlapping, provide opportunities for the two areas to be mutually helpful, and provide a more meaningful experience for pupils."[2]

The Forty-sixth Yearbook of the National Council for the Study of Education states that "children should by the end of each year . . . have experienced growth in the broader areas of the *physical* and *biological* environment, such as the following:

The Universe: Study of the stars, the sun, the moon, the planets and their inter-relationships; causes of day and night, seasonal changes, tides, eclipses, and (less completely) of the vastness of the Milky Way and of galactic systems beyond our own.
The Earth: Origin, formation of mountains, weathering of rock into soil,

2 Glenn O. Blough, Julius Schwartz, and Albert J. Huggett, *Elementary School Science and How to Teach It,* New York, Dryden, 1958, p. 327.

erosion, volcanism, prehistoric life, and the forces that are changing and have changed the earth.

Conditions Necessary to Life: What living things need in order to exist, how they are affected by changes in the environment and the struggle for existence.

Living Things: Variety, social life, adaptations for protection, life cycles of plants and animals, how they obtain food, their economic importance, and man's influence upon nature.

Physical and Chemical Phenomena: Common chemical and physical phenomena such as light, sound, gravity, magnetism, and electricity; changes in matter; and phenomena associated with radiant energy and atmospheric changes.

Man's Attempt to Control His Environment: In gardens, on farms, in orchards, inventions and discoveries; use of power and of minerals; his control over living things; his study of places he cannot reach directly; and other such topics."[3]

A fundamental tenet of science education emphasizes the relatedness of science to the total curriculum, especially in the areas of health and social studies. Through the integration of health and science, both areas can be re-enforced, and the subject matter can be more functional and coherent for the pupils. The practical application of this integration is found in current practices used by some teachers to extend and broaden concepts. Three illustrations are cited as examples. First, when pupils study about light (physical science) it seems appropriate to include a study of the eye (biological science or health). Second, when the human ear is being studied, learnings can be enhanced through a study of sound. Third, the study of electricity has a practical application when integrated with safety.

SCIENTIFIC METHOD OF DEVELOPING HEALTH CONCEPTS

It is common knowledge that the elementary school pupil possesses an intrinsic urge to learn about himself and his environment. This seemingly innate desire provides self-motivation—a desirable

[3] National Society for the Study of Education, *Forty-sixth Yearbook*, Part I, "Science Education in American Schools," Chicago, University of Chicago Press, 1947, pp. 75–76.

prerequisite to effective learning. For the most part when a pupil wants to know, or is self-motivated, he asks questions and more questions. Even before he starts to school he begins to ask questions. "Why Daddy?" is only the beginning of what should be a lifetime of intelligent inquiry. "Why do I get hungry when I play?" "Where does the sun go when it sets?" "Why do we grow two sets of teeth?" "Where does a light go when it goes out?" "How can medicine when swallowed stop a headache?" "Do people have to die?" "What makes it rain?" "Why do I get out of breath when I run?" These questions are indicative of the normal, ceaseless flow of inquiry that is characteristic of the curiosity aroused and stimulated by health and science in the daily life of the elementary school child. Certainly one criterion for daily evaluation might be *how many intelligent questions* have been asked by pupils as a result of teaching. Through the integration of health and science, the teacher can plan meaningful experiences "around the solving of problems which are significant to the pupils, rather than answering unimportant questions that stress the recall of unrelated scientific facts."[4]

Health and science are "child-centered" because the subject matter comes from the everyday world of the pupils. Also, the method of acquiring the subject matter is familiar. During the preschool years, the child uses some of the same methods used in school to find out about himself and his world. After entering school he acquires additional ways to learn. Hence, as an elementary school pupil, when he is faced with a problem to solve, it is natural for him to ask questions, investigate, observe, manipulate, construct, experiment, read, and discuss in order to arrive at acceptable solutions and meaningful generalizations. As he grows and matures he becomes more skillful in these methods and functions at increasingly higher levels of operation.

Thus, health and science involve more than subject matter, facts, and concepts; they involve a way of solving problems, a way of thinking known as the scientific method.

Health teaching might well be characterized by the use of the scientific method in the development of health concepts. Among other things this method involves two significant factors, namely, a problem and the process of solving it. In order to use the scien-

4 Blough, Schwartz, and Huggett, *op. cit.,* p. 8.

tific method to develop health concepts, pupils become involved in the learning process of formulating and stating a problem. "A problem is a task which a child can understand but for which he does not have an immediate solution. Problem solving, accordingly, is the process by which the child goes from the task or problem as he sees it to a solution which for him, meets the demands of the problem."[5]

The pupils are further involved in the learning process as they participate in the necessary steps of the scientific method in solving problems relating to health and science. The following three outcomes are apparent: (1) health concepts tend to be learned more thoroughly, (2) skills of scientific thinking involved in approaching and solving problems tend to become more functional, and (3) the scientific approach tends to help pupils develop a scientific attitude. Therefore it seems imperative that the teacher's plan include both the concept and the procedure,[6] since the pupils will be learning both.

As an example, a lesson plan for Grade 6 might include the following: (1) Science and health concepts previously developed with the pupils: Food is prepared for the use of the body by the process of digestion.[7] (2) Health concept for this lesson: Digestion changes food so that it can pass into the blood and be used by the cells. Guides for the teacher are followed by purposeful activities involving steps in scientific thinking.

I. Help the pupils to identify, define, and limit the problem.
   Question decided upon with the pupils: How does food that we eat get into our blood?
II. Encourage pupils to formulate tentative hypotheses as they tell from their own experiences what they know about the problem, and what they think is the solution.
III. Guide pupils to suggest appropriate methods for solving the problem, and authoritative sources to use for checking accuracy and authenticity of information gathered.
   Ways to Find the Answers to Today's Question:
   1. Conduct an experiment.

[5] David H. Russell, *Children's Thinking,* Boston, Ginn, 1956, p. 251.
[6] For a discussion of the procedure for teaching by the scientific method, see Chapter 7, "Planning for Health Teaching."
[7] Blough, Schwartz, and Huggett, *op. cit.,* p. 326.

2. Ask the school nurse to come to our classroom and talk with us on the question.

3. Locate and read in the health science books about the digestive and circulatory systems.

4. Study charts showing these two systems.

5. See if we can find additional information at home.

IV. Assist pupils in making careful, accurate observations while gathering pertinent information.

Conduct the following experiment:

1. Remove a small piece of shell from the large end of an egg.

2. Make a small hole through both the shell and the lining in the small end of the egg.

3. Insert a small glass tube through the hole in the small end. Seal around the hole with sealing wax.

4. Place the egg in the top of a bottle with enough water to cover the larger end.

5. Observe the results the next day.[8]

V. Assist the pupils to appraise and verify the information.

Ask the school nurse to use charts on the digestive and circulatory systems in verifying for the children what has happened. Check the conclusions by reading from the following textbooks:

Barnard, J. D., Celia Stendler, and Benjamin Spock, *The Macmillan Science-Life Series*, New York, Macmillan, 1959; Book 4, pp. 159–171; Book 6, pp. 138–142.

Bauer, W. W., D. W. Baruch, E. R. Montgomery, E. T. Pounds, *et al.*, *The Basic Health and Safety Program*, Fair Lawn, N.J., Scott, Foresman, 1957–60; Grade 4, *Going on Ten*, pp. 34, 37, 39–41, 88, 89, 203; Grade 5, *About Yourself*, pp. 148–162; Grade 6, *About All of Us*, pp. 238–240, 242.

Brownell, C. L., R. Evans, and L. B. Hobson, *ABC Health Series*, New York, American, 1959; Grade 5, *Among Friends*, pp. 116, 126, 132, 183; Grade 6, *Crossroads*, pp. 43, 68, 80, 99, 194–204, 219, 230–236.

Byrd, Oliver E., *et al.*, *The New Road to Health Series*, Summit, N.J., Laidlaw, 1960; Grade 5, *Your Health*, pp. 142–145, 126–136, 151–154, 164.

Frasier, G. W., H. D. MacCracken, and D. G. Decker, *Singer Science Series*, Syracuse, N.Y., Singer, 1959; Grade 4, *Singer Science Discoveries*, pp. 191–194; Grade 5, *Singer Science Ex-*

---

[8] Through the process of osmosis, the liquid in the bottle passes through the membrane of the egg. The pressure of additional liquid in the egg causes displacement of some liquid into the glass tube.

periments, pp. 140–145, 150–157; Grade 6, *Singer Science Problems,* pp. 136–137, 146–151, 156, 157.

Hallock, G. T., R. L. Allen, and E. Thomas, *Health for Better Living Series,* Boston, Ginn, 1958; Grade 5, *Keeping Healthy and Strong,* pp. 7, 171, 198–214, 219; Grade 6, *Teamwork for Health,* pp. 53, 54, 163, 164, 195–197.

Irwin, L. W., *et al., Health, Happiness and Success Series,* Wilkes-Barre, Pa., Lyons and Carnahan, 1958; Grade 5, *Health for Better Living,* pp. 55, 57, 97–101.

O'Keefe, P. R., *et al., Winston Health Series,* Philadelphia, Winston, 1960; Grade 5, *Getting Acquainted,* pp. 76–80; Grade 6, *Knowing Yourself,* pp. 127–133.

Schneider, Herman, and Nina Schneider, *Health Elementary Science,* Boston, Health, 1959; Grade 5, *Science in Our World,* pp. 251–255.

VI. Assist the pupils to summarize and organize the relevant information and to draw conclusions. Record the experiment as follows:

Purpose:

How does the food that we eat get into our blood?

Materials:

Egg, small glass tube, sealing wax, bottle, water.

Procedures:

1. Remove a small piece of shell from the large end of an egg.
2. Make a small hole through both the shell and the lining in the small end of the egg.
3. Insert a small glass tube through the hole in the small end. Seal around the hole with sealing wax.
4. Place the egg in the top of the bottle with enough water to cover the large end.
5. Observe the results the next day.

Observations:

The water passed through the lining of the egg.

Conclusions:

Based on the observations of the experiment, the statements made by the school nurse, and the information from health and science books, the following conclusion seems warranted. The digested food passes through the walls of the blood vessels of the stomach and intestines in much the same way that the water passed through the lining of the egg.

VII. Plan ways with the pupil to use the information in solving other problems.

1. Make a list of foods that are easily digested.
2. Discuss why infants are given liquid or soft diets.
3. Plan a day's menu for a convalescent person.

Obviously, one of the basic aims of elementary education should be to teach pupils how to think. According to this premise, the pupils need to study the reasoning process, or the way they arrived at the solution to their problem. For instance, under the teacher's direction, the pupils might prepare a guide to follow in certain learning situations that center around problem-solving. The following is submitted as an example of this procedure.

STEPS WE USE TO SOLVE PROBLEMS

1. We discuss our problem and state it in question form.
2. We discuss what we know about the problem. We attempt to make sensible guesses about the solution.
3. We list how and where we get the information on the particular problem.
4. We gather information.
5. We check the information to be sure that it is accurate and authentic.
6. We record the answers we accept.
7. We use the information.

This discussion should not be construed to mean that every time a health or science problem arises these steps should be followed verbatim or that, when used, every step should be taken for the problem approached. However, "if they have intelligent guidance, pupils can make great strides in ability to solve problems in this manner. Contact with this way of problem solving cannot come too early in a child's school experience. It takes a long time to become an accurate solver of problems."[9]

For the most part, through the study of health and science, pupils can experience the scientific way of thinking as they work. In other words, while developing health concepts the pupils practice skills needed in everyday life situations involving (1) making wise choices, (2) drawing valid conclusions, and (3) making intelligent decisions. Thus, it is hoped that behavior is influenced to the extent that the

9 UNESCO, *700 Science Experiments for Everyone*, Garden City, N.Y., Doubleday, 1958, p. 20.

pupils begin to develop scientific attitudes. Among the desirable behavioral changes would be a tendency on the part of the pupil to:

1. Not jump to conclusions
2. Look for reliable sources for information
3. Respect authorities
4. Maintain an inquiring and open mind
5. Evaluate a mistake as a step toward achievement
6. Change his mind when he discovers he is wrong
7. Face problems rather than avoid them
8. Think before he acts, rather than act and think later
9. Feel optimistic about his own ability to solve problems
10. Look at himself objectively as he relates to others and to his environment

ACTIVITIES INVOLVING THE INTEGRATION OF HEALTH AND SCIENCE

Pupils learn health and science in many ways. Experimentation and/or demonstration prove to be successful ways for helping pupils develop health concepts. In addition, experiments and demonstrations can and should lead to other ways of learning. After working an experiment, and observing and noting the results, the pupils need to turn to authoritative sources to check their conclusions. Therefore, they read, use visual aids (pictures, graphs, charts, models, films, filmstrips, slides), hold interviews, take field trips, and the like, in order to appraise and verify the information before drawing conclusions.

The opportunities for integrating health and science are numerous. The resourceful teacher is limited only by imagination and ingenuity. As an example, in the following fourth-grade lesson a science demonstration is used to introduce a unit on disease.

Teacher: What do you suppose would happen if I took a plant and put a cover over it for a day or so?
Pupil: It would die.
Teacher: Why?
Pupil: No air.
Teacher: (Writes the word *air* on the board.) Yes, it needs air in order to live.
Teacher: We also need air in order to live. Now, let us take a deep breath

	and hold it. (Pause) See, you cannot hold it very long because you need air to breathe. Yes, we know that living things need air. But where do we find air?
Pupil:	Everywhere.
Teacher:	Yes, just about everywhere.
Teacher:	Can you see air?
Pupil:	No.
Teacher:	Can you hear air?
Pupil:	Yes, sometimes.
Teacher:	Let's see if we can show that air is in many places. Why do you suppose I can't push this egg in this milk bottle? (Teacher uses a hard boiled egg.)
Pupil:	Air keeps it out.
Teacher:	Now I want you to look closely and listen. (Teacher puts a piece of burning paper in the bottle. One end of the egg is placed in the mouth of the bottle. If the experiment is successful the egg is "sucked" into the milk bottle.)
Teacher:	Now do you know what happened?
Pupil:	(Pupils form hypothesis.)
Teacher:	Three things happened: First, some of the warm air expanded in the bottle and pushed out around the egg; second, when the rest of the air cooled inside the bottle, that air contracted; third, the air outside in trying to get in pushed the egg into the bottle. Can you suggest how we might get the egg out?
Pupil:	Try to blow air into the bottle. (Teacher tips bottle up, blows hard into it, and removes mouth quickly. If the experiment is successful, the egg should be forced out of the bottle by air.)
Teacher:	Why do you think the egg came out of the bottle?
Pupil:	The pressure of the air blown into the bottle pushed the egg out.
Teacher:	So we see that air is not only just about everywhere, but that it also has pressure, and has great force to get into places.
Teacher:	Let's read something else interesting about air. Open your health textbook to the table of contents and find the chapter dealing with disease. Read the selection silently to find out about some tiny enemies of the body. (Pupils read silently. Teacher assists pupils with new and difficult words.)
Teacher:	Did you find out?
Pupil:	Yes.
Teacher:	What are these tiny enemies called?
Pupil:	Germs.
Teacher:	(Writes the word *germs* on the board.) Where are they found?

Pupil: In the air, in water, in the soil, and in the body.

Teacher: Today, we learned many places where air is found, and that we
          need air in order to live. We read in our books that tiny enemies
          called germs are in the air, as well as in other places. Now what
          sort of problems does that present for us? Let's try in the next
          few days to learn many things about germs. To begin let us see
          what some of the class members would like to find out about
          germs. (Pupils write their own questions on the board.) How
          would you like to work on these problems? How should we go
          about solving this problem? This problem? (And so on.)

SCIENCE CONCEPTS INHERENT IN THE TEACHING OF HEALTH

Thus far it has been suggested that (1) health and science subject
matter can be integrated and (2) the development of the scientific
way of thinking can be inherent in the methods that the teacher
uses with the pupils to develop the concepts. With this in mind,
certain specific science concepts that are inherent in both health
and science have been selected as examples of integration. Many
fine sources would yield this information. Among the concepts given
here, are some suggested by Blough, Schwartz, and Huggett.[10] For
the purpose of organization, these science concepts have been listed
under the same categories (foods and nutrition, exercise and physical
activity, first aid, and so on) used to identify the concepts for teaching health in Chapter 9, "Health Teaching Content for the Various
Grade Levels." In addition, some suggested activities for teaching
are included.

SCIENCE CONCEPTS INHERENT IN THE STUDY OF VARIOUS HEALTH TOPICS

FOODS AND NUTRITION

Concept: Air is essential for life.

Experiment: Air can enter a plant through the leaf.[11]

Procure a leaf with a long stalk attached and seal it into a hole through

[10] *op. cit.*

[11] This and several of the following experiments are taken from UNESCO,
op. cit., p. 440.

a cork. Fit this with a side tube, and seal the cork into a flask containing
water. Suck air from the side of the tube. Air bubbles will be seen to
issue from the end of the stalk.

Experiment: To show the respiration of a plant.

Place the plant in a test tube held in a weighted wooden block. Put
this in a bowl containing lime water and cover the plant with a jar.
Keep the plant in a dark place for several hours or examine it the next
day.

The lime water will be milky, showing that CO_2 was given off; the
rise in the level shows that a considerable amount of oxygen was taken in.

Activity: Discuss the reasons for the pressurized cabins on airplanes and
submarines. Discuss problems of air pressure for space travel.

Concept: Living things reproduce their kind in a variety of ways.

Experiment: Observing the development of flowers into fruit.

Collect specimens of flowers in different stages of maturity, from newly
opened buds to specimens in which the petals have fallen. Cut each
ovary open and note the changes that occur during the seed development.

Look over a quart of freshly picked peas or string beans and pick out
the pods that are not completely filled. Open these and compare them
with fully filled specimens. The abortive seeds are the remains of the
ovules that were not fertilized by pollen.

Concept: Chemical changes play an important part in our lives.

Experiment: Testing food for starch.

Cut open a potato. Apply diluted iodine to its surface. Mix a small
amount of cornstarch in water. Apply the diluted iodine to the mixture;
also apply it to a slice of bread and a small amount of milk. Cut open
an orange. Apply the iodine to its surface. (The change of color to
bluish purple indicates the presence of starch.)

Experiment: Testing food for carbohydrates.

Cut open an apple. Apply Benedict's solution to its surface; also apply
the solution to a soda cracker. Heat some raisins in water, then apply
the solution. (The change of color to blue indicates the presence of
sugar.)

Experiment: Testing for protein.

1. Apply copper sulfate and washing soda to a slice of bread.
2. Apply copper sulfate and washing soda to a small amount of peanut
   butter.
3. Apply copper sulfate and washing soda to a slice of cheese.
   (The change of color to red indicates the presence of protein.)

Experiment: Testing for acids.

1. Test a small amount of vinegar with blue litmus paper.
2. Test a small amount of grapefruit juice with blue litmus paper.
3. Test a small amount of lemon juice with blue litmus paper.
4. Test a small amount of sour milk with blue litmus paper.
    (The change of color of the blue litmus paper to red indicates the presence of acid.)

Activity: Make a chart to record the facts learned about the foods tested. Mark an X to show the materials each food contains.

Materials in Foods

Foods	Acids	Protein	Starch	Sugar
Bread			X	
Crackers				X
Milk				
Cheese				
Potatoes				
Apples				
Grapefruit				
Oranges				
Raisins				
Peanut Butter				
Meats				

SLEEP, REST, AND RELAXATION

Concept: The body needs rest and oxygen.

Experiment: To show the effect of exercise on the pulse.

Have each pupil select a partner. Have them take each other's pulse rate at rest and after vigorous exercise.

Activity: Record the results and draw conclusions.

SAFETY

Concept: Fire out of control is a very destructive force.

Experiment: How a fire extinguisher works.

To demonstrate the action of a fire extinguisher use baking soda and vinegar. Place a tablespoon of baking soda in a drinking glass and slowly pour vinegar on it. The bubbles will be extinguished. This should be a teacher-demonstrated experiment, because it involves the use of matches.

Concept: Electrical energy can be converted into other forms of energy —heat, light, motion, and sound.

Experiment: How a flashlight works.

Wrap the end of a short piece of bell wire around the base of the bulb. Set the bulb firmly on the center terminal of a flashlight cell. Press the free end of the wire against the bottom of the cell.

Activities: Show how a fuse works and why it is necessary. Discuss the benefits and hazards resulting from modern household electrical appliances. Demonstrate the safe use of household electrical appliances.

Concept: All machines lose some of their efficiency because of friction.

Experiment: To observe where friction occurs.

Examine toys and other available items to note where parts rub together. Find roller skates that need oiling. Oil the bearings on one of the skates and note the ease with which the oiled bearing turns.

CLOTHING

Concept: Changes in air conditions determine the weather.

Experiment: To show how a themometer registers temperature of air.

Part 1. Place an electric fan near a dish of ice cubes. Place a thermometer in a position to receive the air being blown over the ice cubes. Note the temperature. Relate this information to the kinds of clothes to wear on cold days.

Part 2. Place a thermometer near the hot air coming from a boiling tea kettle. Note the temperature. Relate this information to the kinds of clothes to wear.

Note: As a safety precaution when an electric fan or boiling water is used, it may be advisable that the teacher conduct the experiment while the pupils make the observations.

Activity: Discuss the reasons why an electric fan can make one feel cooler during summer heat.

Experiment: To show how a thermometer works.

Fill a thin glass bottle with colored water. Insert a long glass tube through the small hole in the cork stopper. Place the hands around the bottle. The heat of the hands should warm the water and cause it to rise in the tube.

THE HUMAN ORGANISM—ITS STRUCTURE, FUNCTION, AND CARE

Concept: The body is a wonderful mechanism that performs many duties.

Experiment: To test the sense of smell.

Have pupils seated in their desks facing the front of the room. Have windows and doors of the room closed for the few minutes it takes to perform this experiment. From the back of the room, pour about two tablespoonsful of household ammonia on a piece of cheesecloth. Ask the pupils to raise their hands as soon as an odor is detected.

Activity: Discuss ways the sense of smell can protect us from danger. Compare the various mechanisms of the body to a machine. Demonstrate how the joints give leverage to the body. Demonstrate how muscles give flexibility to the body.

Concept: The organs in the body work together as a unit.
Experiment: Making a simple device for listening to the heartbeat.
Borrow a stethoscope and have pupils use it to listen to the heart action. When a stethoscope is not available a very satisfactory demonstration model can be made from a small funnel, a glass T-tube or Y-tube, and some rubber tubing. Slip a piece of rubber tubing about 8-cm. long over the tip of the funnel. (Any kind of small funnel will do, such as a glass laboratory funnel or the kind used to fill babies' milk bottles.) Insert the T-tubes into the other end of the short piece of rubber tubing and attach longer pieces of tubing to both arms of the T-tube. To use the stethoscope, have one pupil hold the funnel firmly over his heart, while another holds the end of the long tubes in his ears. Heart sounds will be heard very clearly—though, of course, pupils will not be able to interpret them. A physician uses a stethoscope to find out if the heart action is normal.
Activity: This experiment, should naturally lead into a discussion of what the heart does and its importance in maintaining good health. Activities that might injure the heart and diseases that sometime result in heart impairment might also be discussed.
Experiment: To observe the pulse beat.
Place a thumbtack in the large end of a toothpick. Hold the hand out with the palm up and the wrist level. Place the head of the thumbtack on the wrist at the point where the pulse is felt. Observe the toothpick as it moves each time that the heart beats.

Concept: The body needs plenty of water.
Experiment: Water is used with soap for cleansing purposes. Place 2 teaspoons of beef fat or lard in an evaporating dish. Heat the dish with a small flame until the fat is melted. Add 3 cc. of a 33% solution of sodium hydroxide. Warm the dish slowly with a small flame. Add a small amount of salt to make it solid. Stir constantly. Continue the heating until there is a thick uniform mass in the dish. Allow time for cooling. Cut into small cakes of soap for the children.
Activity: Study the action of soap and water on cleaning the hands. Examine the hands with a microscope before and after washing them with soap and water.

Experiment: How to make an experimental filter.
Fit a one-hole stopper carrying a short length of glass tube into the small end of a lamp chimney. Put a little cotton wool in the bottom and then a layer of small clean pebbles. Wash some coarse sand well and place a layer above the pebbles. Next wash some fine sand and make a thicker layer in the filter. Grind some wood charcoal and make into a paste of water. Pour the charcoal paste evenly over the surface of the sand. Secure some very muddy water and pour it in the top of the filter. Collect the filtrate in a clean glass placed below the filter.
Activity: Visit the filtration plant in your community to observe the process of purifying the water. Discuss the ways water can be purified.

Concept: Light is bent or refracted when it passes from a medium of one density to another.
Experiment: A water-drop microscope.
Place a drop of water carefully on a plate of glass. Bring your eye close to the drop and look at something small through the water drop and glass. This serves as a simple microscope.
Experiment: Making a coin appear with refraction.
Place a coin in the bottom of a teacup on a table. Stand away and arrange your line of vision so that the edge of the cup just interferes with your seeing the coin in the bottom. Hold this position while another person pours water carefully into the cup.
Activity: What do you observe? How do you account for this? Apply this information to a study of the camera. Discuss lenses of eyeglasses used for farsightedness, nearsightedness, and astigmatism.

Concept: Light that is not reflected by opaque objects is absorbed by them.
Experiment: Making reflected beams of light.
Hold a comb in a sunbeam falling on a piece of white cardboard. Tilt the cardboard so that the beams of light are several centimeters long. Place a mirror diagonally in the path. Observe that the beams which strike the mirror are reflected at the same angle. Turn the mirror and observe how the reflected beams turn.
Experiment: To show how to see around corners.
Securely attach a mirror to a stick. Stand facing a partly closed door. Hold the mirror outside the door opening and note what is seen.
Activity: Assist the pupils to conclude that reflected light can enable one to see around a corner. Make a simple periscope so that light will be reflected from objects that one would not otherwise be able to see. Discuss the uses of periscopes.

Concept: Pitch depends upon the number of vibrations per sound made by the sounding body.

Experiment: To note the vibration of objects.

Part 1. Run a toy fire truck with a siren sound turned on. The faster the truck runs, the higher the note it produces.

Part 2. Blow across the mouth of empty bottles of different shapes and sizes to note the sounds produced.

Concept: The respiratory system supplies oxygen to the body and gets rid of carbon dioxide.

Experiment: To show that expired air contains carbon dioxide.

Put some clear lime water in a glass jar. Place the end of a glass tube in the lime water and blow through it for a few minutes. The lime water turns milky when it comes in contact with carbon dioxide.

Experiment: How the lung works.

Cut the bottom off a large bottle. Fit a cork to the neck with a Y-tube in it. On each of the lower limbs of the Y, tie a rubber balloon or some small bladder.

Tie a sheet of brown paper or sheet of rubber around the bottom of the jar, with a piece of string knotted through a hole and sealed with wax. Pulling this string lowers the diaphragm, and air enters the neck of the Y-piece, causing the balloons to dilate.

The rubber balloons represent the lungs, the tube represents the windpipe, and the open bottom jar represents the bony thoracic girdle. Lowering the diaphragm reduces the pressure inside the chest cavity and air flows into the lungs. Raising the diaphragm reverses the flow of air. Try moving the diaphragm with the clamp closed.

REFERENCES

Barnard, J. Darrell, *et al., The Macmillan Science-Life Series,* New York, Macmillan, 1959.

Beck, Robert H., Walter W. Cook, and Nolan C. Kearney, *Curriculum in the Modern Elementary School,* New York, Prentice-Hall, 1953.

Blackwood, P. E., "How Can Science Learnings Be Incorporated into the Elementary School Curriculum?" *Science Education,* April, 1956.

Blough, Glenn O., Julius Schwartz, and Albert J. Huggett, *Elementary School Science and How to Teach It,* rev. ed., New York, Dryden, 1958.

Craig, Gerald S., *Science for the Elementary School Teacher,* Boston, Ginn, 1958.

Dunfee, Maxine, and Julian Greenlee, *Elementary School Science: Research, Theory and Practice,* Washington, D.C., Association for Supervision and Curriculum Development, National Education Association, 1957.

Frasier, George Willard, Helen Dolman MacCraken, and Donald Gilmore Decker, *Singer Science Series,* Syracuse, N.Y., Singer, 1959.

National Council for the Social Studies, National Education Association, *Science and the Social Studies,* Yearbook, Washington, D.C., the Council, 1957.

National Society for the Study of Education, *Forty-sixth Yearbook,* Part I, "Science Education in American Schools," Chicago, University of Chicago Press, 1947.

Russell, David, *Children's Thinking,* Boston, Ginn, 1956.

UNESCO, *700 Science Experiments for Everyone,* Garden City, N.Y., Doubleday, 1958.

INTEGRATION OF HEALTH AND PHYSICAL EDUCATION

1   *What are some of the factors which tend to cause widely divergent practices in elementary school physical education?*

2   *What are some of the problems involved in the responsibility for teaching physical education in the elementary school?*

3   *What is the relationship between health education and physical education?*

4   *What are some valid generalizations in health which have a special relationship to physical education?*

5   *What are some of the ways in which opportunities for health experiences can be utilized through physical education?*

The physical education program in the elementary school is characterized by widely divergent practices. This is a condition that exists from one broad geographical location to another, and also may likely be the case as far as different elementary schools in a given community are concerned. For example, it is not too uncommon to find some schools in a certain community carrying out very satisfactory physical education programs, while those in other schools in the same community may be practically undeveloped. Of course, various valid reasons may be set forth to indicate why it is difficult to carry on physical education in the elementary school in the same manner as other aspects of the curriculum.

Generally speaking, there are three presently existing conditions for this. These conditions involve problems related to (1) the program of activities, (2) teaching responsibility, and (3) facilities. All of these factors are closely interrelated and highly interdependent. However, they are at the same time separate enough entities and have unique enough problems to warrant separate discussions.

THE PROGRAM OF ACTIVITIES

In general, elementary school physical education activities may be arbitrarily divided into three broad categories, *game activities, rhythmic activities,* and *self-testing activities.* With perhaps relatively few exceptions, almost any elementary school physical education activity can be classified in one of these categories.

Game Activities

Games have an extremely important place in the school program for children of all ages. In general, games played in small groups are enjoyed most by children at the primary level. Games that involve chasing and fleeing, tag, and one small group against another, as well as those that employ fundamental skills, are best suited to children at the lower elementary levels. In addition, children at this age level enjoy the type of game that has an element of surprise, such as those that entail running for a goal at a given signal.

Children at the upper elementary level, and often as low as the third grade, are interested in various kinds of team games. Often, at this level, games that involve various skills are offered in the program so that children will have an opportunity to use throwing, catching, and like skills in game situations.

Rhythmic Activities

One of the most desirable mediums for child expression through movement is found in rhythmic activities. One need look only at the function of the human organism to see the importance of rhythm in the life of the elementary child. The heart beats in rhythm, the digestive processes function in rhythm, breathing is done in rhythm; in fact, almost anything in which human beings are involved is done in a more or less rhythmic pattern.

At the primary level, fundamental rhythmic activities, found in the locomotor movements of walking, running, jumping, hopping, leaping, and galloping, and the nonlocomotor or axial movements, such as twisting, turning, and stretching, form the basis of skills for all types of rhythmic patterns. Creative rhythms help children to express themselves in just the way the accompaniment "makes them feel" and to give vent to expression, so necessary in the life of the child.[1] Other rhythmic activities suitable for use at the primary level include, among others, folk dances and singing games.

Children at the upper elementary level, if they have had a sufficient background of rhythmic activities at the primary, enjoy activities such as more complicated forms of folk dancing, mixers, square dancing, and social dancing.

Self-Testing Activities

Those physical education activities which are based on the child's desire to test his individual ability in such a way that he attempts to better his individual performance may be placed in the broad category of self-testing activities. Included in this broad category are stunts and tumbling activities and skills.

Stunts and Tumbling Activities. Stunts and tumbling are so closely related that it would perhaps be futile to attempt to show the difference, if any, existing between them. Stunts are concerned predominantly with certain kinds of imitations and the performance of a variety of kinds of movements that utilize such abilities as balance, coordination, flexibility, agility, and strength. Tumbling involves various kinds of body rolls and body springs that encourage the development of these same abilities.

Skills. Physical education skills are concerned with such elements as running, jumping, throwing, catching, and kicking, along with others that are involved in correct methods of performance of various kinds of physical education activities. Although skills are placed in the category of self-testing activities, it should be clearly understood that successful skill performance in all phases of the elementary physical education program—games and rhythmics as well as self-testing activities—is dependent largely upon the amount of proficiency that the individual possesses. There are certain basic motor skills, such as running, that are common to many different kinds of physical education activities. On the other hand, there are other skills, such as those involved in various methods of throwing

[1] See the following chapter for a discussion of creative rhythms.

(side-arm throw, underhand throw, and the like), which may be peculiar to certain specific activities.

Because of the importance of the development of certain kinds of motor skills for best performance in physical education activities, one would think that this area of teaching in physical education would receive a great amount of attention. On the contrary, the teaching of physical education skills is one of the most neglected phases of the entire elementary physical education program. This is indeed a paradoxical situation because the successful performance and resultant enjoyment received from a physical activity depends in large measure upon how well a child can perform the elements involved in it. Yet, at a time in the child's life that is ideal for learning motor skills, we find that this important phase is almost entirely left to chance.

Although each child is born with a certain potential, teachers should not subscribe to the notion that skills are a part of the child's inheritance. In order for a child to participate satisfactorily with his peers, he must be given the opportunity to learn the necessary physical education skills under careful guidance of skillful teachers.

The elementary school has long been considered to be the educational segment in an individual's life that provides the best opportunity for a solid educational foundation. The need for the development of basic skills in reading, writing, and arithmetic has seldom been challenged as an essential purpose of the elementary school. Why, then, should there be a neglect of such an important aspect of learning as that existing in the development of motor skills?

It was previously mentioned that perhaps the ideal time to learn motor skills is in childhood. The muscular pliability of the elementary-age child is such that there is a desirable setting for the acquisition of various kinds of such skills. He is at a stage in life when he has a great deal of time for practice—a most important factor because practice is needed in order to learn—and at this age level he does not seem to become weary of repeating the same thing over and over again. In addition, the elementary child has a limited number of established skills to obstruct the learning of new ones. Because of this, skill learning should be facilitated, provided that competent teaching in the area of motor skills is available. Consequently, there should be little or no future problem of "unlearning" skills that the child might have had to learn incorrectly "on his own."

Experimental research on the influence of specific instruction in various kinds of physical education skills is somewhat limited. However, more and more scientific evidence is being accumulated which appears to indicate that children in the early elementary years are mature enough to benefit from instruction in such skills as throwing and jumping. Unfortunately, this type of instruction is found lacking in far too many elementary physical education programs.

Time Allotment for Activities

A question which often arises in connection with physical education activities is the one concerned with the amount of time that should be spent in each of the three categories. Any recommendation in this regard must necessarily be arbitrary, due to the various influencing factors surrounding local conditions. As a guide for teachers in helping them meet the needs of children through a balance of activities, the following ranges of time are suggested for the various categories: game activities, 30–50 percent of total time; rhythmic activities, 15–30 percent of total time; self-testing activities, 15–30 percent of total time.

Sources of Activities

In recent years many fine sources of elementary school physical education activities have been published. The following list of books, which is by no means complete, is representative of references which the reader might wish to consult:

Andrews, Gladys, Jeannette Saurborn, and Elsa Schneider, *Physical Education for Today's Boys and Girls,* Boston, Allyn and Bacon, 1960.

Halsey, Elizabeth, and Lorena Porter, *Physical Education for Children,* New York, Dryden, 1958.

Humphrey, James H., *Elementary School Physical Education,* New York, Harper, 1958.

Jones, Edwina, Edna Morgan, and Gladys Stevens, *Methods and Materials in Elementary Physical Education,* 2nd ed., New York, World, 1957.

Miller, Arthur, and Virginia Whitcomb, *Physical Education in the Elementary School Curriculum,* Englewood Cliffs, N.J., Prentice-Hall, 1957.

Salt, E. B., *et al.*, *Teaching Physical Education in the Elementary School,* 2nd ed., New York, Ronald, 1960.

Sehon, Elizabeth L., *et al.*, *Physical Education Methods for Elementary School,* 2nd ed., Philadelphia, Saunders, 1953.

Vannier, Maryhellen, and Mildred Foster, *Teaching Physical Education in Elementary Schools,* 2nd ed., Philadelphia, Saunders, 1958.

TEACHING RESPONSIBILITY

There are a variety of different ways in which the responsibility for the provision of physical education learning experiences for elementary children may be delegated. A recent study revealed that the following four general patterns of instruction are those which are most widely used:

1. Classroom teacher with *no* help from a specialist or consultant in physical education.
2. Classroom teacher with the help of a specialist or consultant in physical education attached to the *school staff* (or to several schools' staffs).
3. Classroom teacher with the help of a specialist or consultant in physical education from the *central staff.*
4. *Special teacher* of physical education who does the physical education teaching in some or all of the grades in one or more schools.[2]

The question as to where the major responsibility for teaching physical education in the elementary school should be placed has been given an unprecedented amount of attention in very recent years. This has no doubt been brought about by the various arguments which have been set forth favoring the placing of the responsibility for teaching with either the regular classroom teacher or the person especially trained in physical education.

The proponents in favor of placing it with the regular classroom teacher have generally maintained that:

1. The contact that the classroom teacher has with the child gives this person an outstanding opportunity to understand the child as a growing organism.
2. Classroom teachers are prepared to guide, uninterruptedly, the process of total growth and development.

[2] Elsa Schneider, *Physical Education in Urban Elementary Schools,* Washington, D.C., Department of Health, Education and Welfare, Office of Education, 1959.

3. The transition that the child must make from the family circle to one teacher creates a difficult enough adjustment for him, without having him adjust to more teachers.

4. The classroom teacher is in a better position to carry on a child-centered procedure, as against the possibility that the specialist may be concerned with subject matter only.

5. The classroom teacher is in a better position to integrate physical education with the other subject-matter areas of the curriculum, because she knows precisely the status of her class in this area.

On the contrary, those persons who advocate the use of the special teacher tend to believe that:

1. There is a limit to the many competencies which the classroom teacher should be expected to acquire.

2. Without the help of the specialist, the efforts of the classroom teacher might be "spread too thin," and thus she might neglect an important area of the child's total education.

3. While classroom teachers may now be receiving better professional preparation than in the past, at the same time there are many more activities of an extraclass nature that add to their burden.

4. The child should have the benefit of teaching from a person especially prepared in the field of physical education.

5. All classroom teachers are not likely to have an interest in teaching physical education, for various personal reasons.

It may be interesting to note the point of view on this matter expressed by the National Conference on the Role of the Special Teacher of Art, Music and Physical Education in the Elementary School, held January 16–18, 1957, under the sponsorship of the Elementary Schools Section of the U.S. Office of Education.[3] In essence, it was the majority feeling of this conference that "when a special teacher comes into a classroom to teach a lesson in art, music, or physical education, his or her arrival is not a signal to the classroom teacher to leave the room and take a little rest. Rather, it is a signal for the two teachers to continue a partnership of effort that began when they planned the lesson together." In summarizing the place of the specialist in the elementary school the conference composed the following statement: "Art, music, and physical education are essential to the education of children. Experiences in these areas are best provided with the classroom teacher and the

[3] A report of the conference appears in *School Life,* March, 1957, under the title "Role of the Special Teacher."

specialist working cooperatively, each making his unique contribution. Specialists in these areas provide direction to and enrichment for these experiences. Through such services as cooperative planning, working with children, participating in in-service education activities and interpreting the contributions which can be made by these areas, the specialist promotes a better understanding, develops individual potentialities, and encourages a greater use of art, music, and physical education."

It is obvious that the conference placed a great deal of emphasis upon the aspect of cooperation between the classroom teacher and the specialist. Certainly, this approach is to be strongly recommended instead of trying to justify one plan as having a certain degree of merit over the other.

Consideration of the matter of teaching responsibility from a purely realistic point of view indicates the importance of involving the classroom teacher in the program. One factor which points this up quite clearly is the ratio of pupils to special teachers of physical education in the elementary schools. Estimates of this ratio can be made with a relatively high degree of accuracy. In the previously mentioned study by Schneider,[4] 523 school systems with some 6.5 million children enrolled at the elementary school level participated in the study. It was indicated that approximately 3700 elementary physical education teachers were employed by the schools participating, or one physical education teacher for every 1700 children. As another example, in one state with an elementary school enrollment of some 400,000 children there were approximately 100 elementary physical education teachers, or a ratio of one teacher to each 4000 children. When viewed from this perspective it becomes luminously clear that the classroom teacher should accept some degree of teaching responsibility if children are to derive the optimum benefits attributed to physical education.

THE PROBLEM OF FACILITIES

For purposes of discussion "facilities" refers to areas of space, either indoor or outdoor, where the teaching of physical education might take place. The lack of such space is a reason often given for inadequate programs at the elementary level, and often persons delegated the responsibility of setting up organized programs have

[4] Schneider, *op. cit.*

become discouraged because of an apparent lack of facilities. Although complete programs may be carried on in places that have the finest facilities, it is entirely possible to develop a program irrespective of the limitations.

Generally, and in the case of certain kinds of activities, it is usually most desirable for a program to take place out of doors whenever possible. If there is a sufficient amount of outdoor space available, it may be developed as seems necessary for the best possible use. It is not uncommon, however, to find elementary schools with adequate outdoor space not developed for optimum use. For example, such things as cutting down a few trees, grading, and providing drainage could convert unused space into a play area to be used for outdoor physical education activities.

Numerous schools, particularly some in the larger metropolitan districts, find it difficult to conduct outdoor programs because of the absence of a play area as such. However, in some instances schools have been able, through the cooperation of city officials, to use blocked-off sections of city streets adjacent to the school during a part of the school day. Although it is a rare practice, it is not outside the realm of possibility to use parts of the school building roof for certain outdoor recreational activities.

With regard to indoor facilities, the near-ideal situation would be for every elementary school to have a gymnasium or one or more activity rooms as indoor teaching stations for physical education. In recent years various estimates have been made regarding the approximate number of elementary schools which have adequate indoor facilities in the way of gymnasiums and/or playrooms.[5] Of a total of 12,217 elementary school buildings included in the study cited, it was reported that 4177 buildings, or 34 percent provide "excellent or adequate" gymnasiums. Of these gymnasiums, 3632, or 87 percent are found in schools located in states "where winter weather conditions are likely to restrict the use of outdoor space for teaching purposes." It is interesting to note that swimming pools were found in only 110 of the 12,217 buildings.[6]

5 *Ibid.*

6 An inquiry form was sent to all cities with a population of 30,000 and over, and to one-third of the cities with a population of 10,000 to 30,000, for a total of 619 school systems. Replies were received from 86 percent of these school systems.

It is difficult to determine whether there is a definite trend to include gymnasiums in new elementary school building construction. However, it is known that in some parts of the country gymnasiums are a part of the facilities of such new buildings. For example, it was recently reported that most of the newer elementary schools in the city of Chicago have been built with 50 x 90 ft. gymnasiums with motor-driven folding-door dividers that can be used to make two teaching stations of 45 x 50 ft.[7]

In those elementary schools where indoor facilities as such are not provided, it becomes necessary to carry on the program by other means, and not to abandon hope because the school is not fortunate enough to have them. Some schools without gymnasiums, playrooms, or multiple-purpose rooms carry on effective programs by making use of vacant rooms or by converting storage rooms into play space. However, with the present crowded conditions many schools are utilizing all available area for classroom space.

In the absence of a gymnasium or vacant room, it is sometimes possible to use corridor space for the indoor program. This space does not lend itself readily to certain aspects of the program because the noise involved in some activities might be distracting to pupils and teachers in nearby classrooms. Nevertheless, this part of the building may be used for certain types of activities.

When all other possibilities have been exhausted, it is necessary to operate the indoor program in the regular classroom. At first glance this might appear to be impossible. Nevertheless, with wise planning and organization, it is entirely possible to conduct a satisfactory program. It is more advantageous when the classroom has movable seats, so that the room can be cleared for activity. However, even in rooms in which seats are of the stationary type, the pupils may engage in a number of worthwhile activities.

Although chasing and fleeing games may not be adaptable to school corridor and classroom, games of circle formation, stationary relays, and quiet types of games that require little space afford much enjoyment for children. Further, rhythmic activities, such as folk dancing, may be used to advantage where space is limited. For primary children, story plays, miming, and singing games are very good activities that may be conducted in the regular classroom.

[7] *Physical Education Newsletter,* June 12, 1960.

352ELEMENTARY SCHOOL HEALTH EDUCATION

Although some of these activities may have little to offer in the way of vigorous physical activity, they do provide relief from the stress and tension of the school day. In addition to the games and rhythms programs certain self-testing activities may be used where there is a minimum amount of space. These pursuits, important in the development of skill and agility, may be used in a form of group work, with each group engaging in a different type. Activities of this nature that have been used successfully include ball-handling, balance-beam activities, rope-skipping, target-throwing, and the performance of numerous stunts.

Although the recommendations set forth here are not useful for all types of elementary schools, they may be applied in certain specific situations. In the final analysis the way in which the physical education program is adapted to available facilities depend to a large extent upon the resourcefulness and ingenuity of the person responsible for carrying out the program.

THE RELATIONSHIP OF HEALTH EDUCATION AND PHYSICAL EDUCATION

It has been demonstrated many times that pleasurable exercise is of essential importance in stimulating the growth and development of children. It is pretty much common knowledge that muscles of the body grow in strength, size, and endurance as a result of enjoyable physical activity. Also, this kind of activity favorably influences such vital organs of the body as the heart and lungs, thus improving the performance of the circulatory and respiratory systems. Indeed, children of elementary school age during periods of organized play are engaging in activities which are designed to maintain and improve their health status.

It is interesting to note that there exists the somewhat paradoxical phenomenon that relatively few members of the adult population of America recognize the value of enjoyable exercise as a means of contributing to sound health. If one were to analyze the underlying causes for this apathetic attitude toward pleasurable physical activity, there would no doubt be a number of contributing factors. One of these factors might possibly be that many of our present-day adults did not develop an understanding and appreciation of the importance of physical exercise to health in their early years. Those who have the responsibility of providing physical education learning experiences for elementary children should be reminded that boys and girls should be made aware of the health values resulting from participation in physical education activities. The idea for such a procedure is not necessarily of recent origin. In fact, a strong recommendation in this connection is found in the following statement made by Warnock many years ago:

> I believe that without an integration of these two fields of education, neither field is making its fullest contribution to complete living. No one, I think, would question the fact that skill in motor activities and joy in participation in those activities are important factors in healthful living. And on the other hand any motor activity program which excludes all reference to or consideration of physical, mental, social, and spiritual health, and makes no pretense at developing socially desirable attitudes, habits, and knowledges, is unworthy of the name "physical education."[8]

Teachers should not rely entirely upon the children themselves to develop an appreciation of the contribution that physical education makes to health. On the other hand, teachers should avail themselves of every opportunity to interpret the health values of physical education to children. If this were done in a systematic manner throughout the various educational levels, one might speculate that an appreciation for and a zeal to participate in pleasurable physical activity and exercise might be carried on into adult life.

HEALTH EXPERIENCES THROUGH PHYSICAL EDUCATION

In attempting to develop possible ways in which opportunities for health experiences can be utilized through physical education, it might be well to consider some valid generalizations. The following list, suggested by Cowell, is submitted as a guide for teachers in helping them to integrate health learning experiences with physical education:

1. As food is burned in the body cells it furnishes power to move; the faster we move, the more fuel is used.

8 Florence M. Warnock, "Opportunities for Teaching Health in the Elementary School Through Motor Activities," *Journal of Health and Physical Education*, October, 1934, p. 15.

2. Muscles become bigger as the number of muscle cells becomes greater and as the cells increase in size with exercise. Muscles weaken with disuse.

3. The normal heart and circulatory system becomes stronger and more efficient in moving blood to active areas when repeatedly required to do so.

4. In sedentary existence, or where only a few sports are used, certain body muscles may not develop sufficiently.

5. Precluding accidents, a normal healthy child cannot do himself permanent organic injury by physical exertion.

6. The rise in temperature during a physical activity increases the metabolic rate of the body and adds to the effectiveness of the circulatory and respiratory adjustments occurring during exercise. Hence it promotes the more efficient carrying out of muscular work.

7. Regular and progressive exercise is the essential feature of training, and in the healthy man the development of his heart corresponds with that of his muscular system.

8. Persons out of training should not compete in any sport with persons who are in training and accustomed to the sport.[9]

As children engage in games, rhythms, and self-testing activities the teacher, through careful and skillful guidance, can take advantage of the excellent opportunity to interpret many of the above aspects of health and growth.

SOME SPECIFIC WAYS OF INTEGRATING HEALTH AND PHYSICAL EDUCATION

The practical examples of teaching procedures which follow are intended to show how health and physical education can be successfully integrated in given teaching-learning situations. It should be borne in mind that when this particular type of procedure is used it should perhaps be done in connection with the time allotted to health teaching, rather than during the regular physical education period. In other words, physical education is used as a learning medium for the development of a certain health concept rather than devoting time during the regularly allotted period for physical education. The first procedure shows how the study of "Foods"

[9] Charles C. Cowell, *Scientific Foundations of Physical Education*, New York, Harper, 1953, pp. 216–217.

might take place with a group of second-grade children, in the game "Run for Your Supper."

Teacher: We sometimes hear people say that a healthy child is a hungry child. How many of you boys and girls run into the house quickly when your mother calls you to come in and eat?

Pupil: Sometimes I don't want to go in and eat because I have more fun playing

Teacher: Yes, and I believe that is true of most children. However, we need to have strong muscles so that we can play. Because of this we need to eat certain kinds of foods, and perhaps we should eat at regular times. Now we are going outside, and I want to tell you about a new game we are going to play. The name of the game is "Run for Your Supper." Why would this be a good game for us to learn just at this time?

Pupil: Because we are studying about food and how it makes you feel like playing if you eat right.

Teacher: Yes, that's right, and what does the name of this game make you think of?

Pupil: That you should hurry in when you're called to supper.

Pupil: You just said that we need strong muscles to play, so kids should take time out to eat.

Teacher: Very good, Tom. An automobile would soon quit running if we didn't put gas in it, wouldn't it? Now I am going to explain the game to you here in our room, and I want to see if you can remember how to play it when we get outside. We will form a circle and hold hands. One person will be chosen to be "it," and that person will walk around the outside of the circle. "It" will suddenly stop between two children and say "Run for your supper!" Those two children will run in different directions around the circle. They will see which one of them can get back first to the place he left. The person to get back first can select "it" for the next time.

Pupil: This game is something like another one we played. I can't remember the name.

Teacher: Does anyone remember the name of that game?

Pupil: I think it was "Slap Jack."

Teacher: Yes, that was it.

Pupil: I don't see how you do this.

Pupil: Neither do I.

Teacher: Very well, let's take a little time so some of you can show how we do it. Rose, Otto, and Ronny, come and stand in the front of the room, please. Rose you be "it" and show us what you would do.

Pupil: I will stand between Otto and Ronny.

Pupil: And Ronny and I will run now.

Pupil: Be sure to shake hands.

Pupil: Do we take hold of hands when we go between the two players?

Teacher: Rose, take hold of Ronny's and Otto's hands and see what happens.

Pupil: No, that won't work; they can't run if their hands are being held.

Pupil: How about if we put our hands on the two players' shoulders and said, "Run for your supper"? Everyone would know then that I was really "it."

Teacher: I think that is a fine idea. Shall we try it that way?
            (The children proceed to the playground and participate in the game for a time, and then the teacher evaluates it with them.)

Teacher: Shall we review some of the things we learned in the game "Run for Your Supper"? Can someone tell us? Kathy?

Pupil: We make a circle and "it" runs and chooses two to run. The next "it" is chosen by the last one back.

Teacher: Do you think the game "Run for Your Supper" will help you remember anything about what we are studying?

Pupil: Well, you should come in and eat when you are called instead of staying out to play some more.

Teacher: Can you give us one reason for that, Paul?

Pupil: Well, then you will be able to play more, because you need food to be strong and play games.

Pupil: Good food helps make you strong, and maybe if you were hungry you would run faster.

Teacher: That might be. Can you think of ways we could make the game better?

Pupil: Try not to run into each other.

Teacher: Yes. Can you think of any way we could change this game so the players could have more turns?

Pupil: Couldn't we have more circles and have an "it" for each one?

Teacher: That sounds like a good idea. Why don't we try that when we play a circle game again?

The second procedure illustrates how a better understanding about certain aspects of safety from poison plants might be developed with a group of fourth-grade children in the game "Poison."

Teacher:	Well, boys and girls, it certainly looks like spring is here, with the lawns starting to turn pretty and green.
Pupil:	It sure does, and spring is my favorite time of the year.
Pupil:	Mine too. I like to walk in the woods and hunt for flowers.
Pupil:	And snails and turtles, too.
Teacher:	There are also some other things one might find in the woods this time of year. Do you know what they might be?
Pupil:	Spiders?
Teacher:	Well, yes, but I was thinking of something else that grows, like plants or flowers.
Pupil:	You mean moss or honeysuckle or something like that?
Teacher:	Well, yes, but what I had in mind was something not quite so nice and pretty.
Pupil:	Oh! Are you thinking of poison ivy?
Teacher:	Right, Jack, and also poison oak and sumac. I wonder if some of you have had trouble with one of these three, or at least know someone who has.
Pupil:	I've had poison ivy.
Pupil:	My brother had it too.
Teacher:	I can see that many of you know something about these three enemies of ours, and so this new game I am going to teach you this morning should have real meaning.
Pupil:	What is the name of the game?
Teacher:	It is very well-named I think. It is called "Poison." To play it we first join hands and form a circle. (Children form a circle.) Now I will draw a circle on the inside of your circle about a foot in front of your toes. You will remain with your hands grasped, and on my signal of "go," you will try to pull someone into the circle. Anyone who steps into the circle is said to be "poisoned." As soon as a person is "poisoned," someone calls out "poison," and the one who is "poisoned" becomes "it" and gives chase to the rest of you. Those of you who are being chased will run to various places designated as "safety," such as wood, stone, metal, or something of that nature. All persons tagged are poisoned and become chasers. After those not tagged have reached safety, I will call out "change," and they must run to another place of safety. Those poisoned attempt to tag as many as possible. We will continue the game until all but one have been poisoned.
Pupil:	Let's use wood and metal for "safety."
Teacher:	All right, Fred, wood and metal it is. Now let us start the game on the "go" signal.

(The children participate in the game and the teacher evaluates it with them.)

Teacher: Now that you have played "Poison," is there anything you might think of to improve it?

Pupil: Maybe if you drew the circle a little farther away from our circle it might be tougher to be poisoned.

Teacher: Yes, you might be right, Tom. Another 6 inches or so might help.

Pupil: I think we have too many safe places; it makes it hard for the chasers.

Teacher: Perhaps we could cut it down to one type of material. I wonder how this game will help you in relation to some of the poison plants we talked about.

Pupil: Well, for one thing, staying out of the circle is like staying on the path in the woods and not getting into the bushes.

Teacher: That's right, Frank. Even though we might know what sumac, oak, and ivy look like, we will perhaps be much safer if we stay on the path.

Pupil: I heard that you can catch poison ivy from other people if they have it on their clothes or something like that.

Teacher: Perhaps then we should also avoid coming in contact with anyone who has been poisoned, for we might be affected that way too.

Pupil: Just like in the game; I didn't get pulled into the circle, but Jimmy did, and he touched me and I was poisoned.

Teacher: Yes, we must be careful in many ways in the summer to avoid the discomfort caused by poison ivy, poison oak, and poison sumac.

These illustrations are representative of the numerous possibilities for using physical education as a learning medium in the development of health concepts. This procedure has met with a great deal of success by teachers who have made application of it.

REFERENCES

Harnett, Arthur L., and John H. Shaw, *Effective School Health Education,* New York, Appleton-Century-Crofts, 1959, chap. 8.

Hein, Fred V., and Allan J. Ryan, "The Contributions of Physical Activity to Physical Health," *The Research Quarterly,* May, 1960.

Humphrey, James H., *Elementary School Physical Education*, New York, Harper, 1958, chap. 11.

Humphrey, James H., "Physical Education and Science Concepts," *Elementary School Science Bulletin*, March, 1960.

Humphrey, James H., "Teaching Physical Education in the Elementary School—Whose Responsibility?" *The Physical Educator*, October, 1961.

Johnson, Granville B., Warren R. Johnson and James H. Humphrey, *Your Career in Physical Education*, New York, Harper, 1957, chap. 14.

Oberteuffer, Delbert, *School Health Education*, 3rd ed., New York, Harper, 1960, chap. 17.

INTEGRATION OF HEALTH AND CREATIVE EXPRESSION

16

1 Why should the teacher plan for the pupils to have a variety of different experiences in creative expression?
2 What are the therapeutic values of creative expression?
3 What are some of the art media which can be used by the pupils for creative expression relating to health learnings?
4 What contributions can each facet of the total music program make to the health of the child?
5 How can the various forms of creative dramatics contribute to the total health of the child?

Of concern to educators today is the problem of how to release the individual and develop him to the fullest extent of his potentialities. Daily the teacher is challenged by the marvels of the human mind, and the development of that which otherwise might not be put to use—for not to use mental power is to lose it. Democracy is only beginning to understand the *power of the individual* as the greatest power in the world today.

It is in this context that creativity comes into focus. In recent years, it has received attention in the numerous and various aspects of human endeavor. To a large extent, it appears that recent creative thinking has resulted in or contributed to such advancements as better food, clothing, housing, transportation, communication, medical care, working conditions, employment opportunities, recreation, health, education, improved human relations, and new hopes for an even better world of the future.

THE ELEMENTARY SCHOOL CHILD
AND CREATIVITY

Childhood and creativity go together. Young children are naturally creative. They have vivid imaginations. They pretend. They enjoy "make-believe." They are original and ingenious in their thoughts and actions. They ask questions. They want to know "why." Their thoughts can soar to heights unknown. To the elementary school child the world is full of adventure, excitement, and wonder. Each child is born with, and therefore possesses, intellectual ability—unknown in quantity and quality.

Children differ widely in their interests, abilities, and needs. Thus, the elementary school curriculum should be designed to provide a balance of daily experiences through which the child might find varied and appropriate opportunities to express himself creatively. It is assumed that there is a place for creativity in all school subjects. No longer is creative expression thought of only in such areas as art, music, writing, and dramatics. More and more the value of creativity is recognized in areas of learning that were formerly thought of as being rather routine. Through the nurture of the individual's creative ability, he can be guided to the threshold of new ideas and discoveries in such areas as health, arithmetic, geography, history, science, and physical education.

As discussed in previous chapters and repeated here for emphasis, concept development is essential in all learning. Creative thinking is based essentially upon the *concepts learned through experience*. Thus it should follow that the richer the concept, the more possibilities for its expression. It is suggested that the essence of creativity lies in (1) an abundance and wealth of ideas; (2) thoughts and feelings to express; and (3) a variety of media for expression. In other words, creative expression to be effective might well be integrated with the whole program of instruction. Creativity tends to clarify, stimulate, and extend the pupil's learnings and, thereby, causes the individual to operate at higher levels of his ability and with wider ranges of competency.

Creative expression should enable the teacher to gain insight into what the pupil thinks and how he feels. How a child feels about himself and his world can be viewed through his behavior. In other words children's actions can speak louder than their words. Guided self-expression can offer the pupil appropriate releases for inner tensions, and at the same time enable him to add stature to his own feelings of worth. Freedom to be creative tends to make pupils happier, more relaxed, more productive, more purposeful, and mature in all aspects of their total health. The creative teacher exercises skill by (1) recognizing and accepting the ideas of each pupil; (2) guiding and channeling, but not controlling, the development of his ideas; (3) assisting the pupil to bring his ideas to fruition; and (4) enabling him to present his ideas to others. Through such procedures, creative activities can have a kind of therapeutic value. This approach constitutes one very effective way of reaching all children. The therapeutic value of creative expression has long been recognized by both the teaching and medical professions.

HEALTH AND CREATIVE EXPRESSION

Children probably use language for creative expression more than any other medium. A pupil tends to feel a need for an adequate vocabulary of appropriate words to express his thoughts and feelings clearly and in a form which conveys the precise meanings to others.

Some pupils who do not express themselves well in oral or written communication may do well in other media. Creative expression can appear in many different forms and through many different media—such as the extension of one's self through expression in art, music, and dramatics. It is becoming recognized more and more that art, music, and dramatics have a vast potential contribution to make to the total health of the individual. An educational program which includes experience in these three areas should help children to:

Discover and develop special aptitudes and talents
Express themselves creatively
Communicate feelings and thoughts in a creative and aesthetic manner
Experience the feeling of adequacy that accompanies achievement at some
    levels of endeavor
Understand, appreciate, and improve their environment
Extend physical skills which involve better body dynamics
Develop emotional stability by releasing inner tensions and fears
Develop self-confidence and self-control

Enjoy the finer aspects of life
Use leisure time more wisely
Develop social relationships among children of similar interests
Enrich other areas of learning
Develop life-long avocational or vocational interests

HEALTH AND CREATIVE ART ACTIVITIES

For many years art has been considered an important part of the elementary school program. It is one of the most natural means of expression for the young child. With whatever materials he finds available, an elementary school pupil rather intuitively will spend his own time manipulating and experimenting to find ways to express himself. Consequently, during the elementary years the major emphasis is on a basic art program, which makes it possible for pupils to have experiences with a large variety of materials, rather than on a meager program limited to the use of a few materials.

Art in the elementary school should perhaps be creative and exploratory. One of its unique contributions lies in providing firsthand experiences with various processes involving the use of numerous materials. The resourceful teacher knows that the first step toward a successful art program for pupils is the availability of numerous materials to care for their individual needs, aptitudes, and interests. As in other areas of learning, a pupil may have a particular aptitude for one facet of art rather than another. In other words, a pupil who finds little satisfaction in painting scenery for a health play, may be especially adept at sawing, cutting, nailing, making holes, and finishing a fence for a garden scene in the same play.

Creative art experiences need skillful guidance by the teacher, from the stimulation of the ideas to the finishing of the product. A knowledge of the creative process takes on added significance as the teacher provides numerous opportunities for the pupils to learn the use of the various art media. These experiences usually follow a somewhat planned sequence, as follows:

1. There is a manipulative stage when the pupil becomes acquainted with the art media. The pupil learns the names of the materials and tools. He handles them, and discusses their use and care.
2. There is an experimental stage when the pupil learns "firsthand" how he can use the material or tool to create colors, forms, balance, contrast,

emphasis, and lines. He learns from the experiences of experimenting, without the pressure of having to produce something acceptable.
3. There is an expressive or productive stage when the pupil selects and uses certain media to express his thoughts and feelings.

It should be remembered that in all art activities, the emphasis should be upon the total development of the child as well as upon the mastery of skills and techniques. Creative art activities can contribute to the total health of the individual. On the other hand, health teaching provides opportunities for self-expression through art. The examples given here indicate a few of the ways creative teachers might attempt to integrate the use of some of the various art materials and tools to further health teaching.

Color Media

Crayons, colored chalk, finger paints, water colors, tempera paints, and charcoal are some of the media that may be used in art activities to summarize and record health concepts. Spatter, stencil, and sponge painting provide variation and interest to the work with colors.

HEALTH ACTIVITIES INVOLVING COLOR MEDIA

Make a colored drawing showing circulatory system, or other systems of the body.
Color a series of original pictures showing how germs are transmitted.
Make a finger painting for a bedroom picture.
Make a charcoal drawing to show ways to avoid fires.
Color original pictures for a calendar showing safety practices for each month of the year.
Color place mats for the teachers in the building. Use spatter, stencil, or sponge painting.
Color scenery for a health play, "Vacation Fun."
Design prints for dress or shirt material.

Three-Dimensional Construction

The tools and materials used in three-dimensional construction provide for common group interests as children give expressions to their feelings through creative endeavors. Construction might include the making of such items as:

1. Dioramas (panoramic scenes constructed in miniature) for depicting activities related to health.
2. Relief maps of areas showing physical features.
3. Mobiles (a number of shapes usually suspended from a wire frame and moving freely in space).
4. Stabiles (a number of shapes usually attached to a stationary base).
5. Miniature buildings and equipment.
6. A scroll theater (a box fixed to resemble the stage in a movie theater) on which to run original stories and plays written and illustrated by the pupils. The scroll, on which these illustrated stories or plays are pasted, can be rolled on a roller at one side of the opening of the box, and fastened to another roller on the opposite side of the box. By means of a crank, the scroll is rolled across the opening in the box. One child usually rolls the scroll, while another child reads the script and explains the illustration.

HEALTH ACTIVITIES INVOLVING THREE-DIMENSIONAL CONSTRUCTION

Make a movie to show the processing of cheese to use in the scroll theater.
Make a diorama to show the natural habitat of fur-bearing animals that supply raw materials for clothing.
Make a diorama to show what constitutes a desirable picnic area.
Make a diorama to show safety in water sports.
Make mobiles to show what constitutes a good breakfast.
Make mobiles to show items needed for good grooming.
Make stabiles to show vegetable garden pests.
Make stabiles to show the parts of vegetables we eat: leaf—cabbage, lettuce; root—carrot; flower—cauliflower.
Construct a relief map to show well-known vacation areas in the United States. Use pipe-cleaner figures to identify the sports—skiing in Vermont, water sports in Florida.
Construct a relief map to show areas that produce raw materials for clothes.
Construct a grocery store with shelves, counters, refrigerators, and so on.
Construct equipment used in a bakery, such as mixer, weighing machine, bread troughs, ovens.
Construct a miniature dairy farm with buildings.

Creative Crafts

Carving, modeling, weaving, making toys and games, costuming, pipe-cleaner crafts, and papier-mâché puppets and masks furnish media for pupils to use in connection with their study of health.

Make a shuffleboard.

Make a bat stand and bags for the bases in softball.

Make bean bags.

Make a shoe-shine box.

Make picture puzzles.

Make toys such as kites and airplanes.

Weave paper place mats for a party at school to enjoy products of milk.

Make aprons and smocks to wear when preparing food.

Construct a weaving loom. Weave cloth pot holders and place mats.

Make large papier-mâché models of the different breeds of dairy cows.

Make soap carvings of the different kinds of seafood.

Make papier-mâché masks for a play about animals that give us raw materials for clothing.

Make papier-mâché puppets for a health play about people who supply our food.

Mold items such as meats, fruits, vegetables, milk products and bakery items to be used in the classroom's grocery store.

Make pipe-cleaner dolls to illustrate safety in and near the water.

Make costumes for the pupils in a health play on the story of bread.

Make life-size cardboard figures for a display window in the classroom. Dress the figures for different summertime activities, such as church parties, picnics, swimming.

Lettering

Lettering aids pupils to label and identify health materials for exhibits, displays, bulletin boards, charts, posters, and booklets. Block and stick printing can be used for decorative purposes, too.

Make and label a health picture book for younger children.

Make a chart showing good manners when eating.

Make picture charts showing a good breakfast, lunch, and dinner.

Cut block prints to use for making get-well cards.

Make and label a pictorial chart of the four food groups.

Make and label a chart showing various types of bread.

Make a pictorial calendar for the vegetable garden. Record planting dates, growth of plants, and harvesting of vegetables.

Make a chart indicating the pupil responsible for each duty involved in vegetable gardening.

Make a booklet of types of tools used for the vegetable garden.

Make posters of safety rules for the school grounds.

Make and label a display of resources used to produce synthetic materials.

Make an exhibit of foods containing the various vitamins.

Make a poster of the vegetable seeds planted in the garden. Attach the package container for each kind of seed.

Letter appropriate captions for a bulletin board centered around good manners for the cafeteria.

Use stick prints to decorate a paper tablecloth and napkins for breakfast in the classroom.

Compile a book of simple recipes that include milk.

Arrange the central hall bulletin board and display case for special health drives, such as, Junior Red Cross, Dental Health Week, Easter Seals for Crippled Children, and the like.

Murals and Friezes

For purposes of this discussion a mural will refer to a wall decoration with one specific theme, while a frieze will mean a wall decoration composed of a series of related themes.

HEALTH ACTIVITIES INVOLVING MURALS AND FRIEZES

Make a mural to show poisonous plants in the community.

Make a mural to show foods which help us to have good teeth.

Make a mural to show ways to rest and relax.

Make a mural to show the different kinds of fruits.

Make a series of murals to show various ways fruits are processed.

Make a mural to show milk products.

Make a frieze to show the story of cotton from the seed to our clothes.

Make a frieze to show the story of milk from the cow to the table.

Make a frieze to show the story of bread; include planting the grain, threshing the grain, grinding the grain, making bread, wrapping bread, and delivering bread.

Make a frieze to show health services available at the health center.

HEALTH AND CREATIVE MUSIC ACTIVITIES

Music is considered a very important part of the curriculum offerings in the elementary school. From the beginning of his formal education, the child should experience the joys that come from participating in each facet of the total music program, that is (1) singing, (2) rhythmic activities, (3) music appreciation, (4) instrumental music, and (5) creative music. Each facet has a potential unique contribution to make to the total health of the individual.

Music offers avenues for creative expression at all levels of the elementary school. Rather frequently, children at play can be observed humming an original tune, singing a familiar couplet to music of their own, or trying a new step to music they enjoy. Indeed, it appears that music holds a unique fascination for most children. The resourceful teacher can capitalize upon the pupil's desire for self-expression through music as a means of furthering his growth and development—emotionally, socially, physically, and intellectually, as well as furthering his knowledge in the various aspects of his total health.

Health offers innumerable opportunities for creative activities in music. The activities listed below are intended as illustrations of ways that health can be integrated with creative expression in such areas as singing, rhythmic activities, music appreciation, and instrumental music.

Health and Creative Singing

Experience has shown in many cases that children delight in singing original tunes in answer to health questions asked by the teachers. For example, the teacher sings: "How did you brush your teeth to-day?"

The pupil sings his own tune and words in response. Or, the teacher might sing:

When should you wash your hands?
When do you need to take a bath?
How do you feel about losing a ball game?
What do you do to get ready for breakfast?

Which dance do you like best?
Why do you like to drink milk?

Pupils sing their own tunes and words in response.

Children have been known to create health songs—sometimes the music as well as the lyrics—but more frequently they write words to familiar tunes. The classic example is probably the music for "Here We Go Round the Mulberry Bush." To this melody, the pupils add their own words and actions, such as:

> This is the way we wash our hands,
>   Wash our hands,
>   Wash our hands.
>
> This is the way we skip to school,
>   Skip to school,
>   Skip to school.
>
> This is the way we shine our shoes,
>   Shine our shoes,
>   Shine our shoes.

Creative songs have a freshness and charm of their own. This aspect of creativity needs stimulation, encouragement, and recognition, for its value lies in what happens to the pupil once he finds another avenue for expression and enjoyment.

Health and Creative Rhythms

Creative rhythm is the art of movement. Among other things, the rhythmic program is designed to foster the development of physical coordination for children during these years of rather rapid body change and growth.

The emphasis in creative rhythms is on movement of the entire body, to the end that pupils gain poise, balance, and agility. Thus, through bodily movements, the pupil interprets music and sounds.

A part of creative rhythmic expression is the selection of music that best suits the purposes for which it is intended. Under teacher guidance, children can participate in the selection of such music. For instance, if the pupils are to march, they can select the march they like best, and create their own marching formations. If the pupils are presenting an original skit on "How Germs Are Transmitted," they can select the music that best suits the mood for the undesirable housefly as he tramps across a garbage pile. Once the music is selected, the pupils under teacher guidance can create their own rhythmic movements to portray the "villain."

Music sets the mood for creative rhythms. In planning, the teacher should include a balance in the music to which the children create rhythmic movements. Consequently, there will be music that is fast, slow, loud, soft, heavy, light, and so on.

Health and Music Appreciation

Probably words can never express the intangibles associated with the aesthetic values one can derive from listening to good music. Few would dispute its value in terms of its contributions to one's health. The teacher's attitude toward music is extremely important. It is the teacher who has the responsibility of creating an atmosphere in which there is the time to listen to music, simply for the joy of listening. In such an atmosphere, pupils may want to discuss what they hear and how they feel, or they may want to express their thoughts and feelings through other media. Sometimes, it is enough simply to want to listen again.

Health and Creative Instrumental Music

Children like to create sounds and music. A child may pick out a tune on the piano; he may create a tune on his song flute or whatever instrument he has at hand. Elementary school children can make simple instruments on which to create music. They can tune water glasses, carve willow whistles, and make rhythmic instruments such as bells, cymbals, drums, maracas, rattles, rhythm sticks, sandblocks, tambourines, and triangles. In singing, the child uses his voice to create sounds and tunes, and in this facet of music, he needs opportunities to create sounds and music with instruments.

Health offers many activities with which creative instrumental music can be integrated. For example, during periods of relaxation, pupils can move around the classroom to the varying tempo produced on the homemade instruments. Children can rest at their desks to the soft music played on tuned water glasses. Summarizing activities to health units can be enhanced by original instrumentations worked out to add atmosphere to the presentation.

HEALTH AND CREATIVE DRAMATICS

Through the ages, creative expression through dramatics has been an effective means used by man to communicate his thoughts and feelings to others. As with other media of creativity, dramatics can contribute to the total health of the individual. It is through dramatics that children can (1) release or greatly reduce tensions and fears; (2) resolve real and imaginary problems in a satisfactory manner; (3) develop feelings of empathy based on deeper understandings; (4) build sound patterns of behavior; (5) learn to express themselves well through speech, gestures, and bodily movement; and (6) develop feelings of security, adequacy, and belongingness while sharing common experiences with their peers.

Creative dramatic experiences involve (1) dramatic play, (2) pantomime, (3) informal dramatizations, (4) puppetry, and (5) formal dramatizations. Dramatics, as a creative approach to learning, is especially adaptable to health teaching. The remainder of this chapter will deal with various suggestions for the integration of health and creative expression through dramatics.

Health and Dramatic Play

Dramatic play characterizes the spontaneous, undirected activities in which children engage during early childhood, including kindergarten and first grade. Through dramatic play, children make believe they are adults, and live through the adult life they see going on around them. They identify themselves with people by playing the role of mother, father, teacher, relatives, milkman, grocer, and the like.

Role-playing provides a creative approach to learning. Among other things, it makes language development purposeful, and at the same time it can reveal the child—his talents and abilities as well as his fears and misinterpretations—to the teacher. The major emphasis in dramatic play is upon the role. For the most part, pupils volunteer for the role they want to play. In so doing, it is important that the pupil assume the role and identify with it to the extent that he expresses the feelings involved without inhibitions.

Dramatic play in health offers as many possibilities as there are roles to play in a given lesson or unit. For instance, pupils might role-play:

The school nurse explaining to the pupils about how to prevent common
   colds
The dentist examining teeth
Mother preparing a meal
Mother shopping at a supermarket
Father helping the children to get ready for bed
Mother buying school clothes for the children
Big sister setting the dinner table
The policeman directing traffic at the street crossing nearest the school

Under teacher guidance, the pupils can show the teacher what they have learned in health by selecting the characters they want to portray, and creating the dialogue and actions. Usually pupils want to repeat the "play." In so doing, they change their roles and much of the dialogue each time the roles are played.

Health and Pantomime

Through pantomime, a pupil expresses his thoughts and feelings by the use of facial expressions, gestures, and movements without speaking. Any lines to be spoken, read, or sung are done by others than the pupil doing the acting. Since pantomime requires only physical expressions, it has real value for the shy, timid child, who will act a part that requires no talking. This applies equally well to the child with a speech defect or impediment. As valuable as it may be as a means of expression for certain pupils, it should be understood that pantomime constitutes one important part of the creative dramatic experience for all children.

Health and Informal Dramatization

Dramatic play and pantomime represent activities which are adapted to the growth and development of the young child, who is still self-centered, and normally plays as an individual even when among other children. As the pupil begins to relate himself to others, he is ready for a type of dramatization which involves interaction with groups of children. Therefore, informal dramatization comes after the pupil has had some experiences with dramatic play and pantomime. Informal dramatization is characterized by its spontaneity, naturalness of expression, and simplicity of organization. Very little if anything is needed in the way of stage and properties. The child's imagination seems to fill the gap. For instance, a chair can serve as the dining-room table in one informal dramatization, and the same chair can be a washbowl in the next play. To the child, the "play's the thing." It is self-sustaining and self-sufficient.

Among other things, informal dramatization develops creativity, originality, imagination, and fluency of speech among pupils. It can aid also in the development of social understandings. Through sociodrama, or informal dramatizations based upon a social problem, the pupil can express his own feelings directly or indirectly toward a problem. In this manner he learns how to meet the problem by trying different solutions and observing the consequences. For instance, there could be such problems as: How late should children be permitted to watch television on a school night? Should all children in the home be treated alike? How can a child, who is a leader most of the time, become a good follower in the group? Through informal, unrehearsed dramatizations of problems similar to these, the pupil has an opportunity to think through a problem or situation by being in someone's position other than his own; consequently, he gains insights and a different perspective in terms of what seem to be possible best solutions. In sociodrama, the emphasis is upon the social problem or situation, whereas, in role-playing the emphasis is on the role.

Another aspect of informal dramatization is psychodrama. However, since psychodrama deals with emotional problems which the child is experiencing, it is usually handled in private and by a specialist in mental health.

Health and Puppetry

Puppets serve as players in carrying out dramatic interpretations. Since pupils identify puppets with human beings, puppets can be used to help pupils develop positive and objective understandings relating to the lives of others. The use of puppets can stimulate creativeness, individuality, inventiveness, and originality on the part of those involved. The effectiveness of a production depends upon the manipulation of the puppets, and the use of the voice to carry the mood and intent and to portray vividly the feelings to be communicated.

Puppets serve as another means which the teacher might use to reach the shy, withdrawn, or self-conscious child, who refrains from appearing before an audience. Since the necessity for personal appearance is eliminated, the child who finds other audience situations difficult may do quite well concealed behind the puppet stage. Pupils with speech impediments have been known to speak fluently and distinctly in a puppet show once they have identified themselves with the puppets.

Puppets offer a variety of possibilities for teaching health. One procedure which has been successful is that in which puppets have been used to introduce a health unit. This procedure is particularly effective with primary children, because it tends to hold their interest while a new topic is being initiated. Puppets are suitable at any grade level, and constitute an essential part of a balanced program in dramatics for the elementary school child.

Health and Formal Dramatization

Formal dramatization differs from other forms of dramatics in that it necessitates more thorough planning of the plot, characterizations, lines, staging, and costumes. On the other hand, formal dramatizations relating to health contain elements of the other forms of creative dramatics, that is, (1) the enacting of a role (role-playing); (2) the use of facial expressions, gestures, and movements (pantomime); (3) the emphasis on a social problem or situation (informal dramatization); (4) the use of the voice to carry the intent and mood, and to portray feelings to be communicated (puppetry); and (5) staging and costuming (puppetry). Moreover, formal dramatization provides highly motivated, functional situations for improving the language arts skills, from the decision to write the health play to the final curtain at the end of the production. Therefore, it is extremely important that the purposes for a formal dramatization be clearly defined in terms of inherent learning experiences rather than as an extravaganza for the entertainment of an audience.

Formal dramatization can utilize creativeness in (1) writing the play; (2) varying the dialogues and actions; (3) producing simple costumes and staging; and (4) working out personal interpretations, as the individual releases himself to become the character he is portraying.

For illustrative purposes two original health plays by fifth-grade pupils are included as examples of how formal dramatizations can be used, either to introduce or to summarize health teaching units.

CARE OF OUR TEETH

(Original play to introduce a health unit on teeth)

Characters:

Molly, a girl in the fifth grade at school
Susan, a girl in the fifth grade at school
Henry, a boy in the fifth grade at school
John, a boy in the fifth grade at school
Dr. Waters, a dentist

ACT I

(Scene: Living room of Henry's home. Time: Saturday afternoon.)

Molly: I wish it would stop raining or snowing or whatever that is that's coming down.

John: So do I. I like a good snowstorm, but this drizzle is terrible.

Susan: Mother says it's just right for catching colds, so we had better play inside.

Henry: Here, have some nuts. We might as well do something since we can't go out.

John: Boy! These shells are really hard!

Molly: What are you trying to do, crack that nut with your teeth? Are you crazy?

Susan: Now, isn't that a silly thing to say?

Henry: Nobody will deny that the cave men had to use their teeth more than we do, but remember that article Miss White read to us about teeth? It said that the study of skeletons shows that the cave men *did* have trouble with their teeth. Poor fellows, they couldn't run to a dentist and get help right away.

Molly: Even in the early days of our country, people didn't know much about what caused poor teeth and how to prevent decay. If a tooth ached, they just had to have someone pull it out without anything to stop pain or save the tooth.

John: Oh! It doesn't hurt to have a tooth taken out now. Dentists have gas and Novocain. There's nothing to it.

Susan: So, there's nothing to it, Brave Boy! Remember you have your permanent teeth now. If you lose a few you'll be sorry.

John: Well, I can get some ready-made teeth. The dentist can make them. My mother has some and they look just like her own.

Molly: You know, I think the way you treat your teeth, maybe you'd better start planning on those "ready-made" teeth. Come to think of it, maybe all of us should check ourselves. Probably we all do things that aren't good for our teeth.

Henry: Such as what?

Molly: Oh, forgetting to brush them, for instance.

Susan: I have an idea. Let's ask Dr. Waters how we can take care of our teeth. He'll be able to tell us all about it. He'll be about ready to leave the office now, so let's telephone to find out if he can talk with us.

John: That's a good idea. Maybe he'll show me how he makes those teeth like my mother's.

ACT II
(Scene: Dentist's office. Time: Same afternoon.)

Henry: Good afternoon, Dr. Waters. Could you spare a few minutes to answer some questions about our teeth?

Dr. Waters: I'd be glad to, children. Come into my office and have chairs, I was expecting you. What are some questions you would like to have me discuss with you?

John: Dr. Waters, why shouldn't I crack nuts with my teeth? What difference does it make?

Dr. Waters: Oh, John, you should never crack nuts with your teeth. You might crack the enamel of a tooth, and in time it would cause you to have much pain. You might even lose your tooth after the enamel has been cracked. You are much too young to have ready-made teeth. Your playmates would laugh at you, and say, "We told you so, but you wouldn't listen." Would you like that?

John: No, Dr. Waters, I wouldn't like that. I guess you're right. I'll stop right now doing such foolish things with my teeth before it's too late.

Susan: Tell us more about the care of teeth that we should know, Dr. Waters.

            (Dr. Waters is telling the children more about the care of teeth as the play ends.)

THE COUNTY HEALTH DEPARTMENT[1]

(Original play to summarize a unit on the county health department)

Characters:

    Mr. John Jones, a father who has moved his family into a new neighborhood

    Mrs. Mary Jones, a mother

    Catherine Jones, the 11-year-old daughter

    Bill Jones, the 9-year-old son

(Scene: Living room of the Jones's home. Time: 4:15 P.M. on Monday after the family moved into the neighborhood.)

Bill: (Entering.) Mother, where are you? I'm home.

Mother: (Entering.) Hello, Bill. How was your first day in the new school?

Bill: Oh, I liked it. My teacher's name is Mrs. Henry. She said my transfer records were all right except for one thing. She thought I should have been weighed and measured and had my eyes and ears checked. I haven't had all that done since I was in the first grade.

Mother: You mean we should take you to a doctor for a physical examination?

Bill: Oh, no. Mrs. Henry said there's a nurse whose services the county health department furnishes to the school. She'll give me the "once-over" one day this week.

Mother: That is wonderful. I'll be glad to get her report. Where is Catherine? Didn't she come on the school bus with you?

Bill: Oh, yes. She stopped to talk with Susan who lives next door. Here comes Catherine now.

Catherine: (Entering.) Hello, Mother. Guess what Susan was telling me. She has a baby sister, too; and you won't have to go all the way back to town to get Nell checked by a doctor. Susan's mother takes their baby to the health department clinic near here. You can go there too.

Mother: That is interesting. How much will it cost?

Catherine: Susan says it is a county clinic, and most of the money for the health services comes out of the taxes.

Bill: That's the same place our school nurse is from—the one I was telling you about.

[1] This script was prepared by the fifth-grade pupils at Tracy's Elementary School, Tracy's Landing, Maryland, under the guidance of the teacher, Mrs. Margaret Perrie.

Mother: Oh, I know what that is. I remember seeing a sign at the local drugstore that said there was going to be a square dance next week to help raise money for the clinic. Catherine, here comes your father. Bill and you go and help him bring in the groceries, please. (Exit Catherine and Bill.)

Father: (Entering.) Hello, Mary. I'm glad to be home. It is a rather long drive to work, but I think it will be worth it to live in this community. I like what I've seen and heard about it since we arrived.

Mother: I do, too. Catherine was just telling me about the local health department's clinic where I can take the baby for a check-up.

Father: That's one thing I heard about in the car pool today. The men were telling me that this county has a health department that can help us in many ways. They said I could take a sample of the water from our well to them to test to make sure it is safe for drinking.

Mother: Oh, that's fine. I won't have to boil our drinking water once we find that it is safe. Now, we need to get someone to check our sewage system.

Father: The health department will send a man here to check the sewage system for us. Let's see, I wrote down some of the many services of the health department about which the men told me. It is amazing. (Reading.)

1. The health department inspects the dairy farms that supply milk for us.
2. They inspect the dairy, too.
3. They inspect the food stores and eating places in this county.
4. They inspect the local places that supply seafood.
5. They inspect the swimming pools.
6. They regulate garbage-disposal plants.
7. They even give free chest X rays.
8. They hold regularly scheduled health clinics, too.

Mother: With all of those services, this is certainly a good county in which to live.

Father: Yes, I'm glad that we moved here. Of course, our taxes take care of much of the expenses involved in the services of the health department. However, we can give it our cooperation and support its efforts, too.

Mother: I bet you mean that dance they're having. I saw the poster about it, too.

Father: Yes, I do. Let's plan to attend.

Mother: We can enjoy the dance. It will give us an opportunity to get acquainted with our neighbors. I'm sure people who can work together well enough to have a health department function like this one must be nice people to know. It does make me feel that we have moved into a nice neighborhood. A healthy, safe community is extremely important to a family like ours.

Through creative dramatic experiences the children developed a clearer understanding of the importance of the health department in their community.

REFERENCES

Anne Arundel County Public Schools, *Art Guidebook for Elementary Teachers,* Annapolis, Md., 1958.

Association for Supervision and Curriculum Development, National Education Association, *Freeing Capacity to Learn,* Washington, D.C., the Association, 1960.

DeFrancesco, Italo L., *Art Education, Its Means and Ends,* New York, Harper, 1958.

Durland, Frances C., *Creative Dramatics for Children,* Yellow Springs, Ohio, Antioch, 1952.

Gerbracht, Carl, and Robert J. Babcock, *Industrial Arts for Grades K-6,* Milwaukee, Bruce, 1959.

Klausmeier, Herbert J., Katharine Dresden, Helen C. Davis, Walter Arno Wittich, *Teaching in the Elementary School,* New York, Harper, 1956, pp. 427–504.

Lease, Ruth, and Geraldine B. Siks, *Creative Dramatics in Home, School and Community,* New York, Harper, 1952.

Lowenfeld, Victor, *Creative and Mental Growth,* New York, Macmillan, rev. ed., 1952.

Lowenfeld, Victor, *Your Child and His Art,* New York, Macmillan, 1957.

Russell, David R., *Children's Thinking,* Boston, Ginn, 1956, pp. 305–329.

Shaw, Earline, *et al.,* "Singing Health," *Health Education Journal,* January, 1961.

Sheehy, Emma D., *Children Discover Music and Dance,* New York, Holt, 1959.

Zirbes, Laura, *Spurs to Creative Teaching,* New York, Putnam, 1959.

APPENDIX: SOURCES OF

HEALTH TEACHING AIDS

AND MATERIALS

The following sources of health teaching aids have been of use to many teachers of health in the past and are presented here as a guide to teachers and prospective teachers who are interested in exploring their resources. It is suggested that teachers write to various of the organizations listed, requesting information as to specific offerings.

Numerous other sources of health teaching aids may come to the attention of teachers. These should be evaluated in the light of the discussion presented in the chapter on health teaching aids.

It is suggested to students that, as a class activity, letters be sent to some or all of the sources listed to determine just what the current offerings are; in the case of organizations providing free and inexpensive materials, students may request samples of these for study and evaluation.

PUBLISHERS

Following are some the publishers that provide health education text-books for the elementary school. These books are prepared for specific grade levels and their vocabulary and presentation are adjusted accordingly.

American Book Company of New York
Benefic Press of Chicago
Bobbs-Merrill Company of Indianapolis
Ginn and Company of Boston
Laidlaw Brothers of River Forest, Illinois
Lyons and Carnahan of Chicago
Macmillan Company of New York
Scott, Foresman and Company of Chicago
John C. Winston Company of Philadelphia

In addition to the series of health books designed for children, some publishers also provide film libraries which include items of interest to health teachers. These companies include: The McGraw-Hill Book Company, Film Division, and Encyclopaedia Britannica Films. It should be noted that the great majority of films which have been produced are more suitable for the junior and senior high school and colleges than for the elementary school grades.

381

EDUCATION DEPARTMENTS AND HEALTH DEPARTMENTS

Most departments of education and health provide a variety of teaching aids that are useful in elementary school health and safety teaching. These aids usually include films of various kinds; information concerning communicable diseases and other health and safety problems; and information concerning local sources of health and safety information, including possible health, physical fitness, and safety programs presented on radio and television.

The teaching aids of education departments and health departments are usually provided free of charge or are loaned without rental fee. In the case of the large and relatively expensive items such as moving pictures, the department usually sends them without charge on request, and the borrower is expected merely to pay the cost of return postage.

It is recommended that teachers request their local and state education and health departments to provide a listing of all health and safety teaching aids that are available.

FEDERAL AND WORLD HEALTH ORGANIZATIONS

The United States Bureau of Documents, Washington 25, D.C., provides an exhaustive listing of government publications, of which a considerable number are concerned in some way with health. These publications are available at low cost. A complete listing of them may be obtained by writing to the Bureau; moreover, on request the Bureau will provide a weekly listing of government publications which may be examined for useful items.

The World Health Organization (WHO) publishes a magazine every two months which is an excellent source of information on the status of world health problems and health achievements in the various parts of the world. Interested persons should write to the Regional Office in Washington, D.C., where the WHO is combined with the Pan-American Sanitary Bureau.

In addition to the WHO magazine, teachers may obtain back issues of other WHO publications, including some concerned with the history and functions of this organization. Much of the information is presented in pictorial form and is suitable for use in elementary health teaching.

PROFESSIONAL ORGANIZATIONS

A number of professional organizations may be contacted for information concerning various aspects of health. The following are among those which may be contacted. Each will provide a listing of its offerings on request.

The American Association for Health, Physical Education, and Recreation, 1201 16th Street, N.W., Washington 6, D.C.

The American Dental Association, 222 East Superior Street, Chicago 11.

The American Medical Association, 535 North Dearborn Street, Chicago 10. (This organization provides information and a variety of teaching aids relative to various aspects of health. In addition, it publishes a popular magazine called *Today's Health,* which contains a variety of health articles of interest to those who teach health.)

The American Public Health Association, 1790 Broadway, New York 19.

The American School Health Association, Room 617, 228 North LaSalle Street, Chicago. (*The Journal of School Health,* published by the Association, is devoted specifically to school health education and contains articles of interest to teachers. Some of these are concerned with basic information on the various health topics such as mental health or communicable diseases; some deal with matters of curriculum and methods of teaching health.)

The American Social Hygiene Association, 1790 Broadway, New York 19.

The National Committee for Mental Hygiene, 1790 Broadway, New York 19.

PRIVATE AGENCIES

The following organizations are among those private agencies which devote their energies to making a concerted attack upon one or more disease entities. In recent years there has been a tendency for organizations of this kind to concern themselves increasingly with the general field of health and health education. For example, the American Tuberculosis Association provides information relative to many health subjects other than tuberculosis, and in some communities certain of these agencies have combined forces and have undertaken projects concerned with public health education generally.

In most cases the name of the agency suggests the kind of free or inexpensive material that is provided. However, since these are rich sources of information and of teaching aids, they should be contacted as to their current offerings. The larger agencies have offices in most of the larger communities of the United States, and the telephone book may, therefore, be consulted for the local address.

The American Cancer Society, 47 Beaver Street, New York 4.

The American Heart Association, 1790 Broadway, New York 19.

The American Red Cross, 18th and E Streets, Washington 16, D.C.
The National Foundation, 1026 Connecticut Avenue, N.W., Washington, D.C. (This used to be the National Foundation for Infantile Paralysis. It is now concerned with rheumatoid arthritis and certain birth defects, as well as with polio.)
The National Safety Council, 425 North Michigan Avenue, Chicago.
The National Tuberculosis Association, 1790 Broadway, New York 19.

Two organizations provide a library of booklets, some of which amount to authoritative statements on health subjects ranging from sex education to mental health and child development. These organizations are the Public Affairs Committee, 22 East 38th Street, New York 16, and Science Research Associates, 57 West Grant Avenue, Chicago 10.

COMMERCIAL AND BUSINESS CONCERNS

Many business concerns provide quantities of high-quality aids. These are largely free or very inexpensive, and it is recommended that the interested student or teacher write to these organizations for listings of available materials.

The following list of sources does not purport to be complete. Rather, it is merely a listing of those sources which the authors have found to be especially useful because of their offerings of health, safety, and in some cases, physical fitness information and/or materials.

Aetna Life Insurance Company, 151 Farmington Avenue, Hartford 15, Connecticut (health and safety materials).
American Automobile Association, 1712 G Street, N.W., Washington 6, D.C. (safety and "sportsmanlike driving" materials).
American Institute of Baking, 400 East Ontario Street, Chicago 11 (charts and other materials concerned especially with nutrition).
Bristol-Myers Company, 45 Rockefeller Plaza, New York 20 (materials concerned especially with good grooming).
Cereal Institute Incorporated, 135 South LaSalle Street, Chicago 3 (especially concerned with nutrition).
Continental Baking Company, 630 5th Avenue, New York 20 (especially concerned with nutrition).
International Cellucotton Products Company, 919 North Michigan Avenue, Chicago 11 (materials include posters and films such as those concerned with colds and menstruation).
Metropolitan Life Insurance Company, 1 Madison Avenue, New York 10 (an extremely varied offering for both children and teachers).

National Board of Fire Underwriters, 85 John Street, New York 38 (materials concerned with safety).

National Dairy Council, 111 North Canal Street, Chicago 6 (a rich offering concerned especially with nutrition).

Prudential Insurance Company of America, Newark, New Jersey (pamphlets on health, safety, and disease).

Wheat-Flour Institute, 309 West Jackson Boulevard, Chicago 6 (these materials have special reference to nutrition).

INDEX

Adams, Fay, 311
Adams, Robert F., 227
Andersen, Donald, 227
Andrews, Gladys, 346
Arithmetic, integration of health and, 231–256
Attitudes, 61

Barber, Lois S., 50
Beck, Robert H., 308
Bibliotherapy and health, 288–290
Blaney, Clarabelle, 302
Blough, Glenn O., 325
Bowen, Louise, 268
Broderick, G., 212
Brown, Ruth, 301, 304
Burton, William H., 268

Casteline, Elaine, 227
Chaplin, J. P., 81
Child health, 26–42
Children's Physical Developmental Clinic, 26
Clark, D. L., 91
Color media, 364
Combs, Arthur W., 309
Comprehensive skills, development of, 137–138
Concepts, scientific method of developing, 326–332
    suggested for development, 168–198
Continuous plan, 44–45
Cook, Walter W., 308
Cowell, Charles C., 354
Creative art activities, 363–364
Creative crafts, 365–366
Creative expression, and integration of health, 360–384
Creative singing, 368–369
Creativity and the elementary school child, 361–363
Creswell, William H., 50
Curriculum, 43–57

Curriculum (cont.)
    organization, 52–56
    areas of living version, 55–56
    broad fields version, 54–55
    subject version, 53–54
Cycle plan, 45–46

Dawson, Mildred A., 276
Development of school health programs, 8–11
Discussion leader, 78
Dodd, Alan L., 323
Dramatic play, 371–372
Dramatization, 375–379
Duker, Sam, 260
Dullea, Irene, 278
Dunham, F., 212

Effective speaking, 72–74
Elementary education, scope of, age and grade levels, 2–3
    curriculum offerings, 2
Exercise, 34–37

Foster, Mildred, 347

Group discussions, 76–78

Hagaman, Neva, 95
Halsey, Elizabeth, 346
Hanna, Lavone A., 95
Hendricks, Richard, 71
Huggett, Albert J., 325
Humphrey, James H., 35, 346
Health advertising, 85–92
Health interests, 161
    procedures for determining, 161–162
    relationship to health needs, 149
Health learning experiences, 46–52
    ways of providing, 46–52
    opportunistic teaching, 47–48
    separate subject, 46–47

Health needs, 149–151
  as criteria for curriculum content, 151–159
  kinds of, 152–153
  procedures for determining, 154–155
  relationship to health interests, 149–150
Health teaching, 7–8, 22–23
  planning for, 94–147
  responsibility for, 23
Health topical areas, 168–198
Healthful school living, 7, 20–21
  responsibility for, 21–22

Integration:
  of health and arithmetic, 231–256
    in development of arithmetic concepts and health concepts, 239–243
    health activities in the development of arithmetic concepts and skills, 232–238
    as a tool in developing health concepts, 243–256
  of health and creative expression, 360–384
    in color media, 364
    in crafts, 365–366
    in creative dramatics, 371–380
    in creative singing, 368–369
    in murals and friezes, 367
    in music activities, 367–368
    in music appreciation, 370
    in pantomime, 372
    in puppetry, 373–374
    in rhythms, 369–370
    in three dimensional construction, 365
  of health and language arts, 257–303
    by listening, 259–276
    by reading, 281–297
    by speaking, 276–281
    by writing, 297–305
  of health and other curriculum areas, 48–52
  of health and physical education, 342–359
    opportunities for, 353–354
    specific ways of, 354–358
  of health and science, 323–341
    through activities, 332–334

Integration (cont.)
  of health and science (cont.)
    through concepts inherent in the teaching of health, 334–340
  of health and social studies, 307–322
    in activities involving health, 318–322
    in health climate of the classroom, 309–310
    through health concepts in social studies content, 311–318

Jones, Edwina, 346

Kearney, Nolan C., 308
Klausmeier, H. J., 62
Knowledge, health, 61

Language, facets of, 258
  and health, 80–85
  sequence of development, 258–259
Language arts, integration of health and, 257–305
Learning, 59
  activities, 63–64
  experiences, 63–64
  meaning of, 59
  nature of, 62–63
Lee, J. Murray and Dorris May, 49, 59, 95
Listening and health, 259–276
Loomis, R. E., 91
Lowdermilk, R., 212
Lowell, Bernard, 212

Method, 59–60
  derivation of, 60
  meaning of, 59
Miller, Arthur, 346
Moore, Virginia D., 50
Morgan, Edna, 346
Movement, 34–37
Music activities, 367–368
Music appreciation, 370
Murals and friezes, 367

Ness, Carmen Oved, 48
Nutrition, 37–38

Objectives of health education, 11–12
Oral communication, 71–93

Oral reports, 144–146
  preparing, 144–146
  presenting, 144–146
Organization and administration of health education, 14–25
  community level, 16
  individual school level, 17–25
  state level, 15
Orientation, 1–12

Packard, Vance, 85
Panel discussions, 78–79
Perrie, Margaret, 377
Physical activity, 34–37
Physical education, facilities, 349–352
  game activities, 343
  health experiences through, 353–354
  integration of health and, 342–359
  specific ways of, 354–358
  relationship to health education, 352–353
  rhythmic activities, 343–344
  self-testing activities, 344–345
  sources of activities, 346–347
  teaching responsibility, 347–349
  time allotment, 346
Physical fitness, 28–42
  meaning of, 32–40
Porter, Lorena, 346
Potter, Gladys L., 95
Preparation and presentation of "talks," 74–76

Question and answer sessions, 79–80

Rabelais, Francois, 11
Reading and health, 281–297
  following up, 139
  guiding silent, 137
  and the health series for the elementary school, 287–288
  individualized, 290–291
  and vision, 291–297
  a teaching plan for, 292–297
Reinhardt, Emma, 3
Resource unit, 95–97
Rest and relaxation, 40
Russell, David, 328

Salt, E. B., 347
Saurborn, Jeannette, 346

School health program, coordination of, 23–25
School health service, 6–7, 17–18
  responsibility for, 19–20
Science, activities involving integration of health and, 332–334
  concepts inherent in teaching of health, 334–340
  and integration of health, 323–341
  trends in teaching science and health, 324–326
Schneider, Else, 346
Schubert, L., 75
Schwartz, Julius, 325
Scott, Harry A., 68
Scope of elementary education, 1–2
Scope of the school health program, 5–8
Sehon, Elizabeth, 347
Shane, Harold G., 151
Shaver, Dorothy, 299, 302, 303
Snyder, Raymond A., 68
Social studies, and integration of health, 307–322
  activities involving health, 318–322
  health concepts inherent in, 311–318
Speaking and health, 276–281
  health activities involving speaking, 279–281
Stevens, Gladys, 346
Symposiums, 78–79

Teachers, competencies needed by, 68–70
  experiences needed by, 68–70
  qualifications of, 65–70
Teaching, meaning of, 59
Teaching aids and materials, 200–229
  adhering boards, 223–224
  bulletin boards, 218–219
  cartoon strips, 228
  demonstration, 225–226
  exhibits, 221–222
  field trips, 225
  flash cards, 222–223
  general considerations, 203–209
  follow up, 207–209
  preparation, 205–206
  presentation, 206–207
  selection, 204
  health clubs, 228

Teaching aids and materials (*cont.*)
  health plays, 226–227
  models, 219–220
  motion pictures and other films, 210–212
  notebooks and scrapbooks, 227
  parades, 228
  photographs, 228
  puppets, 228
  radio, 215–216
  reading materials, 209–210
  recordings, 216–217
  slogans, 227
  small animal experiments, 226
  sources of, 381–385
  specimens, 220–221
  television, 212–215
  versus teacher substitutes, 201–203
Teaching content, 149–198
  criteria for selection of, 149–163
  development of, 166–167
  grade placement of, 165–166
  sequence of, 167–168
  scope of, 165
  for various grade levels, 164–198
    clothing, 179–181
    exercise and physical activity, 170–172
    first aid, 177–178
    foods and nutrition, 167–170
    health services, 193–195
    human organism, 181–192
    mental, social and emotional health, 195–198

Teaching content (*cont.*)
  for various grade levels (*cont.*)
    safety, 174–177
    sleep, rest and relaxation, 172–174
    stimulants and narcotic drugs, 178–179
Teaching and learning, 58–70
Teaching machines, 224–225
Teaching unit, 97–146
  evaluation of, 125
  an example of, 101–124
  form, 98
  in health and social studies, 310
  interrelatedness of parts, 98
  introduction of, 130–133
  planning, 97–99
  summarizing of, 124, 147
  teaching of, 133–136
Tiegs, Ernest W., 311
Total personality health, 27–30

Understanding the child, 65–67

Vannier, Maryhellen, 347

Warner, Mary P., 164
Warnock, Florence, M., 353
Whitcomb, Virginia, 346
Wiksell, Wesley, 260
Word recognition skills, 138
Writing and health, 297–305

Zollinger, Marian, 276